The Wide White Page

The
Wide White Page

Writers Imagine
Antarctica

EDITED BY

Bill Manhire

VICTORIA UNIVERSITY PRESS

VICTORIA UNIVERSITY PRESS
Victoria University of Wellington
PO Box 600 Wellington

First published 2004

National Library of New Zealand Cataloguing-in-Publication Data
The wide white page : writers imagine Antarctica /
edited by Bill Manhire.
ISBN 0-86473-485-9
Includes bibliographical references.
1. Antarctica—In literature. I. Manhire, Bill, 1946-
808.8032989—dc 22

Printed by South Wind, Singapore

*Study the treasures under the Antarctic
and make use of them even after my death.*
—Nobu Shirase

Contents

Introduction

For the ANTARTICK POLE is not yet
but shall answer in the Consummation.
—Christopher Smart, *Jubilate Agno*

1

At times the imagination travels so far ahead of the facts that
it seems to bring them into being. Long before it was found,
Antarctica existed as an aesthetic hypothesis. The Greeks
supposed the earth to be a sphere, and, since universal
symmetry required the harmonious balance of things, also
supposed a place which would be 'opposite' to the Arctic.
Thus the continent would regularly appear on maps hundreds
of years before ever it was sighted or landfall made. Captain
James Cook, who in December 1774 glimpsed Antarctica's
outer palisades, thought that because of the extremities of ice
and weather no one would ever venture further south. Now
there is a permanent base at the South Pole. Now there is a
Lonely Planet guide.

Beyond the realms of climate and geology, the early history
of Antarctica is a tale of the centuries-long search for the place
which bore that name—or for that overlapping unknown
southern continent, *Terra Australis Incognita*. Even 100 years
ago Antarctica was indistinct, a location where anything might
be found and anything might happen—and where a man (it
usually was a man) might be tested in ways that might be good
for his immortal soul. Ursula K. Le Guin's story 'Sur' has a
female narrator who is a fictional Latin American contemporary
of Shackleton, Scott and Amundsen. She speaks of Antarctica
lying 'on our maps and globes like a white cloud, a void, fringed

here and there with scraps of coastline, dubious capes, supposititious islands, headlands that may or may not be there . . .' Today the processes of exploration and definition continue, though now within the real if mobile borders—for Antarctica doubles its size in winter—of an entity which nobody owns, and which has no native population to produce anything that might resemble a national literature. Unlike comparable collections of non-fiction, which include the work of explorers, environmentalists, scientists, even of tourists, *The Wide White Page* mostly makes room for authors who have never been to Antarctica. It samples some of the ways in which Antarctica has been devised by the human imagination.

2

This selection begins with Dante's famous account of Ulysses's last voyage, a narrative which—with its southbound ocean journey culminating in mysterious peak, violent storm, and savage whirlpool—uncannily anticipates the trials of some later Antarctic travellers, including Coleridge's Ancient Mariner and Poe's Arthur Gordon Pym. In Bishop Joseph Hall's *Another World and Yet the Same* (1605), we first meet another familiar Antarctic possibility—the use of the unknown southern land as a site for utopian or dystopian speculation. Flourishing sub-branches of the genre include chirpy science fiction, lost-race and lost-world adventures, and claustrophobic horror tales. Then there are the 'true' histories—retellings which variously endorse, qualify or reprove a number of legendary figures from the heroic age of exploration, especially of course Robert Falcon Scott. More recent writing about Antarctica touches on issues to do with scientific research, tourism, and environmental vulnerability, either current or (as in the case of Kim Stanley Robinson) projected into the future.

Certainly when Antarctica was entirely a matter of

supposition, it was a very convenient location for imaginary voyage narratives which satirised European customs. *Another World and Yet the Same* looks forward to *Gulliver's Travels* in its willingness to take certain kinds of European behaviour to ridiculous or antipodal extremes. It initiates elements which will recur in later lost-race tales, and even in stories based on the heroic age of exploration, where men are decent and behave better than their fellows in, say, contemporary London. Such things as Hall's anthropological mockery of gluttony and fickleness and—inaugurating a preoccupation threaded through much Antarctic writing—his horror at the thought that women might exercise significant power, are all designed to make points about his own time and place.

In such satire, the natural environment is not the point and does not need to be convincing. Joseph Hall knows about the likelihood of ice, but his ice is occasional and perfunctory. Rivers are frozen only where it suits his purposes. Subsequently, as the southern ocean was actually entered and traversed, Antarctic narratives began to incorporate authenticating detail from the published reports of returned explorers. Edgar Allan Poe's *Narrative of Arthur Gordon Pym of Nantucket* borrows all it can from the surface features of seafaring narratives in order to guarantee its plunge into the purely imaginary, while the 'ice, mast-high', as evoked by the Ancient Mariner, is no figment of anyone's imagination— even if it owes more to Arctic exploration than to the tales of Antarctic travellers.[1] Plausibility begins to matter. Valery

1   It is probably true that in nineteenth-century England the Arctic got more attention than the Antarctic. A musical, *The Antarctic*, was performed on Boxing Day, 1875, at London's Strand Theatre. It was essentially a drawing-room comedy, a romantic tale with musical items, and had very little to do with its own title. The heroine's father, Ultramarine, a famed 'Antarctic navigator', leaves his daughter in the care of a friend, Old Bastille, announcing as he departs on yet another voyage, 'I'm going to the South Pole. The North Pole has a sickening and unjust monopoly.'

Bryusov's futuristic 'The Republic of the Southern Cross' depicts a vast social collapse—the disease of contradiction— which may well spring from a kind of totalitarian capitalism;[2] nevertheless his story is designed to resemble a formal report, or an article from an academic journal.

While fact and reasonable supposition had entered the imaginative frame, it was hardly at the expense of adventurous speculation. Like remote valleys in the Himalayas or the Andes, the Antarctic continent offered a generous, flexible location—geographically beyond reproach, but still suffic- iently uncharted to be able to host any number of narrative surprises. A standard piece of explorer dialogue in popular novels late in the nineteenth century, or early in the twentieth, tended to go something like this:

> 'Good grief, is that an opening in the side of the extinct volcano?'
>   'Why . . . yes, I do believe it is.'
>   'Well, don't just stand there: let's investigate!'
>   'Now, if we can just squeeze through . . .'
>   'Good God! A temperate valley at the heart of the icy waste.'
>   'Yes, and what do you suppose are those figures over there?'
>   'I don't know, it seems odd to say so . . . but they seem to be wearing sheets . . . or could it be togas . . .'
>   'You don't suppose . . .'

And of course they turn out to be the ancient Greeks, or the ancient Romans, or Elizabethan buccaneers who have somehow been blown off course. In one extraordinary late example—Dennis Wheatley's 1946 war novel, *The Man Who Missed the War*—they are the lost race of Atlantis. Wheatley's Antarctica also contrives to embrace displaced Irish

2 'The problem of the future historian will be to determine how much this system was responsible for the outbreak and spread of that fatal disease which brought to destruction the town of Zvezdny, and with it, perhaps, the whole young Republic.' (p.70)

leprechauns in the course of an adventure which sees the satanic Atlanteans, safe in their polar fastness, controlling the world's weather in order to support the Nazis and foil the D-Day landings. Wheatley was not the first, nor anything like the last, to make weather central to a polar narrative.

The powerful and persistent dimension which Antarctic (and Arctic) fiction adds to lost-world geography is the hollow earth. Among some speculative thinkers there was a vigorously held hypothesis that the earth was hollow and that there were openings at both poles.[3] It was possible not just to travel through the earth, but also to live within it. Indeed, as in Robert Paltock's novel, *The Life and Adventures of Peter Wilkins* (1751), other peoples already lived there.[4] As the retired US army captain John Cleves Symmes asserted in 1818, the earth was 'hollow, habitable within', and 'open at the pole twelve or sixteen degrees'. One adherent of hollow-earth theory was Edgar Allan Poe. He had ties with one of its most vocal advocates, Jeremiah N. Reynolds, while the perplexing end of his *Narrative of Arthur Gordon Pym of Nantucket* (1838), with its hero swept into the embrace of some other-worldly polar entity, implies passage to a realm which is as much physical as spiritual.

Poe's novel has undoubtedly been the most influential of all hollow earth narratives. There is an earlier, perhaps satirical novel by the pseudonymous Captain Adam Seaborn, *Symzonia* (1820), in which the crew of the ship *Explorer* sail into the hollow earth and make a range of subterranean discoveries. But *Pym* is quite unironically informed by the imaginative possibility of the hollow earth, as are a number of subsequent tales of mystery and imagination composed under its influence (some, like those by Jules Verne and H.P. Lovecraft, are sequels

---

3 The idea has been traced back at least as far as Athanasius Kircher in his *Mundus Subterraneus* (1664).

4 See p.40, and note pp.301–2.

of a sort). As well as many formulaic narratives, there are also a few later books which are far more playful in the ways they deal with Poe and the hollow-earth tradition. For example, in Rudy Rucker's *The Hollow Earth* (1990), Edgar Allan Poe himself leads an expedition to the South Pole in search of Symmes Hole, as the southern entrance was sometimes known. There are plenty of in-jokes for aficionados of hollow-earth literature. The adventurers enter the hollow earth and even meet the people known as Tekeli-li, while Poe meets his hollow-earth replica, MirrorPoe.[5]

Then there is Peter Delpeut's droll film, *The Forbidden Quest* (1992). This is ostensibly a documentary feature, based around an interview with a retired ship's carpenter who reminisces about the fictional 1905 *Hollandia* south polar expedition, of which he is the only surviving member. The interview is intercut with archival images from actual early twentieth-century expeditions, notably film by Ponting, who travelled with Scott, and photographs by Hurley, who went with Shackleton. The *Hollandia*'s aim had apparently been to search for the southern entry to the hollow earth, and indeed we learn that the adventurers encountered Arctic savages and a polar bear, all of whom had made their way through the hollow earth from its northern entrance.

5　See also the 1977 story by Howard Waldrop and Steve Utley, 'Black as the Pit, from Pole to Pole', which pastiches a number of authors, including Verne, Melville, and Lovecraft, as we follow the adventures of Frankenstein's monster on his journey south through the hollow earth, and Richard Lupoff's novel *Circumpolar!* (1984), in which Charles Lindbergh, Amelia Earhart and Howard Hughes are involved in a circumpolar air race, entering the hollow earth through the South Pole opening, while their rivals enter through the North.

3

Antarctic writers vary in the degree to which they feel bound to make their explorers convincing. John Martin Leahy makes odd, cartooning gestures, most obviously in his characters' names (Stanley Livingstone, Darwin Frontenac), for he has his eye on the yarn, the reader's gasp of astonishment or horror—somewhat flatly elicited in his case. H.P. Lovecraft, on the other hand, models his explorers on Byrd because he wants to persuade his reader to believe in a world in which, eventually, the unspeakably alien will be revealed. He gets his surface right in order to journey to the depths.

One of the major strands of Antarctic storytelling involves representations of the known human surface. Poets and novelists have been drawn to the historical record. This usually means fresh articulations and re-visionings of the heroic age of exploration, especially of the Scott and Shackleton expeditions, often resulting in stories where terms like heroism and sacrifice, though muted, still ring with some conviction.[6] The heroic-age explorers themselves had their own literary interests which canvassed the same certainties. Tennyson and Browning both travelled to the Pole with Scott. And they were, many of them, men who wrote and reflected. They kept their diaries, and in their huts at Cape Evans or Cape Royds they produced sketches, stories, poems.

Photographic naturalism was not necessarily what all of them wished to meet on the page. We know that Griffith Taylor and Debenham took books by Poe and Verne to the ice in 1911 (Wheeler, 133), while the young Douglas Mawson, given the opportunity to contribute to *Aurora Australis* (1908–1909),

---

6 Not so now. US aircrew based at McMurdo talk about flying to 'Pole': what was destiny for Scott has become just one more destination on the US military network. Sir Edmund Hillary's overland tractor journey to the South Pole in January 1958, the first since the sledging parties of Scott and Amundsen, has not yet prompted any works of fiction.

wrote a piece which might have come straight out of Verne or Conan Doyle. In his story 'Bathybia', a sledging party finds 'the ruin of a huge volcano of unprecedented proportions'. Slowly the air grows warm and moist. The men build a raft and set sail on a river, only to encounter 'a dangerous-looking spider-like monster' and witness a fight between a water-bear and a rotifer, 'both of giant size'. There are exploding giant toadstools, and a frozen creature which, when thawed out, attacks members of the sleeping expeditionary party—at which point the narrator wakes to find that it was all a dream! 'As I sleepily drew on my clothes, regretful at sacrificing Bathybia for Cape Royds, I meditated how much can happen in dreamland during a short quarter hour.' Perhaps Mawson— one of Antarctica's great, heroic pragmatists—is inviting us to consider how reality can reprimand overheated fantasy, but it seems more likely that his vision of the unexplored Antarctic interior is shaped as much by popular fiction as by his own experience. No doubt there are men and women now wintering over at Scott Base or the South Pole who are busy producing new variants of *The Thing*.[7]

The canonical Antarctic document, however, is Scott's journal, especially its final passages which incorporate letters to several individuals and one 'to the public'. It is a work of

---

7 *The Thing* is probably better known to many than even Scott's diaries. It began life in 1938 as John W. Campbell, Jr's twelve-chapter novella *Who Goes There?* In Campbell's tale, a somewhat perfunctorily sketched alien creature—it has three red eyes and blue hair like crawling worms—gets loose in an Antarctic base; its power lies in its ability to impersonate, even duplicate, the life forms it destroys—dogs, men and (somewhat bizarrely) cattle. Who is human, and who a monster? What can outward appearances tell us about anyone, including our nearest neighbours? In Campbell's text there are references to Byrd and to *The Ancient Mariner*. The story has twice been made as a feature film (1951, 1982; in 1951 with an Arctic setting); the screenplay of the 1982 production has been novelised by Alan Dean Foster (1982).

art, written as he was dying, acutely conscious of his own capacity to make an end. Scott wrote with an intense sense of audience. In his diaries, this is repeatedly evident—for example in the way he talks about reaching the pole 'without the reward of priority', a phrase which acknowledges yet glides quietly past the irreducible fact of Amundsen's victory. Or there is his wonderfully 'composed' reference to 'these rough notes' in one of his very last notations. Or, as Anne Michaels points out in the footnote to her poem 'Ice House', there is his decision (moving or chilling?) to strike out the word 'wife'— in the instruction, 'Send this diary to my wife'—and replace it with 'widow'. Ursula K. Le Guin ranks Scott's diary 'with Woolf's or Pepys's diaries, as a personal record of inestimable value, written by an artist'—and so 'his testimony turns mere waste and misery into that useful thing, tragedy'.

I have not included the famous last passages from Scott's journal, preferring to reproduce one of his much earlier 'Impressions', where it seems to me that he uses language with more sense of its lyrical possibilities than either of his poetry-writing contemporaries, Wilson and Shackleton.[8] There is in 'Impressions on the March' a sort of rhythmic layering and listing which will remind some readers of a subdued version of a poet Scott is unlikely ever to have read, Walt Whitman. Literary impressions go only so far. Scott was also the man who wrote in his diary (Tuesday, 9 May 1911): 'Science—the rock foundation of all effort!' He may have been conscious of the impression he made on the page, but he was

---

8 'Shackleton—"the frustrated poet" to his biographer, "a born poet" in the eyes of Frank Hurley—wrote a fair amount of verse and once declaimed some of it to a fellow-officer during the war, adding that it was by someone named Shackleton. "That explorer-man?" said the officer. "I never knew he was a poet!" Shackleton replied, "Then why the devil did you think he became an explorer?"' (Anthony Lane, *The New Yorker*, 12 April 1999, p.99).

not the sort of artist to explicitly make things up. Fiction was one thing; fact another.

The challenge for those who rework Antarctic history as fiction is that there is little they can do to match, let alone enhance, true-life stories such as Scott's and Shackleton's, or a tale like Apsley Cherry-Garrard's in *The Worst Journey in the World*, a book which has hardly been out of print since its publication in 1922. Some of the best writing reworks past events sympathetically—like the poems of Chris Orsman and Melinda Mueller, or Kare Holt's *The Race* and Beryl Bainbridge's *The Birthday Boys*, or David Young's *Inexpressible Island*. Or there is the young Vladimir Nabokov— eventually to become the author of *Pale Fire* and *Lolita*— whose short play, *The Pole*, written just over a decade after Scott's death, takes the explorer entirely at his word.

Others, taking their cue from the biographer Roland Huntford, see Scott as representative of all that was misguided and blinkered about the tail end of empire. Trevor Griffiths's seven-episode television drama *The Last Place on Earth* (1985) is a serious, sustained attack on Scott, putting a case counter to the devout portrait of *Scott of the Antarctic*, the 1948 film which starred John Mills and was mostly filmed on a Swiss glacier. Then there is the Brechtian mockery of the left-wing English playwright Howard Brenton, whose own *Scott of the Antarctic* (1972) is set on an ice rink and contains, as well as Scott and his four polar companions, Jesus and the Devil, Neil Armstrong, Captain Cook, and Sir Francis Chichester. The New Zealand playwright Stuart Hoar in turn borrows the 1948 film title for a short radio and stage play in which Scott, Wilson, Bowers and Cherry-Garrard are played by women, and two other characters—Husky, a sledge dog, and 'the Audience'—are played by men. And eventually there remains only a kind of anarchic comedy, as in the Monty Python sketch, *Scott of the Sahara*—'the story of three people and a woman united by fate who set out in search of the fabled Pole of the Sahara and found . . . themselves.' Yes, indeed: the truly heroic journey is inward and self-discovering (cf Coleridge's Ancient Mariner), but in the world of Monty Python it, too, is enlisted in the ranks of comic platitude.

Scott's journal was lightly edited for publication—a scandal in the eyes of those who detect a plot to disguise evidence of incompetence. There is a story that the explorer's last words were not those to which the original notebook is opened in the glass case in the British Library, but rather, 'Don't believe a thing Evans tells you.' Thus the contest between Scott and his second-in-command (who would in 1927 publish a bad boys' adventure novel, *The Mystery of the 'Polar Star'*) went on to the end, and after. Such a story is far too good to check. But supposing it true, its effect is not to undermine but to humanise. Why should pettiness cancel out courage? Perhaps Robert Falcon Scott was neither the hero nor the fool of empire but simply a brave, resourceful human being—subject, despite his will, to circumstance and a number of ordinary human failings.

This is why Derek Mahon's wonderful villanelle catches so well the mixed feelings many now have about heroic-age Antarctica. His title, 'Antarctica', evokes the ethos of a whole time and place, but the poem's focus is on the iconic line uttered by Oates before walking to his death. Oates's words are adjusted and deepened by repetition—yet they rhyme always with the twinned heroic and unheroic dimensions of the moment:

> *'I am just going outside and may be some time.'*
> *At the heart of the ridiculous, the sublime.*

4

This anthology takes its title from that of a very bad novel about Antarctica, published in London shortly before World

War Two. Beall Cunningham's[9] *Wide White Page*, full of what seem to be fascist sympathies, is a futuristic utopian tale in which the exiled, idealistic Prince Alexis seeks to found a new colony in Antarctica.

'Things have gone too far here,' he tells a potential expedition sponsor. 'We must find a new world. We have exhausted this one. We must go as far as we dare. We must go to the clean ends of the earth.'

Antarctica is the place he has in mind. It is far away from European decadence. Also, germs can't live there. 'Think of the effect of such purity on the enervated bodies of the unemployed.'

For Alexis—as for many other imagined and actual travellers—Antarctica is a bare canvas, a clean slate, a *tabula rasa* awaiting inscription and impression. 'He looked at the great blank of Polar continent, the wide white page upon which he would write a new civilisation . . . A new clean country shall be taken out of a primitive and pure State and developed with the best of an old civilisation; the worst shall be left behind . . .'

And how does the exiled prince feel once he reaches Antarctica?

'Exultantly, he drew in the sharp, hurting Antarctic purity. Here he could breathe and decree.'

Antarctica is often seen as the safe, clean, uncorrupted place where you can start again. J.D. Salinger is reported as saying, 'I can take society well enough, so long as I keep my rubber gloves on. Although lately, I have to say I keep feeling the irrepressible urge to cut off my ear and catch the next train to Antarctica.'[10] Harper in Tony Kushner's *Angels in America*

---

9 Though the novel is full of masculine swagger, Beall Cunningham is almost certainly the Dorothy Beall Cunningham about whom Virginia Woolf was so scathing in her letters (Woolf, 364).

10 Quoted by Joyce Maynard in *At Home in the World* (London: Anchor, 1999), p.108.

may be lost in valium delusions, but her fantasy is typical: 'I want to make a new world here. So that I never have to go home again.' Such yearnings are matched by the actual experience of many who go south. For one recent literary traveller, the novelist and environmental writer Peter Matthiessen, Antarctica is 'the last clean place on earth', an environment where 'the excruciating purity' enables the traveller to *simplify* himself.

Ideas of purity, cleanness, and perfection come up repeatedly in writing about the Antarctic, at least as far back as Poe's shrouded figure whose hue is 'of the perfect whiteness of the snow'. There are of course the physical facts of an unpolluted environment: the ice and snow really are clean. In Antarctica nothing decomposes, not even the bodies of heroes. Scott and his companions, all uncorrupted, are now about twenty-eight metres below the surface of the Ross Ice Shelf, having been carried some fifty-six kilometres from the spot where they died. In about 250 years they will reach the edge of the shelf and 'calve off' into the Southern Ocean.[11]

Purity of environment is matched by purity of motive and behaviour. The heroic-age explorers were felt to be part of the decency of the place to which they travelled, their endeavours pure, simple, clean, untainted. Douglas Stewart's verse play for radio, *The Fire on the Snow*, published and broadcast during World War Two, talks of Scott 'living his dream / On the pure plane of action / Where the white, sparkling scene, / Almost his own creation, / Is stamped with his own design'. As the character Wilson puts it in the same play, 'I have seen this death as the common fate made clearer, / And cleaner, too, this simple struggle on the ice.'

11 Reported in the *Dominion*, 10 November 1998. The journey has been plotted by Ian Whillans of the Byrd Polar Research Centre, Ohio. One of Thomas Keneally's two Antarctic novels, *The Survivor* (1969)—the other is *Victim of the Aurora* (1977)—is in fact about the discovery of the preserved body of the leader of an early polar expedition.

There were several everyday extensions of such assumptions. One was moral. The Alliance of Honour, a fervent morals association which flourished in the first half of the twentieth century, was much opposed to masturbation, deeming it 'the special sin'. No members of Scott's polar party, the Alliance asserted, had been 'victims of the vice' (Wheeler, 57). Another was ruthlessly commercial. *Captain Scott Cigarettes* were advertised as 'HANDMADE'—also as 'ABSOLUTELY PURE'.

5

Cleanness and purity are very much tied up with sexuality in Beall Cunningham's strange novel, in perhaps familiar ways. The colony will be a success only while it remains—like Scott's own expedition to the Pole—an entirely masculine enterprise. It is not long before the comradely southern Utopia comes to be threatened by the presence of a woman who is married to one of the younger members of the colony. Things turn out well, however. Alexis says to his second-in-command:

> *'So you really think we can go ahead with our plan for wives in Antarctica?'*
>
> *'Yes, sir, I do. There's something about this big white country that shows up a little dirt so clearly. The very conditions of our life—a hard fight with physical odds, order, and discipline, work, above all work; all that, which is Antarctica, as well as the purity, the hard cold, the beauty— all that will keep men clean.'*

And the woman in question, Magda, is able to say to herself: 'I've been the first woman in Antarctica! I must be the first mother, too!'

The facts and narratives of Antarctica have been mostly manhandled since the beginning. Ursula K. Le Guin's story, 'Sur', with its all-female polar expedition, plays against a relentlessly male tradition. Unlike the Arctic, Antarctica never had a Mary Shelley. The first woman to step onto the Antarctic continent, Caroline Mikkelsen, wife of the captain of a whaling factory ship, did so in 1935. The first novel in English by a woman, probably Beall Cunningham's own *Wide White Page*, was published the following year.

One of the most persistent notes in writing about Antarctica—both fiction and non-fiction—is the way in which the continent itself is gendered as female. To some extent it becomes a rival for the affections of the male explorer. Early in the film *Scott of the Antarctic*, Kathleen Scott is given the lines: 'You knew the Antarctic before you knew me. I knew you'd go back.' Daphne Clair's *Frozen Heart* (1980) portrays a resourceful young female journalist and psychologist whose ultimate achievement is to melt the cold heart and icy blue gaze of a male scientist who—like Captain Scott—has pledged himself to the south.

When he finally declares his love, she is briefly incredulous.

'You can't mean that. I don't mean as much to you as that. More than Antarctica.'

'More than my cold mistress?' says the man of science. 'I'd give her up tomorrow if you would be my wife.'

Like some of the natural wildernesses in other exploration literature, Antarctica is a kind of female body which must be mastered and penetrated by bold, resourceful males. She is not a savage female waiting to be tamed, however,[12] but a pure virgin who must be woken gently and warmed into passionate life. John Leahy's frozen woman (see note, p.307–8) is not entirely remote from Amundsen's cry (Amundsen, 194), 'Beauty is still sleeping, but the kiss is coming, the kiss that shall wake her!' And in a poetic moment Admiral Richard Byrd is able to link arms with both Leahy and Amundsen: 'At

12 Margaret Atwood notes that '[Robert W.] Service habitually personifies the North as a savage but fascinating female, and a talkative one at that'. (Atwood, 18)

the bottom of this planet is an enchanted continent in the sky, pale like a sleeping princess. Sinister and beautiful, she lies in frozen slumber.' (Tetley, 63)

Given the ubiquity of the metaphor, it would confuse things enormously to have real women in Antarctica. Not only would they be rivals for male attention, they would also provoke impure impulses, and thus corrupt the clean decency of heroic endeavour. Admiral Reedy probably knew exactly what he was saying when in 1968 he described Antarctica as 'the womanless white continent of peace'.

6

The full range of imaginative interpretations of the Antarctic is not represented in *The Wide White Page*.

For example, penguin picture books are missing. I have turned away Bessie, the Messy Penguin, Ponny the Penguin, Yap the Penguin, Willy Nilly, Percy the Penguin, Chilitoes, Flip the Baby Penguin, Peppi and Poppy (a toy and 'real' penguin who go searching for Santa), the Penguin that Hated the Cold, the Penguin Who Wanted to Fly, Hector Penguin, Johnny Penguin, Mac the Macaroni, Tacky the Penguin, Cuddly Dudley, and many of their cheerful friends.

Nor have I searched as hard as perhaps I should have for the song lyrics from the musical, *Aurora Australis*, which was reviewed in *China Daily* (26 September 1994).

> *Poor old Qin, the main character, can't ski or sledge, so he has to lag behind his skiing companions each day. And of course, it doesn't take long before he's thoroughly exhausted and ill.*
>
> *The end result is an appealing character; a scientist who is determined to reach his destination against all odds. Isolated by his fellow travellers and confronted with the harsh winter, Qin eventually makes it to the South Pole.*
>
> *And the vast icy wilderness, the back drop of the show,*

together with pop songs 'Ode to the South Pole', 'Let's Pull on the Two Oars' and 'Black Hair, Yellow Hair', casts a legendary snow hero nobody will forget.

Best-selling Australian thriller writer Matthew Reilly's 1998 novel, *Ice Station*, consists of several hundred pages of hi-tech gunbattles at an Antarctic station, but really, the shooting might be happening anywhere. There is plenty of formulaic fiction which has turned to Antarctica in search of a fresh backdrop. There is a Biggles book, for example (*Biggles Breaks the Silence*); there is the X-Files movie. There are a whole range of seafaring adventures—Hammond Innes set at least three novels in Antarctic waters. There are cold-war thrillers, often exploring mining and ecological themes. There are beginning to be novels about Antarctic tourism.

My decision to exclude non-fiction (aside from its manifestations in poetry) has meant that one kind of Antarctic tourist writing has also been excluded—namely the developing genre of the shipboard travelogue. There is already work by Diane Ackerman, Jenny Diski, Helen Garner, and Peter Matthiessen, not to mention any number of weblogs. But then I had already decided to exclude the most famous parts of Antarctic literature, the diary and the memoir, breaking my rule only for Scott's 'Impressions on the March'. Non-fiction would have made this book unmanageable. Quite aside from Cherry-Garrard and his contemporaries, there is excellent recent work by writers like Sara Wheeler, Stephen Pyne, Barry Lopez, Bill Green, and David Campbell.

7

Writers like Wheeler, Lopez, and Matthiessen have the great advantage—and perhaps disadvantage—of having been to Antarctica. Most of the writers in *The Wide White Page* devised their poems and stories at a desk. Some, like Samuel Taylor Coleridge and Edgar Allan Poe, wrote about Antarctica before any landfall had been reported. Like H.P. Lovecraft, Melinda Mueller and Michael Chabon after them, they depended on an imaginative engagement with whatever they could read. More and more in the future, however, the literature of Antarctica is likely to be made by people who have been there, however briefly. Science and tourism take thousands to the continent annually, and now there are artist visits. It becomes clearer and clearer that there is an Antarctica beyond both the hollow earth and those fine ideas of the sublime which early explorers took south along with their sponsors' tobacco and foodstuffs. There is an Antarctica beyond the scenic photograph. A visitor's actual experience of the place can be disorientating and unframed, especially in the middle of the Ross Ice Shelf or on the polar plateau. Like the world of Wallace Stevens's 'The Snowman', there is some sort of reality there which the imagination has not yet made comprehensible to us: the 'Nothing that is not there and the nothing that is.'

Stevens thought it was the imagination's task to make reality—the nothing—orderly and bearable. A number of nations with Antarctic connections now have visiting artists' programmes. The oldest is the US National Science Foundation's Antarctic Visiting Artists and Writers Program, which began in 1957. Most, however, are still finding their way. Antarctica New Zealand's small programme sends two or three artists south each year. The scheme has been going only since 1998, and like a cautious gambler has in its choice of 'Antarctic Arts Fellows' more or less covered the field. In the first year two poets and a painter visited the ice. Since then there have been a children's writer, a fashion designer, a photographer, a choreographer, a ceramics artist, a printmaker, a sculptor and video artist, two more painters, a composer, a sound artist and percussionist, a novelist, a furniture designer. Both Kim Stanley Robinson (NSF) and Laurence Fearnley (Antarctica NZ) have visited the ice and incorporate artist visits into their fiction, though the first publication of Fearnley's 'The Piper and the Penguin' predates the establishment of the New Zealand programme by several years.

Antarctic visitors will always want to write. Something about direct experience of the place tends to require a response which is not simply scientific or scholarly. Weblogs and photographs will not always be enough. Students enrolled for the Graduate Certificate of Antarctic Studies at the University of Canterbury make an annual field trip to Antarctica as part of their programme, and in turn enjoy visits from (or video conferences with) artists and writers who have themselves been there: Margaret Mahy, for instance, or Kim Stanley Robinson. Usually, too, an artist or writer accompanies the students down to the ice as a field tutor.

And in time imaginative accounts of the Antarctic and the Arctic may start to diverge. The two polar 'opposites' are brilliantly brought together in Francis Spufford's *I May Be Some Time: Ice and the English Imagination*, but geographical difference may lead towards distinct imaginative projects. The Arctic is not quite a discrete place (no one speaks of 'Arctica'). It is continuous with several mainlands, and so with the whole impure range of human behaviour. You could walk there from Athens or Karachi or Chicago. But then the North Pole itself is ice floating on water, at a point where latitude runs out. The South Pole is ice, too, perhaps a mile or two deep, but its ice rests on the surface of a continent which is separated from other landmasses by vast expanses of dangerous ocean. Antarctica is there, but hard to get to. The Arctic can be reached, but is perhaps not there at all.

In Julian Barnes's *Flaubert's Parrot* the narrator decides to introduce a quota system on fiction set in South America. 'The intention is to curb the spread of package-tour baroque and heavy irony.' On the other hand, 'Novels set in the Arctic and Antarctic will receive a development grant.' Well, yes, there is room for more, especially work which deals with the

usual human presence in Antarctica, the everyday lives of
people (scientists, support workers, tourists) in their social
relations as well as their engagement with a sometimes baffling
physical environment. Antarctica need not always be far-
fetched: if we cannot walk there, we can at least acknowledge
that people have been living there, in temporary ways, for
about a hundred years. Perhaps some kinds of comedy, even,
may be possible. Whether what comes will be classical or
baroque, or romantic or modernist, or post- all of these,
remains to be seen. It is odd to think that children will
probably be missing.

Bill Manhire
Menton, June 2004

The Death of Ulysses

Dante

'. . . When I from Circe broke at last,
   Who more than a year by Gaeta (before
   Aeneas had so named it) held me fast,
Not sweet son, nor revered old father, nor
   The long-due love which was to have made glad
   Penelope for all the pain she bore,
Could conquer the inward hunger that I had
   To master earth's experience, and to attain
   Knowledge of man's mind, both the good and bad.
But I put out on the deep, open main
   With one ship only, and with that little band
   Which chose not to desert me; far as Spain,
Far as Morocco, either shore I scanned.
   Sardinia's isle I coasted, steering true,
   And the isles of which that water bathes the strand.
I and my crew were old and stiff of thew
   When, at the narrow pass, we could discern
   The marks that Hercules set far in view
That none should dare beyond, or further learn.
   Already I had Sevilla on the right,
   And on the larboard Ceuta lay astern.
"Brothers," I said, "Who manfully, despite
   Ten thousand perils, have attained the West,
   In the brief vigil that remains of light
To feel in, stoop not to renounce the quest
   Of what may in the sun's path be essayed,
   The world that never mankind hath possessed.

Think on the seed ye spring from! Ye were made
　　Not to live life of brute beasts of the field
　　But follow virtue and knowledge unafraid."
With such few words their spirits so I steel'd,
　　That I thereafter scarce could have contained
　　My comrades from the voyage, had I willed.
And, our poop turned to where the Morning reigned,
　　We made, for the mad flight, wings of our oars,
　　And on the left continually we gained.
By now the Night beheld within her course
　　All stars of the other pole, and ours so low,
　　It was not lifted from the ocean-floors.
Five times beneath the moon rekindled slow
　　The light had been, and quenched as oft, since we
　　Broached the hard issue we were sworn to know,
When there arose a mountain in the sea,
　　Dimm'd by the distance: loftier than aught
　　That ever I beheld, it seemed to be.
Then we rejoiced; but soon to grief were brought.
　　A storm came out of the strange land, and found
　　The ship, and violently the forepart caught.
Three times it made her to spin round and round
　　With all the waves; and, as Another chose,
　　The fourth time, heaved the poop up, the prow drowned,
Till over us we heard the waters close.'

Another World and Yet the Same

Joseph Hall

Fooliana is the most vast and ill-husbanded region that ever mine eyes beheld, and yet withal, the most populous. If a man should but go into the Bourse of any town of traffic in this whole nation, he would swear (as one did once of Paris) that the whole world came to trade thither. It lieth just under the *Antarcticke* pole, as the *Pigmy-land* lieth under the *Articke* pole: and hence do I gather (as any man else may) that the extremity of cold in both these opposed regions is cause both of the pigmies' littleness, and the *Foolianders'* blockishness: nature so well gracing herself by effecting the defect of body in one place, and counterpacing it with as great a defect of wit in another. To confirm this, do we not see that such as inhabit the temperate zones are generally perfect both in body and mind? But let this matter be removed unto the cloisters of the Philosophers; I must proceed with my purpose.

Fooliana the great is divided into five lesser *Foolianas*, as namely there is *Fooliana the fickle* in the Eastern frontiers; *Fooliana the craggy* just under the Pole; *Fooliana the fatte* towards the South-west; *Fooliana the fond* between both; and *Fooliana the devoute* towards the West.

Now the inhabitants of all these five are generally tall of body (the cause being the vehemency of the cold climate wherein they live), their hair a pale flaxen, their heads pointed like sugar-loafs, their lips big like a *Moor's*, and their ears thick and spacious. But their conditions do not keep all one form. Some things they have generally in them all, and they are these: whatever stranger arrive amongst them (unless he light in *Fooliana the craggy*) they presently entertain him with all the pleasures that their town-house and table can by any means afford. Come we to any of them all, with a dust-licking *congee* and some three or four *vostra signorias*, *Spaniard* like, and either commend his good face, his new coat, his fine hand, his fair house, or season but his affections with an admiring applause, and this your obsequiousness shall purchase you a host whose courtesy will imagine nothing too dear for you; good words and fair promises are all the moneys that this nation useth; yet they have great store of gold, which they barter away for feathers, bells, timbrels, and garlands.

The inhabitants are of a hard constitution, going bare-breasted, and thin attired in the depth of winter, to take the air better. Marry, in the heat of summer, they wear rug-gowns, and cloaks above that, to keep out the heat better. Yet they have some *Philosophoterical* professors amongst them, that will go almost naked in midst of winter, in contempt of the cold, and their reason is this, that seeing all creatures besides man can be content with hair and hide only, why should not man that is made master to them all, make shift to break through all the battalions of cold, being armed only with his flint of nature, his skin?

You shall never take any of them solitary, for they do continually talk and contend with themselves in argument when they are alone and in game. You shall have them fall terribly out sometimes with themselves only; one word provoking him to tears, and another immediately procuring laughter, and the person being all this while single by himself.

They have also certain sects of people, generally called *Fool-osophers* amongst them, and these have the same credit there that the *Bonzoes* have in *China*. All these give their own allowances unto others, and beg for scraps for themselves, wandering through the verges of *Fooliana*, and where they find a stone with any picture upon it (be it what it will), down they go on all fours with curtsies, and cringes.

They have great store of magnificent cities, but they change their names every other day at the farthest. The chief of which, at my first coming thither, was called *Farfellia*, but ere I went away it was decreed by the whole body of the council that it should thenceforth be called *Butterflies*. The whole frame of this city goeth all upon wheels, and may be drawn like a cart, whither the council's pleasure is to have it. It is recorded to have altered its situation a hundred times since its foundation; and thirty times it hath quite lost its former shape. In the time that I was there it stood seated by the river of *Water-lesse*, and was very shortly to be carried up to the height of *Mount Wantwood*. The rivers are all so frozen over with the extreme cold, that if any town be weary of the old place it may travel the waters into a new one. Every month the form of the city changeth, for every house is separable from the next unto it: so that as soon as ever they find any the least fault with the old neighbours, away goes house and household and all, to seat themselves in a new street.

They do marry wives, and love them pestilently well for a while, keeping themselves truly loyal to their espousals, until they either take some occasion of dislike in their old bedfellow, or chance to behold another that is fairer than she, and then, farewell wife, and welcome with all mine heart, husband, sayeth she, for the wife is commonly as willing to make exchange as the man is. They use a stranger for the first day as if he were their own brother (though they never saw him before); marry the next day they will pass you by, and forget that ever they knew you.

They seldom or never proffer anything which they do not call back again at the next breath they take, before the promise be confirmed. Nor do they ever promise, but they afterwards forswear it, until it be performed; nor do they ever perform anything which they do not afterwards (though all too late) repent and be sorry for.

Fooliana the craggy lieth just under the pole: the farthest of all the land Southward. It is a Mountainous, stony, and eternally frosty country, lying in an air extremely cold—and as extremely dry. Here there is an Iron Rock, just like that Rock of Lodestone which the Geographers say is under the North pole, and this is the reason why the compass, after you are past the *Equinoctial*, declines towards the South, the cause whereof no Geographer or Mariner could ever as yet declare. This land is divided into two duchies, rather spacious than fertile, commonly called *Solitaria the sad*, and *Cholerik-oye*.

The Duke of *Solitaria* is generally called by the name of *Grumble-doro the Great*, a testy and severe man whose subjects are as like in conditions unto him as they are unlike to all the rest of the other *Foolianders*. He hath a huge and spacious palace called *Heart's-Grief-Court*, built all of Ebony and Jet in a most magnificent kind of structure. Over the porch are these words enchased in coral:

> *This is the place where sorrow dwells and care:*
> *Fly far, far hence, all you that mirthful are.*

The people of this nation are generally all hair-begrown, lean, slovenly, swarthy complexioned, rough-headed, sternly visaged, and heavy-eyed, fixing their looks as in amazement, and seldom moving their eyeballs. Their optic organs stand far into their heads, making them look like so many hollow-eyed skulls. Here it is in vain to look either for city or village: they dwell every man in a place far from others, as Hares choose their seats, and profess a kind of life most truly *Hermitical*: partly because they are of too suspicious and fearful a nature to dwell in company, and partly because the Duke hath expressly forbidden all men to build any one house within the sight of another, or within the distance of thus many miles from any habitation whatsoever. They seldom or never stir forth a doors, partly for the continual darkness that covereth all this climate, and partly for their own and their Prince's pleasures; and when they do go abroad they do very seldom salute any one they meet, for this is one statute in their laws: *let no man stir abroad but upon necessity, nor salute any man he meets but upon Thursdays.* Go to any of their houses and knock at the door, you shall stand a good while to cool your toes, and at last be sent away with a snappish answer: for they are the most unsociable creatures under the cope of heaven.

But how do they spend their time, think you? Faith, in imagining and framing fictions to themselves of things never done, nor never likely to be done, in believing these their fictions, and in following these beliefs. This is the reason why they abhor company, and hate to be interrupted in their airy castle-buildings.

You shall have one of them directly persuaded that he is dead, and lying all along under the stool, like a dead carcass. If anyone come to question him, he flieth in his face with most violent fury, supposing him some Necromancer that hath called his soul back again from the dead by his magical enchantments, and from that time forward he wanders all about the country like a ghost, imagining himself henceforth wholly invisible. But if any of his fellows take him and bind him, he forthwith deems him a fury sent from *Pluto*, to fetch back the soul that lately broke away from hell, and now he is in the most pitiful taking that ever was man, imagining his house—which he held to be but his grave before—to be a direct hell to him now.

Another is of opinion that he is become a Mole, and lieth in a cave underground hunting for worms, and turning up the earth with a pike upon his nose provided just for the purpose. If anyone follow him and give him but a little prick, he presently believes himself to be taken by the Mole-catcher, and with miserable cries prepares himself to be hung up on the hedge.

Another believes his nose to be grown of such a size, he gets him a great many thongs to bind it up at his back for the more convenient carriage. Another supposeth himself made all of glass or Potter's earth, and so flies all men's company lest he should be broken amongst them.

From the foot of *Mount-eye*, the river of *Teares* hath his first spring, running through most part of this Province, which is parted into two, by a continual ledge of mountains. These mountains have nothing in them but dire and frightful desolation, nor give harbour to any living thing save Bears and Witches, and these abound all the deserts through. The Bear (a most lumpish, melancholy creature) will lie all the winter through, in a lightless cave, living only upon sleep and licking of his feet. The witches, being blear-eyed and toothless old hags, do nothing but sit muttering charms to raise winds and waters, to cure maladies, and call up the dead, over all which they promise themselves assured authority, and yet in the meantime are starved to death for want of meat. These hills on the one side are all covered with a thick, dark wood, called *Owles-wood*, which is continually haunted with spirits and apparitions, and not for man to enter or to pass through. Here you shall have your *Witch-wolves* in abundance, whose howling if you know not their customs before will set your hair on end with terror. In *Devils-dale*, at the foot of these hills, you shall see many whom that famous enchantress *Choly-melan* is said to have transformed into Lions and Asses, and yet left them both the faces and voices of men.

Here we may not overpass the only wonder of the whole country. 'Tis this. On the side of the highest mountains is *Choly-melan's cave*. It hath a narrow entrance and is almost frozen up with Ice, but it is as it seemeth by the sound, of a large compass within. All the sides of the entry are hung with huge Ice-hickles, which shewing like teeth, do make the place seem like the picture of Hell's-mouth. In this cave they say the souls of melancholic persons are plagued with continual and extreme cold: whosoever offers to look in (as few will that wise are) is presently struck down senseless, where his body lieth a good while dead, expecting the return of his tormented spirit. But he that lays his ear to the ground a little without the hole, oh what howling, sighing, rattling of chains, and falling of Ice-hickles shall he seem to hear? Or he that sleepeth upon any part of this mountain (which I more hardily than warily adventured) good God what *Chimaeras*, *Centaurs*, and thousands of such amazeful apparitions shall he (to his horror) behold in his dreams!

Tab. III.

Boitard Fecit.

A Ganorey Extended for Flight.

Song

Thomas Perry

It is now my brave boys we are clear of the Sea
And keep a good heart if you'll take my advice
We are out of the cold my brave Boys do not fear
For the Cape of good Hope with good hearts we do steer

Thank God we have ranged the Globe all around
And we have likewise the south Continent found
But it being too late in the year as they say
We could stay there no longer the land to survey

So we leave it alone for we give a good reason
For the next ship that comes to survey in right season
The great fields of Ice among them we were bothered
We were forced to alter our course to the Northward

So we have done our utmost as any men born
To discover a land so far South of Cape Horn
So now my brave Boys we no longer will stay
For we leave it alone for the next Ship to survey

It was when we got into the cold frosty air
We was obliged our Mittens and Magdalen Caps to wear
We are out of the cold my brave Boys and perhaps
We will pull off our Mittens and Magdalen Caps

We are hearty and well and of good constitution
And have ranged the Globe round in the brave Resolution
Brave Captain Cook he was our Commander
Has conducted the Ship from all eminent danger

We were all hearty seamen no cold did we fear
And we have from all sickness entirely kept clear
Thanks be to the Captain he has proved so good
Amongst all the Islands to give us fresh food

And when to old England my Brave Boys we arrive
We will tip off a Bottle to make us alive
We will toast Captain Cook with a loud song all round
Because that he has the South Continent found

Blessed be to his wife and his Family too
God prosper them all and well for to do
Bless'd be unto them so long as they shall live
And that is the wish to them I do give.

from
The Rime of the Ancient Mariner
Samuel Taylor Coleridge

Argument
How a Ship having passed the Line was driven by storms to the cold Country towards the South Pole; and how from thence she made her course to the tropical Latitude of the Great Pacific Ocean; and of the strange things that befell; and in what manner the Ancyent Marinere came back to his own Country.

PART I

An ancient Mariner
meeteth three
Gallants bidden to
a wedding-feast,
and detaineth one.

It is an ancient Mariner,
And he stoppeth one of three.
'By thy long grey beard and glittering eye,
Now wherefore stopp'st thou me?

'The Bridegroom's doors are opened wide,
And I am next of kin;
The guests are met, the feast is set:
May'st hear the merry din.'

He holds him with his skinny hand,
'There was a ship,' quoth he.
'Hold off! unhand me, grey-beard loon!'
Eftsoons his hand dropped he.

The Wedding-Guest
is spellbound by the
eye of the old
seafaring man, and
constrained to hear
his tale.

He holds him with his glittering eye—
The Wedding-Guest stood still,
And listens like a three years' child:
The Mariner hath his will.

The Wedding-Guest sat on a stone:
He cannot choose but hear;
And thus spake on that ancient man,
The bright-eyed Mariner.

'The ship was cheered, the harbour cleared,
Merrily did we drop
Below the kirk, below the hill,
Below the lighthouse top.

'The Sun came up upon the left,
Out of the sea came he!
And he shone bright, and on the right
Went down into the sea.

'Higher and higher every day,
Till over the mast at noon—'
The Wedding-Guest here beat his breast,
For he heard the loud bassoon.

The bride hath paced into the hall,
Red as a rose is she;
Nodding their heads before her goes
The merry minstrelsy.

The Wedding-Guest he beat his breast,
Yet be cannot choose but hear;
And thus spake on that ancient man,
The bright-eyed Mariner.

'And now the STORM-BLAST came, and he
Was tyrannous and strong:
He struck with his o'ertaking wings,
And chased us south along.

'With sloping masts and dipping prow,
As who pursued with yell and blow
Still treads the shadow of his foe,
And forward bends his head,
The ship drove fast, loud roared the blast,
And southward aye we fled.

'And now there came both mist and snow,
And it grew wondrous cold:
And ice, mast-high, came floating by,
As green as emerald.

'And through the drifts the snowy clifts
Did send a dismal sheen:
Nor shapes of men nor beasts we ken—
The ice was all between.

'The ice was here, the ice was there,
The ice was all around:
It cracked and growled, and roared and howled,
Like noises in a swound!

'At length did cross an Albatross,
Thorough the fog it came;
As if it had been a Christian soul,
We hailed it in God's name.

'It ate the food it ne'er had eat,
And round and round it flew.
The ice did split with a thunder-fit;
The helmsman steered us through!

And lo! the Albatross proveth a bird of good omen, and followeth

'And a good south wind sprung up behind;
The Albatross did follow,
And every day, for food or play,
Came to the mariner's hollo!

the ship as it returned northward through fog and floating ice.

'In mist or cloud, on mast or shroud,
It perched for vespers nine;
Whiles all the night, through fog-smoke white
Glimmered the white Moon-shine.'

The ancient Mariner inhospitably killeth the pious bird of good omen.

'God save thee, ancient Mariner!
From the fiends, that plague thee thus!—
Why lookest thou so?'—With my cross-bow
I shot the ALBATROSS.

from
The Narrative of Arthur Gordon Pym
of Nantucket

Edgar Allan Poe

We now found ourselves in the wide and desolate Antarctic Ocean, in a latitude exceeding eighty-four degrees, in a frail canoe, and with no provision but the three turtles. The long Polar winter, too, could not be considered as far distant, and it became necessary that we should deliberate well upon the course to be pursued. There were six or seven islands in sight belonging to the same group, and distant from each other about five or six leagues; but upon neither of these had we any intention to venture. In coming from the northward in the *Jane Guy* we had been gradually leaving behind us the severest regions of ice—this, however little it may be in accordance with the generally received notions respecting the Antarctic, was a fact experience would not permit us to deny. To attempt, therefore, getting back, would be folly—especially at so late a period of the season. Only one course seemed to be left open for hope. We resolved to steer boldly to the southward, where there was at least a probability of discovering other lands, and more than a probability of finding a still milder climate.

So far we had found the Antarctic, like the Arctic Ocean, peculiarly free from violent storms or immoderately rough water; but our canoe was, at best, of frail structure, although large, and we set busily to work with a view of rendering her as safe as the limited means in our possession would admit. The body of the boat was of no better material than bark—the bark of a tree unknown. The ribs were of a tough osier, well adapted to the purpose for which it was used. We had fifty feet room from stem to stern, from four to six in breadth, and in depth throughout four feet and a half—the boats thus differing vastly in shape from those of any other inhabitants of the Southern Ocean with whom civilised nations are acquainted. We never did believe them the workmanship of the ignorant islanders who owned them; and some days after this period discovered, by questioning our captive, that they were in fact made by the natives of a group to the south-west of the country where we found them, having fallen accidentally into the hands of our barbarians. What we could do for the security of our boat was very little indeed. Several wide rents were discovered near both ends, and these we contrived to patch up with pieces of woollen jacket. With the help of the superfluous paddles, of which there were a great many, we erected a kind of framework about the bow, so as to break the force of any seas which might threaten to fill us in that quarter. We also set up two paddle blades for masts, placing them opposite each other, one by each gunwale, thus saving the necessity of a yard. To these masts we attached a sail made of our shirts—doing this with some difficulty, as here we could get no assistance from our prisoner whatever, although he had been willing enough to labour in all the other operations. The sight of the linen seemed to affect him in a very singular manner. He could not be prevailed upon to touch it or go near it, shuddering when we attempted to force him, and shrieking out, *Tekeli-li*.

Having completed our arrangements in regard to the security of the canoe, we now set sail to the south-south-east for the present, with the view of weathering the most southerly of the group in sight. This being done, we turned the bow full to the southward. The weather could by no means be considered disagreeable. We had a prevailing and very gentle wind from the northward, a smooth sea, and continual daylight. No ice whatever was to be seen; *nor did I ever see one particle of this after leaving the parallel of Bennett's Islet.* Indeed, the temperature of the water was here far too warm for its existence in any quantity. Having killed the largest of our tortoises, and obtained from him not only food but a copious supply of water, we continued on our course, without any incident of moment, for perhaps seven or eight days, during which period we must have proceeded a vast distance to the southward, as the wind blew constantly with us, and a very strong current set continually in the direction we were pursuing.

*March 1** Many unusual phenomena now indicated that we were entering upon a region of novelty and wonder. A high range of light grey vapour appeared constantly in the southern horizon, flaring up occasionally in lofty streaks, now darting from east to west, now from west to east, and again presenting a level and uniform summit—in short, having all the wild variations of the Aurora Borealis. The average height of this vapour, as apparent from our station, was about twenty-five degrees. The temperature of the sea seemed to be increasing momentarily, and there was a very perceptible alteration in its colour.

March 2. Today, by repeated questioning of our captive, we came to the knowledge of many particulars in regard to the island of the massacre, its inhabitants, and customs—but with these how can I *now* detain the reader? I may say, however, that we learned there were eight islands in the group—that they were governed by a common king, named *Tsalemon* or *Psalemoun*, who resided in one of the smallest of the islands—that the black skins forming the dress of the warriors came from an animal of huge size to be found only in a valley near the court of the king—that the inhabitants of the group fabricated no other boats than the flat-bottomed rafts—the four canoes being all of the kind in their possession,

---

* For obvious reasons I cannot pretend to strict accuracy in these dates. They are given principally with a view to perspicuity of narration, and as set down in my pencil memoranda.

and these having been obtained, by mere accident, from some large island in the south-west—that his own name was Nu-Nu—that he had no knowledge of Bennett's Islet—and that the appellation of the island we had left was *Tsalal*. The commencement of the words *Tsalemon* and *Tsalal* was given with a prolonged hissing sound, which we found it impossible to imitate, even after repeated endeavours, and which was precisely the same with the note of the black bittern we had eaten upon the summit of the hill.

March 3. The heat of the water was now truly remarkable, and its colour was undergoing a rapid change, being no longer transparent, but of a milky consistency and hue. In our immediate vicinity it was usually smooth, never so rough as to endanger the canoe—but we were frequently surprised at perceiving, to our right and left, at different distances, sudden and extensive agitations of the surface—these, we at length noticed, were always preceded by wild flickerings in the region of the vapour to the southward.

March 4. Today, with the view of widening our sail, the breeze from the northward dying away perceptibly, I took from my coat pocket a white handkerchief. Nu-Nu was seated at my elbow, and the linen accidentally flaring in his face, he became violently affected with convulsions. These were succeeded by drowsiness and stupor, and low murmurings of *Tekeli-li! Tekeli-li!*

March 5. The wind had entirely ceased, but it was evident that we were still hurrying on to the southward, under the influence of a powerful current. And now, indeed, it would seem reasonable that we should experience some alarm at the turn events were taking—but we felt none. The countenance of Peters indicated nothing of this nature, although it wore at times an expression I could not fathom. The Polar winter appeared to be coming on—but coming without its terrors. I felt a *numbness* of body and mind—a dreaminess of sensation—but this was all.

March 6. The grey vapour had now arisen many more degrees above the horizon, and was gradually losing its greyness of tint. The heat of the water was extreme, even unpleasant to the touch, and its milky hue was more evident than ever. Today a violent agitation of the water occurred very close to the canoe. It was attended, as usual, with a wild flaring up of the vapour at its summit, and a momentary division at its base. A fine white powder, resembling ashes—but certainly not such—fell over the canoe and over a large surface of the water, as the flickering died away among the vapour and the commotion subsided in the sea. Nu-Nu now threw himself on his face in the bottom of the boat, and no persuasions could induce him to arise.

March 7. This day we questioned Nu-Nu concerning the motives of his countrymen in destroying our companions, but he appeared to be too utterly overcome by terror to afford us any rational reply. He still obstinately lay in the bottom of the boat; and, upon our reiterating the questions as to the motive, made use only of idiotic gesticulations, such as raising with his forefinger the upper lip, and displaying the teeth which lay beneath it. These were black. We had never before seen the teeth of an inhabitant of Tsalal.

March 8. Today there floated by us one of the white animals whose appearance upon the beach at Tsalal had occasioned so wild a commotion among the savages. I would have picked it up, but there came over me a sudden listlessness, and I forbore. The heat of the water still increased, and the hand could no longer be endured within it. Peters spoke little, and I knew not what to think of his apathy. Nu-Nu breathed, and no more.

March 9. The white ashy material fell now continually around us, and in vast quantities. The range of vapour to the southward had arisen prodigiously in the horizon, and began to assume more distinctness of form. I can liken it to nothing but a limitless cataract, rolling silently into the sea from some immense and far-distant rampart in the heaven. The gigantic curtain ranged along the whole extent of the southern horizon. It emitted no sound.

March 21. A sullen darkness now hovered above us—but from out the milky depths of the ocean a luminous glare arose, and stole up along the bulwarks of the boat. We were nearly overwhelmed by the white ashy shower which settled upon us and upon the canoe, but melted into the water as it fell. The summit of the cataract was utterly lost in the dimness and the distance. Yet we were evidently approaching it with a hideous velocity. At intervals there were visible in it wide, yawning, but momentary rents, and from out these rents, within which was a chaos of flitting and indistinct images, there came rushing and mighty, but soundless winds, tearing up the enkindled ocean in their course.

March 22. The darkness had materially increased, relieved only by the glare of the water thrown back from the white curtain before us. Many gigantic and pallidly white birds flew continuously now from beyond the veil, and their scream was the eternal *Tekeli-li!* as they retreated from our vision. Hereupon Nu-Nu stirred in the bottom of the boat; but upon touching him, we found his spirit departed. And now we rushed into the embraces of the cataract, where a chasm threw itself open to receive us. But there arose in our pathway a shrouded human figure, very far larger in its proportions than any dweller among men. And the hue of the skin of the figure was of the perfect whiteness of the snow.

An Antarctic Mystery

Jules Verne

'We Were The First.'

Two days later not one of the survivors from the two
schooners, the *Jane* and the *Halbrane,* remained upon any
coast of the Antarctic region.

On the 21st of February, at six o'clock in the morning, the
boat, with us all (we numbered thirteen) in it, left the little
creek and doubled the point of Halbrane Land. On the
previous day we had fully and finally debated the question of
our departure, with the understanding that if it were settled
in the affirmative, we should start without delay.

The captain of the *Jane* was for an immediate departure,
and Captain Len Guy was not opposed to it. I willingly sided
with them, and West was of a similar opinion. The boatswain
was inclined to oppose us. He considered it imprudent to
give up a certainty for the uncertain, and he was backed by
Endicott, who would in any case say 'ditto' to his 'Mr Burke'.
However, when the time came, Hurliguerly conformed to the
view of the majority with a good grace, and declared himself
quite ready to set out, since we were all of that way of thinking.

Our boat was one of those in use in the Tsalal Archipelago
for plying between the islands. We knew, from the narrative
of Arthur Pym, that these boats are of two kinds, one resembling rafts or flat boats, the other strongly built pirogues. Our
boat was of the former kind, forty feet long, six feet in width,
and worked by several paddles.

We called our little craft the *Paracuta*, after a fish which
abounds in these waters. A rough image of that denizen of
the southern deep was cut upon the gunwale.

Needless to say that the greater part of the cargo of the *Halbrane* was left in our cavern, fully protected from the weather, at the disposal of any shipwrecked people who might chance to be thrown on the coast of Halbrane Land. The boatswain had planted a spar on the top of this slope to attract attention. But, our two schooners notwithstanding, what vessel would ever venture into such latitudes?

Nota Bene.—We were just thirteen—the fatal number. Perfectly good relations subsisted among us. We had no longer to dread the rebellion of a Hearne. (How often we speculated upon the fate of those whom he had beguiled!)

At seven o'clock, the extreme point of Halbrane Land lay five miles behind us, and in the evening we gradually lost sight of the heights that variated that part of the coast.

I desire to lay special stress on the fact that not a single scrap of iron entered into the construction of this boat, not so much as a nail or a bolt, for that metal was entirely unknown to the Tsalal islanders. The planks were bound together by a sort of liana, or creeping plant, and caulked with moss steeped in pitch, which was turned by contact with the sea water to a substance as hard as metal.

I have nothing special to record during the week that succeeded our departure. The breeze blew steadily from the south, and we did not meet with any unfavourable current between the banks of the Jane Sound.

During those first eight days, the *Paracuta*, by paddling when the wind fell, had kept up the speed that was indispensable for our reaching the Pacific Ocean within a short time.

The desolate aspect of the land remained the same, while the strait was already visited by floating drifts, packs of one to two hundred feet in length, some oblong, others circular, and also by icebergs which our boat passed easily. We were made anxious, however, by the fact that these masses were proceeding towards the iceberg barrier, for would they not close the passages, which ought to be still open at this time?

I shall mention here that in proportion as Dirk Peters was carried farther and farther from the places wherein no trace of his poor Pym had been found, he was more silent than ever, and no longer even answered me when I addressed him.

It must not be forgotten that since our iceberg had passed beyond the South Pole, we were in the zone of eastern longitudes counted from the zero of Greenwich to the hundred and eightieth degree. All hope must therefore be abandoned of our either touching at the Falklands, or finding whaling ships in the waters of the Sandwich Islands, the South Orkneys, or South Georgia.

Our voyage proceeded under unaltered conditions for ten days. Our little craft was perfectly seaworthy. The two captains and West fully appreciated its soundness, although, as I have previously said, not a scrap of iron had a place in its construction. It had not once been necessary to repair its seams, so staunch were they. To be sure, the sea was smooth, its long, rolling waves were hardly ruffled on their surface.

On the 10th of March, with the same longitude the observation gave 7° 13' for latitude. The speed of the *Paracuta* had then been thirty miles in each twenty-four hours. If this rate of progress could be maintained for three weeks, there was every chance of our finding the passes open, and being able to get round the iceberg barrier; also that the whaling ships would not yet have left the fishing grounds.

The sun was on the verge of the horizon, and the time was approaching when the Antarctic region would be shrouded in polar night. Fortunately, in re-ascending towards the north we were getting into waters from whence light was not yet banished. Then did we witness a phenomenon as extraordinary as any of those described by Arthur Pym. For three or four hours, sparks, accompanied by a sharp noise, shot out of our fingers' ends, our hair, and our beards. There was an electric snowstorm, with great flakes falling loosely, and the contact produced this strange luminosity. The sea rose so suddenly and tumbled about so wildly that the *Paracuta* was several times in danger of being swallowed up by the waves, but we got through the mystic-seeming tempest all safe and sound.

Nevertheless, space was thenceforth but imperfectly lighted. Frequent mists came up and bounded our outlook to a few cable lengths. Extreme watchfulness and caution were necessary to avoid collision with the floating masses of ice, which were travelling more slowly than the *Paracuta*.

It is also to be noted that, on the southern side, the sky was frequently lighted up by the broad and brilliant rays of the polar aurora.

The temperature fell very perceptibly, and no longer rose above twenty-three degrees.

Forty-eight hours later Captain Len Guy and his brother succeeded with great difficulty in taking an approximate observation, with the following results of their calculations:

Latitude: 75° 17' south.

Latitude: 118° 3' east.

At this date, therefore (12th March), the *Paracuta* was distant from the waters of the Antarctic Circle only four hundred miles.

During the night a thick fog came on, with a subsidence of the breeze. This was to be regretted, for it increased the risk of collision with the floating ice. Of course fog could not be a surprise to us, being where we were, but what did surprise us was the gradually increasing speed of our boat, although the falling of the wind ought to have lessened it.

This increase of speed could not be due to the current for we were going more quickly than it.

This state of things lasted until morning, without our being able to account for what was happening, when at about ten o'clock the mist began to disperse in the low zones. The coast on the west reappeared—a rocky coast, without a mountainous background; the *Paracuta* was following its line.

And then, no more than a quarter of a mile away, we beheld a huge mound, reared above the plain to a height of three hundred feet, with a circumference of from two to three hundred feet. In its strange form this great mound resembled an enormous sphinx; the body upright, the paws stretched out, crouching in the attitude of the winged monster which Grecian Mythology has placed upon the way to Thebes.

Was this a living animal, a gigantic monster, a mastodon a thousand times the size of those enormous elephants of the polar seas whose remains are still found in the ice? In our frame of mind we might have believed that it was such a creature, and believed also that the mastodon was about to hurl itself on our little craft and crush it to atoms.

After a few moments of unreasoning and unreasonable fright, we recognised that the strange object was only a great mound, singularly shaped, and that the mist had just rolled off its head, leaving it to stand out and confront us.

Ah! that sphinx! I remembered, at sight of it, that on the night when the iceberg was overturned and the *Halbrane* was carried away, I had dreamed of a fabulous animal of this kind, seated at the pole of the world, and from whom Edgar Poe could only wrest its secrets.

But our attention was to be attracted, our surprise, even our alarm, was evoked soon by phenomena still more strange than the mysterious earth form upon which the mist curtain had been raised so suddenly.

I have said that the speed of the *Paracuta* was gradually increasing; now it was excessive, that of the current remaining inferior to it. Now, of a sudden, the grapnel that had belonged to the *Halbrane,* and was in the bow of the boat, flew out of its socket as though drawn by an irresistible power, and the rope that held it was strained to breaking point. It seemed to tow us, as it grazed the surface of the water towards the shore.

'What's the matter?' cried William Guy. 'Cut away, boatswain, cut away!' shouted West, 'or we shall be dragged against the rocks.'

Hurliguerly hurried to the bow of the *Paracuta* to cut away the rope. Of a sudden the knife he held was snatched out of his hand, the rope broke, and the grapnel, like a projectile, shot off in the direction of the sphinx.

At the same moment, all the articles on board the boat that were made of iron or steel—cooking utensils, arms, Endicott's stove, our knives, which were torn from our pockets—took flight after a similar fashion in the same direction, while the boat, quickening its course, brought up against the beach.

What was happening? In order to explain these inexplicable things, were we not obliged to acknowledge that we had come into the region of those wonders which I attributed to the hallucinations of Arthur Pym?

No! These were physical facts which we had just witnessed, and not imaginary phenomena!

We had, however, no time for reflection, and immediately upon our landing, our attention was turned in another direction by the sight of a boat lying wrecked upon the sand.

'The *Halbrane*'s boat!' cried Hurliguerly. It was indeed the boat which Hearne had stolen, and it was simply smashed to pieces; in a word, only the formless wreckage of a craft which has been flung against rocks by the sea remained.

We observed immediately that all the ironwork of the boat had disappeared, down to the hinges of the rudder. Not one trace of the metal existed.

What could be the meaning of this?

A loud call from West brought us to a little strip of beach on the right of our stranded boat.

Three corpses lay upon the stony soil, that of Hearne, that of Martin Holt, and that of one of the Falklands men.

Of the thirteen who had gone with the sealing-master, there

remained only these three, who had evidently been dead some days.

What had become of the ten missing men? Had their bodies been carried out to sea?

We searched all along the coast, into the creeks, and between the outlying rocks, but in vain. Nothing was to be found, no traces of a camp, not even the vestiges of a landing.

'Their boat,' said William Guy, 'must have been struck by a drifting iceberg. The rest of Hearne's companions have been drowned, and only these three bodies have come ashore, lifeless.'

'But,' asked the boatswain, 'how is the state the boat is in to be explained?'

'And especially,' added West, 'the disappearance of all the iron?'

'Indeed,' said I, 'it looks as though every bit had been violently torn off.'

Leaving the *Paracuta* in the charge of two men, we again took our way to the interior, in order to extend our search over a wider expanse.

As we were approaching the huge mound the mist cleared away, and the form stood out with greater distinctness. It was, as I have said, almost that of a sphinx, a dusky-hued sphinx, as though the matter which composed it had been oxidised by the inclemency of the polar climate.

And then a possibility flashed into my mind, an hypothesis which explained these astonishing phenomena.

'Ah!' I exclaimed, 'a loadstone! that is it! A magnet with prodigious power of attraction!'

I was understood, and in an instant the final catastrophe, to which Hearne and his companions were victims, was explained with terrible clearness.

The Antarctic Sphinx was simply a colossal magnet. Under the influence of that magnet the iron bands of the *Halbrane's* boat had been torn out and projected as though by the action of a catapult. This was the occult force that had irresistibly attracted everything made of iron on the *Paracuta*. And the boat itself would have shared the fate of the *Halbrane's* boat had a single bit of that metal been employed in its construction. Was it, then, the proximity of the magnetic pole that produced such effects?

At first we entertained this idea, but on reflection we rejected it.

At the place where the magnetic meridians cross, the only phenomenon produced is the vertical position of the magnetic needle in two similar points of the terrestrial globe. This phenomenon, already proved by observations made on the spot, must be identical in the Antarctic regions.

Thus, then, there did exist a magnet of prodigious intensity in the zone of attraction which we had entered. Under our eyes one of those surprising effects which had hitherto been classed among fables was actually produced.

The following appeared to me to be the true explanation.

The Trade-winds bring a constant succession of clouds or mists in which immense quantities of electricity not completely exhausted by storms, are stored. Hence there exists a formidable accumulation of electric fluid at the poles, and it flows towards the land in a permanent stream.

From this cause come the northern and southern auroras, whose luminous splendours shine above the horizon, especially during the long polar night, and are visible even in the temperate zones when they attain their maximum of culmination.

These continuous currents at the poles, which bewilder our compasses, must possess an extraordinary influence. And it would suffice that a block of iron should be subjected to their action for it to be changed into a magnet of power proportioned to the intensity of the current, to the number of turns of the electric helix, and to the square root of the diameter of the block of magnetised iron. Thus, then, the bulk of the sphinx which upreared its mystic form upon this outer edge of the southern lands might be calculated by thousands of cubic yards.

Now, in order that the current should circulate around it and make a magnet of it by induction, what was required? Nothing but a metallic lode, whose innumerable windings through the bowels of the soil should be connected subterraneously at the base of the block.

It seemed to me also that the place of this block ought to be in the magnetic axis, as a sort of gigantic calamite, from whence the imponderable fluid whose currents made an inexhaustible accumulator set up at the confines of the world should issue. Our compass could not have enabled us to determine whether the marvel before our eyes really was at the magnetic pole of the southern regions. All I can say is, that its needle staggered about, helpless and useless. And in fact the exact location of the Antarctic Sphinx mattered little in respect of the constitution of that artificial loadstone, and the manner in which the clouds and metallic lode supplied its attractive power.

In this very plausible fashion I was led to explain the phenomenon by instinct. It could not be doubted that we were in the vicinity of a magnet which produced these terrible but strictly natural effects by its attraction.

I communicated my idea to my companions, and they regarded this explanation as conclusive, in presence of the physical facts of which we were the actual witnesses.

'We shall incur no risk by going to the foot of the mound, I suppose,' said Captain Len Guy.

'None,' I replied.

'There—yes—there!'

I could not describe the impression those three words made upon us. Edgar Poe would have said that they were three cries from the depths of the underworld.

It was Dirk Peters who had spoken, and his body was

stretched out in the direction of the sphinx, as though it had been turned to iron and was attracted by the magnet.

Then he sped swiftly towards the sphinx-like mound, and his companions followed him over rough ground strewn with volcanic remains of all sorts.

The monster grew larger as we neared it, but lost none of its mythological shape. Alone on that vast plain it produced a sense of awe. And—but this could only have been a delusion—we seemed to be drawn towards it by the force of its magnetic attraction.

On arriving at the base of the mound, we found there the various articles on which the magnet had exerted its power; arms, utensils, the grapnel of the *Paracuta*, all adhering to the sides of the monster. There also were the iron relics of the *Halbrane*'s boat, all her utensils, arms, and fittings, even to the nails and the iron portions of the rudder.

There was no possibility of regaining possession of any of these things. Even had they not adhered to the loadstone rock at too great a height to be reached, they adhered to it too closely to be detached. Hurliguerly was infuriated by the impossibility of recovering his knife, which he recognised at fifty feet above his head, and cried as he shook his clenched fist at the imperturbable monster,—

'Thief of a sphinx!'

Of course the things which had belonged to the *Halbrane*'s boat and the *Paracuta*'s were the only articles that adorned the mighty sides of the lonely mystic form. Never had any ship reached such a latitude of the Antarctic Sea. Hearne and his accomplices, Captain Len Guy and his companions, were the first who had trodden this point of the southern continent. And any vessel that might have approached this colossal magnet must have incurred certain destruction. Our schooner must have perished, even as its boat had been dashed into a shapeless wreck.

West now reminded us that it was imprudent to prolong

our stay upon this Land of the Sphinx—a name to be retained. Time pressed, and a few days' delay would have entailed our wintering at the foot of the ice-barrier.

The order to return to the beach had just been given, when the voice of the half-breed was again heard, as he cried out:

'There! There! There!'

We followed the sounds to the back of the monster's right paw, and we found Dirk Peters on his knees, with his hands stretched out before an almost naked corpse, which had been preserved intact by the cold of these regions, and was as rigid as iron. The head was bent, a white beard hung down to the waist, the nails of the feet and hands were like claws.

How had this corpse been fixed to the side of the mound at six feet above the ground?

Across the body, held in place by its cross-belt, we saw the twisted barrel of a musket, half eaten by rust.

'Pym—my poor Pym!' groaned Dirk Peters.

He tried to rise, that he might approach and kiss the ossified corpse. But his knees bent under him, a strangled sob seemed to rend his throat, with a terrible spasm his faithful heart broke, and the half-breed fell back—dead!

The story was easy to read. After their separation, the boat had carried Arthur Pym through these Antarctic regions! Like us, once he had passed beyond the South Pole, he came into the zone of the monster! And there, while his boat was swept along on the northern current, he was seized by the magnetic fluid before he could get rid of the gun which was slung over his shoulder, and hurled against the fatal loadstone Sphinx of the Ice-realm.

Now the faithful half-breed rests under the clay of the Land of the Antarctic Mystery, by the side of his 'poor Pym', that hero whose strange adventures found a chronicler no less strange in the great American poet!

The Republic of the Southern Cross

Valery Bryusov

There have appeared lately a whole series of descriptions of the dreadful catastrophe which has overtaken the Republic of the Southern Cross. They are strikingly various, and give many details of a manifestly fantastic and improbable character. Evidently the writers of these descriptions have lent a too ready ear to the narratives of the survivors from Star City (*Zvezdny*), the inhabitants of which, as is common knowledge, were all stricken with a psychical distemper. For that reason we consider it opportune to give an account here of all the reliable evidence which we have as yet of this tragedy of the Southern Pole.

The Republic of the Southern Cross came into being some forty years ago, as a development from three hundred steel works established in the Southern Polar regions. In a circular note sent to each and every Government of the whole world, the new state expressed its pretensions to all lands, whether mainland or island, within the limits of the Antarctic circle, as also all parts of these lands stretching beyond the line. It announced its readiness to purchase from the various other states affected the lands which they considered to be under their special protectorate. The pretensions of the new Republic did not meet with any opposition on the part of the fifteen great powers of the world. Debateable points concerning certain islands lying entirely outside the Polar circle, but closely related to the Southern Polar state were settled by special treaties. On the fulfilment of the various formalities the Republic of the Southern Cross was received into the family of world states, and its representatives were recognised by all Governments.

The chief city of the Republic, having the name of Zvezdny, was situated at the actual Pole itself. At that imaginary point where the earth's axis passes and all earthly meridians become one, stood the Town Hall, and the roof with its pointed towers looked upon the nadir of the heavens. The streets of the town extended along meridians from the Town Hall and these meridians were intersected by other streets in concentric circles. The height of all the buildings was the same, as was also their external appearance. There were no windows in the walls, as all the houses were lit by electricity and the streets were lighted by electricity. Because of the severity of the climate, an impenetrable and opaque roof had been built over the town, with powerful ventilators for a constant change of air. These localities of the globe have but one day in six months, and one long night also of six months, but the streets of Zvezdny were always lighted by a bright and even light. In the same way in all seasons of the year the temperature of the streets was kept at one and the same height.

According to the last census the population of Zvezdny had reached two and a half millions. The whole of the remaining population of the Republic, numbering fifty millions, were concentrated in the neighbourhood of the ports and factories. These other points were also marked by the settlement of millions of people in towns which in external characteristics were reminiscent of Zvezdny. Thanks to a clever application of electric power, the entrance to the local havens remained open all the year round. Overhead electric railways connected the most populated parts of the Republic, and every day tens of thousands of people and millions of kilograms of material passed along these roads from one town to another. The interior of the country remained uninhabited. Travellers looking out of the train window saw before them only monotonous wildernesses, white in winter, and overgrown with wretched grass during the three months of summer. Wild animals had long since been destroyed, and for human beings there was no means of sustenance. The more remarkable was the hustling life of the ports and industrial centres. In order to give some understanding of the life, it is perhaps enough to say that of late years about seven-tenths of the whole of the world's output of metal has come from the State mines of the Republic.

The constitution of the Republic, according to outward signs, appeared to be the realisation of extreme democracy. The only fully enfranchised citizens were the metal-workers, who numbered about sixty per cent of the whole population. The factories and mines were State property. The life of the miners was facilitated by all possible conveniences, and even with luxury. At their disposal, apart from magnificent accommodation and a *recherché* cuisine, were various educational institutions and means of amusement: libraries, museums, theatres, concerts, halls for all types of sport, etc. The number of working hours in the day were small in the extreme. The training and teaching of children, the giving of medical and legal aid, and the ministry of the various religious cults were all taken upon itself by the State. Ample provision for all the needs and even whims of the workmen of the State factories having been made, no wages whatever were paid; but families of citizens who had served twenty years in a factory, or who in their years of service had died or become enfeebled, received a handsome life pension on condition that they did not leave the Republic. From the workmen, by universal ballot, the representatives of the Law-making Chamber of the Republic were elected, and this Chamber had cognisance of all the questions of the political life of the country, being, however, without power to alter its fundamental laws.

It must be said that this democratic exterior concealed the purely autocratic tyranny of the shareholders and directors of a former Trust. Giving up to others the places of deputies in the Chamber they inevitably brought in their own candidates as directors of the factories. In the hands of the Board of Directors was concentrated the economic life of the country. The directors received all the orders and assigned them to the various factories for fulfilment; they purchased the materials and the machines for the work; they managed the whole business of the factories. Through their hands passed immense sums of money, to be reckoned in milliards. The Law-making Chamber only certified the entries of debits and credits in the upkeep of the factories, the accounts being handed to it for that purpose, and the balance on these accounts greatly exceeded the whole budget of the Republic. The influence of the Board of Directors in the international relationships of the Republic was immense. Its decisions might ruin whole countries. The prices fixed by them determined the wages of millions of labouring masses over the whole earth. And, moreover, the influence of the Board, though indirect, was always decisive in the internal affairs of the Republic. The Law-making Chamber, in fact, appeared to be only the humble servant of the will of the Board.

For the preservation of power in its own hands the Board was obliged to regulate mercilessly the whole life of the country. Though appearing to have liberty, the life of the citizens was standardised even to the most minute details. The buildings of all the towns of the Republic were according to one and the same pattern fixed by law. The decorations of all buildings used by the workmen, though luxurious to a degree, were strictly uniform. All received exactly the same food at exactly the same time. The clothes given out from the Government stores were unchanging and in the course of tens of years were of one and the same cut. At a signal from the Town Hall, at a definite hour, it was forbidden to go out of the houses. The whole Press of the country was subject to a sharp censorship. No articles directed against the dictatorship of the Board were allowed to see light. But, as a matter of fact, the whole country was so convinced of the benefit of this dictatorship that the compositors themselves would have refused to set the type of articles criticising the Board. The factories were full of the Board's spies. At the slightest manifestation of discontent with the Board the spies hastened to arrange meetings and dissuade the doubters with passionate speeches. The fact that the life of the workmen of the Republic was the object of the envy of the entire world was of course a disarming argument. It is said that in cases of continued agitation by certain individuals the Board did not hesitate to resort to political murder. In any case, during the whole existence of the Republic, the universal ballot of the citizens never brought to power one representative who was hostile to the directors.

The population of Zvezdny was composed chiefly of workmen who had served their time. They were, so to speak, Government shareholders. The means which they received from the State allowed them to live richly. It is not astonishing, therefore, that Zvezdny was reckoned one of the gayest cities of the world. For various *entrepreneurs* and entertainers it was a goldmine. The celebrities of the world brought hither their talents. Here were the best operas, best concerts, best exhibitions; here were brought out the best-informed gazettes. The shops of Zvezdny amazed by the richness of their choice of goods; the restaurants by the luxury and the delicacy of their service. Resorts of evil, where all forms of debauch invented in either the ancient or the modern world were to be found, abounded. However, the governmental regulation of life was preserved in Zvezdny also. It is true that the decorations of lodgings and the fashions of dress were not compulsorily determined, but the law forbidding the exit from the house after a certain hour remained in force, a strict censorship of the Press was maintained, and many spies were kept by the Board. Order was officially maintained by the popular police, but at the same time there existed the secret police of the all-cognisant Board.

Such was in its general character the system of life in the Republic of the Southern Cross and in its capital. The problem of the future historian will be to determine how much this system was responsible for the outbreak and spread of that fatal disease which brought to destruction the town of Zvezdny, and with it, perhaps, the whole young Republic.

The first cases of the disease of 'contradiction' were observed in the Republic some twenty years ago. It had then the character of a rare and sporadic malady. Nevertheless, the local mental experts were much interested by it and gave a circumstantial account of the symptoms at the international medical congress at Lhasa, where several reports of it were read. Later, it was somehow or other forgotten, though in the mental hospitals of Zvezdny there never was any difficulty in finding examples. The disease received its name from the fact that the victims continuously contradicted their wishes by their actions, wishing one thing but saying and doing another. [The scientific name of the disease is *mania contradicens*.] It begins with fairly feeble symptoms, generally those of characteristic aphasia. The stricken, instead of saying 'yes,' say 'no'; wishing to say caressing words, they splutter abuse, etc. The majority also begin to contradict themselves in their behaviour; intending to go to the left they turn to the right, thinking to raise the brim of a hat so as to see better they would pull it down over their eyes instead, and so on. As the disease develops contradiction overtakes the whole of the bodily and spiritual life of the patient, exhibiting infinite diversity conformable with the idiosyncrasies of each. In general, the speech of the patient becomes unintelligible and his actions absurd. The normality of the physiological functions of the organism is disturbed. Acknowledging the unwisdom of his behaviour the patient gets into a state of extreme excitement bordering even upon insanity. Many commit suicide, sometimes in fits of madness, sometimes in

70

moments of spiritual brightness. Others perish from a rush of blood to the brain. In almost all cases the disease is mortal; cases of recovery are extremely rare.

The epidemic character was taken by *mania contradicens* during the middle months of this year in Zvezdny. Up till this time the number of cases had never exceeded two per cent of the total number of patients in the hospitals. But this proportion suddenly rose to twenty-five per cent during the month of May (autumn month, as it is called in the Republic), and it continued to increase during the succeeding months with as great rapidity. By the middle of June there were already two per cent of the whole population, that is, about fifty thousand people, officially notified as suffering from 'contradiction'. We have no statistical details of any later date. The hospitals overflowed. The doctors on the spot proved to be altogether insufficient. And, moreover, the doctors themselves, and the nurses in the hospitals, caught the disease also. There was very soon no one to whom to appeal for medical aid, and a correct register of patients became impossible. The evidence given by eyewitnesses, however, is in agreement on this point, that it was impossible to find a family in which someone was not suffering. The number of healthy people rapidly decreased as panic caused a wholesale exodus from the town, but the number of the stricken increased. It is probably true that in the month of August all who had remained in Zvezdny were down with this psychical malady.

It is possible to follow the first developments of the epidemic by the columns of the local newspapers, headed in ever larger type as the mania grew. Since the detection of the disease in its early stages was very difficult, the chronicle of the first days of the epidemic is full of comic episodes. A train conductor on the metropolitan railway, instead of receiving money from the passengers, himself pays them. A policeman, whose duty it was to regulate the traffic, confuses it all day long. A visitor to a gallery, walking from room to room, turns all the pictures with their faces to the wall. A newspaper page of proof, being corrected by the hand of a reader already overtaken by the disease, is printed next morning full of the most amusing absurdities. At a concert, a sick violinist suddenly interrupts the harmonious efforts of the orchestra with the most dreadful dissonances. A whole long series of such happenings gave plenty of scope for the wits of local journalists. But several instances of a different type of phenomenon caused the jokes to come to a sudden end. The first was that a doctor overtaken by the disease prescribed poison for a girl patient in his care and she perished. For three days the newspapers were taken up with this circumstance. Then two nurses walking in the town gardens were overtaken by 'contradiction', and cut the throats of forty-one children. This event staggered the whole city. But on the evening of the same day two victims fired the *mitrailleuse* from the quarters of the town militia and killed and injured some five hundred people.

At that, all the newspapers and the society of the town cried for prompt measures against the epidemic. At a special session of the combined Board and Legal Chamber it was decided to invite doctors from other towns and from abroad, to enlarge the existing hospitals, to build new ones, and to construct everywhere isolation barracks for the sufferers, to print and distribute five hundred thousand copies of a brochure on the disease, its symptoms and means of cure, to organise on all the streets of the town a special patrol of doctors and their helpers for the giving of first aid to those who had not been removed from private lodgings. It was also decided to run special trains daily on all the railways for the removal of the patients, as the doctors were of opinion that change of air was one of the best remedies. Similar measures were undertaken at the same time by various associations, societies, and clubs. A 'society for struggle with the epidemic' was even founded, and the members gave themselves to the work with remarkable self-devotion. But in spite of all these measures the epidemic gained ground each day, taking in its course old men and little children, working people and resting people, chaste and debauched. And soon the whole of society was enveloped in the unconquerable elemental terror of the unheard-of calamity.

The flight from Zvezdny commenced. At first only a few fled, and these were prominent dignitaries, directors, members of the Legal Chamber and of the Board, who hastened to send their families to the southern cities of Australia and Patagonia. Following them, the accidental elements of the population fled—those foreigners gladly sojourning in the 'gayest city of the southern hemisphere', theatrical artists, various business agents, women of light behaviour. When the epidemic showed no signs of abating the shopkeepers fled. They hurriedly sold off their goods and left their empty premises to the will of Fate. With them went the bankers, the owners of theatres and restaurants, the editors and the publishers. At last, even the established inhabitants were moved to go. According to law the exit of workmen from the Republic without special sanction from the Government was forbidden on pain of loss of pension. Deserters began to increase. The employés of the town institutions fled, the militia fled, the hospital nurses fled, the chemists, the doctors. The desire to flee became in its turn a mania. Everyone fled who could.

The stations of the electric railway were crushed with immense crowds, tickets were bought for huge sums of money and only held by fighting. For a place in a dirigible, which took only ten passengers, one paid a whole fortune. . . . At the moment of the going out of trains new people would break into the compartments and take up places which they would not relinquish except by compulsion. Crowds stopped the trains which had been fitted up exclusively for patients, dragged the latter out of the carriages and compelled the engine-drivers to go on. From the end of May train service, except between the capital and the ports, ceased to work. From Zvezdny the trains went out overfull, passengers standing on the steps and in the corridors, even daring to cling on outside, despite the fact that with the speed of contemporary electric railways any person doing such a thing risks suffocation. The steamship companies of Australia, South America and South Africa grew inordinately rich, transporting the refugees of the Republic to other lands. The two Southern companies of dirigibles were not less prosperous, accomplishing, as they did, ten journeys a day and bringing away from Zvezdny the last belated millionaires. . . . On the other hand, trains arrived at Zvezdny almost empty; for no wages was it possible to persuade people to come to work at the Capital; only now and again eccentric tourists and seekers of new sensations arrived at the towns. It is reckoned that from the beginning of the exodus to the twenty-second of June, when the regular service of trains ceased, there passed out of Zvezdny by the six railroads some million and a half people, that is, almost two-thirds of the whole population.

By his enterprise, valour, and strength of will, one man earned for himself eternal fame, and that was the President of the Board, Horace Deville. At the special session of the fifth of June, Deville was elected, both by the Board and by the Legal Chamber, Dictator over the town, and was given the title of Nachalnik. He had sole control of the town treasury, of the militia, and of the municipal institutions. At that time it was decided to remove from Zvezdny to a northern port the Government of the Republic and the archives. The name of Horace Deville should be written in letters of gold among the most famous names of history. For six weeks he struggled with the growing anarchy in the town. He succeeded in gathering around him a group of helpers as unselfish as himself. He was able to enforce discipline, both in the militia and in the municipal service generally, for a considerable time, though these bodies were terrified by the general calamity and decimated by the epidemic. Hundreds of thousands owe their escape to Horace Deville, as, thanks to his energy and organising power, it was possible for them to leave. He lightened the misery of the last days of thousands of others, giving them the possibility of dying in hospitals, carefully looked after, and not simply being stoned or beaten to death by the mad crowd. And Deville preserved for mankind the chronicle of the catastrophe, for one cannot but consider as a chronicle his short but pregnant telegrams, sent several times a day from the town of Zvezdny to the temporary residence of the Government of the Republic at the Northern port. Deville's first work on becoming Nachalnik of the town was to attempt to restore calm to the population. He issued manifestos proclaiming that the psychical infection was most quickly caught by people who were excited, and he called upon all healthy and balanced persons to use their authority to restrain the weak and nervous. Then Deville used the Society for Struggle with the Epidemic and put under the authority of its members all public places, theatres, meeting-houses, squares, and streets. In these days there scarcely ever passed an hour but a new case of infection might be discovered. Now here, now there, one saw faces or whole groups of faces manifestly expressive of abnormality. The greater number of the patients, when they understood their condition, showed an immediate desire for help. But under the influence of the disease this wish expressed itself in various types of hostile action directed against those standing near. The stricken wished to hasten home or to a hospital, but instead of doing this they fled in fright to the outskirts of the town. The thought occurred to them to ask the passer-by to do something for them, but instead of that they seized him by the throat. In this way many were suffocated, struck down, or wounded with knife or stick. So the crowd, whenever it found itself in the presence of a man suffering from 'contradiction', took to flight. At these moments the members of the Society would appear on the scene, capture the sick man, calm him, and take him to the nearest hospital; it was their work to reason with the crowd and explain that there was really no danger, that the general misfortune had simply spread a little further, and it was their duty to struggle with it to the full extent of their powers.

The sudden infection of persons present in the audience of theatres or meeting-houses often led to the most tragic catastrophes. Once at a performance of Opera some hundreds of people stricken mad in a mass, instead of expressing their approval of the vocalists, flung themselves on the stage and scattered blows right and left. At the Grand Dramatic Theatre, an actor, whose rôle it was to commit suicide by a revolver shot, fired the revolver several times at the public. It was, of course, blank cartridge, but it so acted on the nerves of those present that it hastened the symptoms of the disease in many in whom it was latent. In the confusion which followed several scores of people were killed. But worst of all was that which happened in the Theatre of Fireworks. The detachment of militia posted there in case of fire suddenly set fire to the stage and to the veils by which the various light effects are obtained. Not less than two hundred people were burnt or crushed to death. After that occurrence Horace Deville closed all the theatres and concert-rooms in the town.

The robbers and thieves now began to constitute a grave danger for the inhabitants, and in the general disorganisation they were able to carry their depredations very far. It is said that some of them came to Zvezdny from abroad. Some simulated madness in order to escape punishment, others felt it unnecessary to make any pretence of disguising their open robberies. Gangs of thieves entered the abandoned shops, broke into private lodgings, and took off the more valuable things or demanded gold; they stopped people in the streets and stripped them of their valuables, such as watches, rings, and bracelets. And there accompanied the robberies outrage of every kind, even of the most disgusting. The Nachalnik sent companies of militia to hunt down the criminals, but they did not dare to join in open conflict. There were dreadful moments when among the militia or among the robbers would suddenly appear a case of the disease, and friend would turn his weapon against friend. At first the Nachalnik banished from the town the robbers who fell under arrest. But those who had charge of the prison trains liberated them, in order to take their places. Then the Nachalnik was obliged to condemn the criminals to death. So almost after three centuries' break capital punishment was introduced once more on the earth. In June a general scarcity of the indispensable articles of food and medicine began to make itself felt. The import by rail diminished; manufacture within the town practically ceased. Deville organised the town bakeries and the distribution of bread and meat to the people. In the town itself the same common tables were set up as had long since been established in the factories. But it was not possible to find sufficient people for kitchen and service. Some voluntary workers toiled till they were exhausted, and they gradually diminished in numbers. The town crematoriums flamed all day, but the number of corpses did not decrease but increased. They began to find bodies in the streets and left in houses. The municipal business—such as telegraph, telephone, electric light, water supply, sanitation, and the rest, were worked by fewer and fewer people. It is astonishing how much Deville succeeded in doing. He looked after everything and everyone. One conjectures that he never knew a moment's rest. And all who were saved testify unanimously that his activity was beyond praise.

Towards the middle of June shortage of labour on the railways began to be felt. There were not enough engine-drivers or conductors. On the 17th of July the first accident took place on the South-Western line, the reason being the sudden attack of the engine-driver. In the paroxysm of his disease the driver took his train over a precipice on to a glacier and almost all the passengers were killed or crippled. The news of this was brought to the town by the next train, and it came as a thunderbolt. A hospital train was sent off at once; it brought back the dead and the crippled, but towards the evening of that day news was circulated that a similar catastrophe had taken place on the First line. Two of the railway tracks connecting Zvezdny with the outside world were damaged. Breakdown gangs were sent from Zvezdny and from North Port to repair the lines, but it was almost impossible because of the winter temperature. There was no hope that on these lines train service would be resumed—at least, in the near future.

These catastrophes were simply patterns for new ones. The more alarmed the engine-drivers became the more liable they were to the disease and to the repetition of the mistake of their predecessors. Just because they were afraid of destroying a train they destroyed it. During the five days from the 18th to the 22nd of June seven trains with passengers were wrecked. Thousands of passengers perished from injuries or starved to death unrescued in the snowy wastes. Only very few had sufficient strength to return to the city by their own efforts. The six main lines connecting Zvezdny with the outer world were rendered useless. The service of dirigibles had ceased earlier. One of them had been destroyed by the enraged mob, the pretext given being that they were used exclusively for the rich. The others, one by one, were wrecked, the disease probably attacking the crew. The population of the city was at this time about six hundred thousand. For some time they were only connected with the world by telegraph.

On the 24th of June the Metropolitan railway ceased to run. On the 26th the telephone service was discontinued. On the 27th all chemists' shops, except the large central store, were closed. On the 1st of July the inhabitants were ordered to come from the outer parts of the town into the central districts, so that order might better be maintained, food distributed, and medical aid afforded. Suburban dwellers abandoned their own quarters and settled in those which had lately been abandoned by fugitives. The sense of property vanished. No one was sorry to leave his own, no one felt it strange to take up his abode in other people's houses. Nevertheless, burglars and robbers did not disappear, though perhaps now one would rather call them demented beings than criminals. They continued to steal, and great hoards of gold have been discovered in the empty houses where they hid them, and precious stones beside the decaying body of the robber himself.

It is astonishing that in the midst of universal destruction life tended to keep its former course. There still were shopkeepers who opened their shops and sold for incredible sums the luxuries, flowers, books, guns, and other goods which they had preserved. . . . Purchasers threw down their unnecessary gold ungrudgingly, and miserly merchants hid it, God knows why. There still existed secret resorts, with cards, women, and wine, whither unfortunates sought refuge and tried to forget dreadful reality. There the whole mingled with the diseased, and there is no chronicle of the scenes which took place. Two or three newspapers still tried to preserve the significance of the written word in the midst of desolation. Copies of these newspapers are being sold now at ten or twenty times their original value, and will undoubtedly become bibliographical rarities of the first degree. In their columns is reflected the horrors of the unfortunate town, described in the midst of the reigning madness and set by half-mad compositors. There were reporters who took note of the happenings of the town, journalists who debated hotly the condition of affairs, and even feuilletonists who endeavoured to enliven these tragic days. But the telegrams received from other countries, telling as they did of real healthy life, caused the souls of the readers in Zvezdny to fall into despair.

There were desperate attempts to escape. At the beginning of July an immense crowd of women and children, led by a certain John Dew, decided to set out on foot for the nearest inhabited place, Londontown; Deville understood the madness of this attempt, but could not stop the people, and himself supplied them with warm clothing and provisions. This whole crowd of about two thousand people were lost in the snow and in the continuous Polar night. A certain Whiting started to preach a more heroic remedy: this was, to kill all who were suffering from the disease, and he held that after that the epidemic would cease. He found a considerable number of adherents, though in those dark days the wildest, most inhuman, proposal which in any way promised deliverance would have obtained attention. Whiting and his friends broke into every house in the town and destroyed whatever sick they found. They massacred the patients in the hospitals, they even killed those suspected to be unwell. Robbers and madmen joined themselves to these bands of ideal murderers. The whole town became their arena. In these difficult days Horace Deville organised his fellow-workers into a military force, encouraged them with his spirit, and set out to fight the followers of Whiting. This affair lasted several days. Hundreds of men fell on one side or the other, till at last Whiting himself was taken. He appeared to be in the last stages of *mania contradicens* and had to be taken to the hospital, where he soon perished, instead of to the scaffold.

On the 8th of July one of the worst things happened. The controller of the Central Power Station smashed all the machinery. The electric light failed, and the whole city was plunged in absolute darkness. As there was no other means of lighting and warming the city, the people were left in a helpless plight. Deville had, however, foreseen such an eventuality and had accumulated a considerable quantity of torches and fuel. Bonfires were lighted in all the streets.

Torches were distributed in thousands. But these miserable lights could not illumine the gigantic perspectives of the city of Zvezdny, the tens of kilometres of straight line highways, the gloomy height of thirteen-storey buildings. With the darkness the last discipline of the city was lost. Terror and madness finally possessed all souls. The healthy could not be distinguished from the sick. There commenced a dreadful orgy of the despairing.

The moral sense of the people declined with astonishing rapidity. Culture slipped from off these people like a delicate bark, and revealed man, wild and naked, the man-beast as he was. All sense of right was lost, force alone was acknowledged. For women, the only law became that of desire and of indulgence. The most virtuous matrons behaved as the most abandoned, with no continence or faith, and used the vile language of the tavern. Young girls ran about the streets demented and unchaste. Drunkards made feasts in ruined cellars, not in any way distressed that amongst the bottles lay unburied corpses. All this was constantly aggravated by the breaking out of the disease afresh. Sad was the position of children, abandoned by their parents to the will of Fate. They died of hunger, of injury after assault, and they were murdered both purposely and by accident. It is even affirmed that cannibalism took place.

In this last period of tragedy Horace Deville could not, of course, afford help to the whole population. But he did arrange in the Town Hall shelter for those who still preserved their reason. The entrances to the building were barricaded and sentries were kept continuously on guard. There was food and water for three thousand people for forty days. Deville, however, had only eighteen hundred people, and though there must have been other people with sound minds in the town, they could not have known what Deville was doing, and these remained in hiding in the houses. Many resolved to remain indoors till the end, and bodies have been found of many

81

who must have died of hunger in their solitude. It is remarkable that among those who took refuge in the Town Hall there were very few new cases of the disease. Deville was able to keep discipline in his small community. He kept till the last a journal of all that happened, and that journal, together with the telegrams, makes the most reliable source of evidence of the catastrophe. The journal was found in a secret cupboard of the Town Hall, where the most precious documents were kept. The last entry refers to the 20th of July. Deville writes that a demented crowd is assailing the building, and that he is obliged to fire with revolvers upon the people. 'What I hope for,' he adds, 'I know not. No help can be expected before the spring. We have not the food to live till the spring. But I shall fulfil my duty to the end.' These were the last words of Deville. Noble words!

It must be added that on the 21st July the crowd took the Town Hall by storm, and its defenders were all killed or scattered. The body of Deville has not yet been found, and there is no reliable evidence as to what took place in the town after the 21st. It must be conjectured, from the state in which the town was found, that anarchy reached its last limits. The gloomy streets, lit up by the glare of bonfires of furniture and books, can be imagined. They obtained fire by striking iron on flint. Crowds of drunkards and madmen danced wildly about the bonfires. Men and women drank together and passed the common cup from lip to lip. The worst scenes of sensuality were witnessed. Some sort of dark atavistic sense enlivened the souls of these townsmen, and half-naked, unwashed, unkempt, they danced the dances of their remote ancestors, the contemporaries of the cave-bears, and they sang the same wild songs as did the hordes when they fell with stone axes upon the mammoth. With songs, with incoherent exclamations, with idiotic laughter, mingled the cries of those who had lost the power to express in words their own delirious dreams, mingled also the moans of those in the convulsions of death. Sometimes dancing gave way to fighting—for a barrel of wine, for a woman, or simply without reason, in a fit of madness brought about by contradictory emotion. There was nowhere to flee; the same dreadful scenes were everywhere, the same orgies everywhere, the same fights, the same brutal gaiety or brutal rage—or else, absolute darkness, which seemed more dreadful, even more intolerable to the staggered imagination.

Zvezdny became an immense black box, in which were some thousands of man-resembling beings, abandoned in the foul air from hundreds of thousands of dead bodies, where amongst the living was not one who understood his own position. This was the city of the senseless, the gigantic madhouse, the greatest and most disgusting Bedlam which the world has ever seen. And the madmen destroyed one another, stabbed or strangled one another, died of madness, died of terror, died of hunger, and of all the diseases which reigned in the infected air.

It goes without saying that the Government of the Republic did not remain indifferent to the great calamity which had overtaken the capital. But it very soon became clear that no help whatever could be given. No doctors, nurses, officers, or workmen of any kind would agree to go to Zvezdny. After the breakdown of the railroad service and of the airships it was, of course, impossible to get there, the climatic conditions being too great an obstacle. Moreover, the attention of the Government was soon absorbed by cases of the disease appearing in other towns of the Republic. In some of these it threatened to take on the same epidemic character, and a social panic set in that was akin to what happened in Zvezdny itself. A wholesale exodus from the more populated parts of the Republic commenced. The work in all the mines came to a standstill, and the entire industrial life of the country faded away. But thanks, however, to strong measures taken in time, the progress of the disease was arrested in these towns, and nowhere did it reach the proportions witnessed in the capital.

The anxiety with which the whole world followed the misfortunes of the young Republic is well known. At first no one dreamed that the trouble could grow to what it did, and the dominant feeling was that of curiosity. The chief newspapers of the world (and in that number our own *Northern European Evening News*) sent their own special correspondents to Zvezdny—to write up the epidemic. Many of these brave knights of the pen became victims of their own professional obligations. When the news became more alarming, various foreign governments and private societies offered their services to the Republic. Some sent troops, others doctors, others money; but the catastrophe developed with such rapidity that this goodwill could not obtain fulfilment. After the breakdown of the railway service the only information received from Zvezdny was that of the telegrams sent by the Nachalnik. These telegrams were forwarded to the ends of the earth and printed in millions of copies. After the wreck of the electrical apparatus the telegraph service lasted still a few days longer, thanks to the accumulators of the power-house. There is no accurate information as to why the telegraph service ceased altogether; perhaps the apparatus was destroyed. The last telegram of Horace Deville was that of the 27th of June, From that date, for almost six weeks, humanity remained without news of the capital of the Republic.

During July several attempts were made to reach Zvezdny by air. Several new airships and aeroplanes were received by the Republic. But for a long time all efforts to reach the city failed. At last, however, the aeronaut, Thomas Billy, succeeded in flying to the unhappy town. He picked up from the roof of the town two people in an extreme state of hunger and mental collapse. Looking through the ventilators Billy saw that the streets were plunged in absolute darkness; but he heard wild cries, and understood that there were still living human beings in the town. Billy, however, did not dare to let himself down into the town itself. Towards the end of August one line of the electric railway was put in order as far as the station Lissis, a hundred and five kilometres from the town. A detachment of well-armed men passed into the town, bearing food and medical first-aid, entering by the north-western gates. They, however, could not penetrate further than the first blocks of buildings, because of the dreadful atmosphere. They had to do their work step by step, clearing the bodies from the streets, disinfecting the air as they went. The only people whom they met were completely irresponsible. They resembled wild animals in their ferocity and had to be captured and held by force. About the middle of September train service with Zvezdny was once more established and trains went regularly.

At the time of writing the greater part of the town has already been cleared. Electric light and heating are once more in working order. The only part of the town which has not been dealt with is the American quarter, but it is thought that there are no living beings there. About ten thousand people have been saved, but the greater number are apparently incurable. Those who have to any degree recovered evince a strong disinclination to speak of the life they have gone through. What is more, their stories are full of contradiction and often not confirmed by documentary evidence. Various newspapers of the last days of July have been found. The latest to date, that of the 22nd of July, gives the news of the death of Horace Deville and the invitation of shelter in the Town Hall. There are, indeed, some other pages marked August, but the words printed thereon make it clear that the author (who was probably setting in type his own delirium) was quite irresponsible. The diary of Horace Deville was discovered, with its regular chronicle of events from the 28th of June to the 20th of July. The frenzies of the last days in the town are luridly witnessed by the things discovered in streets and houses. Mutilated bodies everywhere: the bodies of the starved, of the suffocated, of those murdered by the insane, and some even half-eaten. Bodies were found in the most unexpected places: in the tunnels of the Metropolitan railway, in sewers, in various sheds, in boilers. The demented had sought refuge from the surrounding terrors in all possible places. The interiors of most houses had been wrecked, and the booty which robbers had found it impossible to dispose of had been hidden in secret rooms and cellars.

It will certainly be several months before Zvezdny will become habitable once more. Now it is almost empty. The town, which could accommodate three million people, has but thirty thousand workmen, who are cleansing the streets and houses. A good number of the former inhabitants who had previously fled have returned, however, to seek the bodies of their relatives and to glean the remains of their lost fortunes. Several tourists, attracted by the amazing spectacle of the empty town, have also arrived. Two business men have opened hotels and are doing pretty well. A small café-chantant is to be opened shortly, the troupe for which has already been engaged.

The Northern-European Evening News has for its part sent out a new correspondent, Mr Andrew Ewald, and hopes to obtain circumstantial news of all the fresh discoveries which may be made in the unfortunate capital of the Republic of the Southern Cross.

The Travellers to the South Pole

Georg Heym

By three o'clock in the afternoon they had finally reached the top of the iceberg; standing there, they could see the vast horizon all around them. Endless white plains, miles wide, full of blue lights, an endless sea gleaming in the sun which hung in the steely blue of the Antarctic ether.

The three travellers took the large sextants from the sled. Godefroy sat down on the runners and calculated longitude and latitude. The other two gazed out into the endless silence, the boundless clear loneliness of the flat icefields. And both of them again had the same sole thought they had been thinking a hundred times every hour: nobody has ever stood here, this silence has been sundered by nobody before. Here, many many miles deep into the Antarctic continent, here, where no penguin or seagull had strayed. They saw their trail behind them, the broad sled-tracks disappearing in the fissured inclines of the frozen mountains. Thus far man had reached, goaded by his obsession, in terrible suffering and privation, frostbitten, like a blind man groping his way behind a demented guide.

Many months, many days of journeying, an eternal sameness of monotonous trudging behind them, far away, where the sun hung in the sky to the north, back there lay the sea, the blue sea, friendly and divine. Evans closed his eyes, swaying from the hips, rocking like a boat on the waves, back there where the firm ice melted into floes, back there where the ship lay on the open roadstead, caressed by a southern wind. His senses alert, he could feel the burning homesickness starting to consume him again, choking his heart out of him. Homesickness: will-less, he yielded to it, let its torments flow over him. Suddenly he thought, smiling as he did so, of what he had once, a long time ago, beyond the ramparts of these travails, called love. What were the torments of jealousy, what was the blind pain of love betrayed, what the worst desolation of a lonely sickbed—what was all of that compared with the homesickness that was dragging him back by the neck. Back, running away, long days and nights of walking, further and further through the autumn night of the Antarctic, and ah! reaching the ship. Going home, to be in his garden, in the evening, a girl beside him on the garden seat, on a warm May evening. God damn it, why didn't he kill these bloody bastards, why didn't he stab the two of them to death in their sleeping-bags, these scoundrels, these crazy dogmatists, these bloodless wonders, these animals. Look at them sitting there. That one doing his calculations on paper covered with lines, crosses and figures. If he had his way, they would be tramping forever through this ghastly wilderness, until one day they withered up, turned to stone with all those calculations. One day they would be standing at the Pole, thin as sticks, living abstractions. Damn, damn, to hell with it. Was that the bliss of solitude, was that what fame felt like? Where had it all gone? It was all suffocated by the homesickness eating away like some terrible cancer at his heart, an eternal suppurating wound. Go on, make yourself at home, he thought. God, I could weep. And for the thousandth time he played with the idea of murdering his companions. Who could do anything to him, who could ever prove he'd done it. Tonight I'll knife them to death. And may they lie frozen in the ice till kingdom come. I'll run away, I'll make the sled as light as I can. And he sat down on a block of ice and crawled deep inside his desperation.

The Japanese gazed off into the iron wall of the horizon, beyond the distant Pole and across fields of ice again, over the sea to Tokyo, into the colourful narrow streets, he could hear the voices singing at the cherry-blossom festival, O how white the land was, all the little houses white with flowers. Now he will enter a tea-house, where the young women are sitting in a circle in front of little teacups, he will slide back the colourful paper screen, and behind the big porcelain vase he will find his little Mi-Ko, there on the sea-grass matting, on the carpet with the silver cranes. She will draw him to her, then she will open her kimono and he will embrace her. Away back there is Japan, back there the islands of eternal fortune lie sleeping. Why didn't he stab these white swine to death, these madmen. 'I'll manage to get to the sea,' he whispered. 'I am Japanese.'

Godefroy summoned them to him. 'We are now at 88° 44' 12" of arc,' he said, and showed them his map. 'We're standing here,' and he marked a black dot on the map. 'Taking the average distance we've covered each day, we'll need about four more weeks to get to the Pole,' his voice grew quieter, 'and you know that the food won't last that long, not even if we put ourselves on even shorter rations. Shall we turn back? Shall we turn back?'—Turn back, turn back, go home—Evans and the Japanese, each waited for the other to say something. Finally Evans said: 'I'm going on. To hell with it, I'm going on.' The Japanese said nothing, but he stared out towards the ghastly south. And when Godefroy put the question to him again, he only shook his head.

And they forced the sled-harness quickly over their shoulders and, silent and desperate, began the arduous descent to the untrodden south.

Not another word was spoken; they pulled stolidly on the sled, setting one foot in front of the other, further and further, deeper and deeper, over unstable crevasses, past gigantic blue chasms that gaped open abruptly like canyons beside them.

But far away from them, a tiny black dot no larger than the head of a pin was dancing in the ashen sky, and that was the Pole. That was the secret.

Sur

Ursula K. Le Guin

A Summary Report of the *Yelcho* Expedition to the Antarctic, 1909–1910

Although I have no intention of publishing this report, I think it would be nice if a grandchild of mine, or somebody's grandchild, happened to find it some day; so I shall keep it in the leather trunk in the attic, along with Rosita's christening dress and Juanito's silver rattle and my wedding shoes and finneskos.

The first requisite for mounting an expedition—money—is normally the hardest to come by. I grieve that even in a report destined for a trunk in the attic of a house in a very quiet suburb of Lima I dare not write the name of the generous benefactor, the great soul without whose unstinting liberality the *Yelcho* Expedition would never have been more than the idlest excursion into daydream. That our equipment was the best and most modern—that our provisions were plentiful and fine—that a ship of the Chilean Government, with her brave officers and gallant crew, was twice sent halfway round the world for our convenience: all this is due to that benefactor whose name, alas! I must not say, but whose happiest debtor I shall be till death.

When I was little more than a child my imagination was caught by a newspaper account of the voyage of the *Belgica*, which, sailing south from Tierra del Fuego, became beset by ice in the Bellingshausen Sea and drifted a whole year with the floe, the men aboard her suffering a great deal from want of food and from the terror of the unending winter darkness. I read and reread that account, and later followed with excitement the reports of the rescue of Dr Nordenskjold from the South Shetland Isles by the dashing Captain Irizar of the *Uruguay,* and the adventures of the *Scotia* in the Weddell Sea. But all these exploits were to me but forerunners of the British National Antarctic Expedition of 1902–1904, in the *Discovery,* and the wonderful account of that expedition by Captain Scott. This book, which I ordered from London and reread a thousand times, filled me with longing to see with my own eyes that strange continent, last Thule of the South, which lies on our maps and globes like a white cloud, a void, fringed here and there with scraps of coastline, dubious capes, supposititious islands, headlands that may or may not be there: Antarctica. And the desire was as pure as the polar snows: to go, to see—no more, no less. I deeply respect the scientific accomplishments of Captain Scott's expedition, and have read with passionate interest the findings of physicists, meteorologists, biologists, etc.; but having had no training in any science, nor any opportunity for such training, my ignorance obliged me to forego any thought of adding to the body of scientific knowledge concerning Antarctica; and the same is true for all the members of my expedition. It seems a pity; but there was nothing we could do about it. Our goal was limited to observation and exploration. We hoped to go a little farther, perhaps, and see a little more; if not, simply to go and to see. A simple ambition, I think, and essentially a modest one.

Yet it would have remained less than an ambition, no more than a longing, but for the support and encouragement of my dear cousin and friend Juana ——— ———. (I use no surnames, lest this report fall into strangers' hands at last, and embarrassment or unpleasant notoriety thus be brought upon unsuspecting husbands, sons, etc.) I had lent Juana my copy of *The Voyage of the Discovery,* and it was she who, as we strolled beneath our parasols across the Plaza de Armas after Mass one Sunday in 1908, said, 'Well, if Captain Scott can do it, why can't we?'

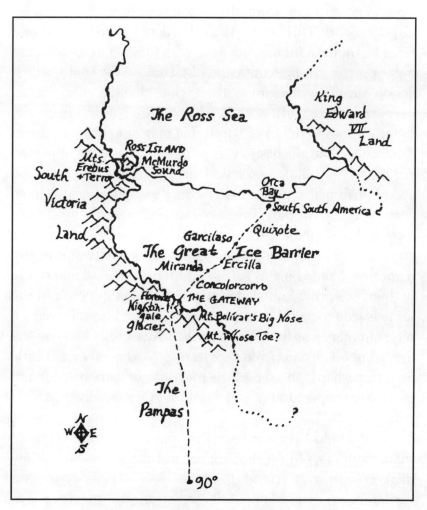

The labels on the map read:

The Ross Sea

King Edward VII Land

Ross Island
Mts. Erebus + Terro
McMurdo Sound

South Victoria Land

Orca Bay

South South America?

Garcilaso   Quixote

The Great Ice Barrier
Miranda   Ercilla

Concolorcorvo
Florence   THE GATEWAY
Nightingale Glacier
Mt. Bolívar's Big Nose
Mt. Whose Toe?

The Pampas

N W E S

90°

The Map in the Attic

92

It was Juana who proposed that we write Carlota ——— in Valparaiso. Through Carlota we met our benefactor, and so obtained our money, our ship, and even the plausible pretext of going on retreat in a Bolivian convent, which some of us were forced to employ (while the rest of us said we were going to Paris for the winter season). And it was my Juana who in the darkest moments remained resolute, unshaken in her determination to achieve our goal.

And there were dark moments, especially in the early months of 1909—times when I did not see how the Expedition would ever become more than a quarter ton of pemmican gone to waste and a lifelong regret. It was so very hard to gather our expeditionary force together! So few of those we asked even knew what we were talking about—so many thought we were mad, or wicked, or both! And of those few who shared our folly, still fewer were able, when it came to the point, to leave their daily duties and commit themselves to a voyage of at least six months, attended with not inconsiderable uncertainty and danger. An ailing parent; an anxious husband beset by business cares; a child at home with only ignorant or incompetent servants to look after it: these are not responsibilities lightly to be set aside. And those who wished to evade such claims were not the companions we wanted in hard work, risk, and privation.

But since success crowned our efforts, why dwell on the setbacks and delays, or the wretched contrivances and downright lies that we all had to employ? I look back with regret only to those friends who wished to come with us but could not, by tiny contrivance, get free—those we had to leave behind to a life without danger, without uncertainty, without hope.

On the seventeenth of August, 1909, in Punta Arenas, Chile, all the members of the Expedition met for the first time: Juana and I, the two Peruvians; from Argentina, Zoe, Berta, and Teresa; and our Chileans, Carlota and her friends

Eva, Pepita, and Dolores. At the last moment I had received word that Maria's husband, in Quito, was ill, and she must stay to nurse him, so we were nine, not ten. Indeed, we had resigned ourselves to being but eight, when, just as night fell, the indomitable Zoe arrived in a tiny pirogue manned by Indians, her yacht having sprung a leak just as it entered the Strait of Magellan.

That night before we sailed we began to get to know one another; and we agreed, as we enjoyed our abominable supper in the abominable seaport inn of Punta Arenas, that if a situation arose of such urgent danger that one voice must be obeyed without present question, the unenviable honour of speaking with that voice should fall first upon myself: if I were incapacitated, upon Carlota: if she, then upon Berta. We three were then toasted as 'Supreme Inca', 'La Araucana', and 'The Third Mate', among a lot of laughter and cheering. As it came out, to my very great pleasure and relief, my qualities as a 'leader' were never tested; the nine of us worked things out amongst us from beginning to end without any orders being given by anybody, and only two or three times with recourse to a vote by voice or show of hands. To be sure, we argued a good deal. But then, we had time to argue. And one way or another the arguments always ended up in a decision, upon which action could be taken. Usually at least one person grumbled about the decision, sometimes bitterly. But what is life without grumbling, and the occasional opportunity to say, 'I told you so'? How could one bear housework, or looking after babies, let alone the rigours of sledge-hauling in Antarctica, without grumbling? Officers —as we came to understand aboard the *Yelcho*—are forbidden to grumble; but we nine were, and are, by birth and upbringing, unequivocally and irrevocably, all crew.

Though our shortest course to the southern continent, and that originally urged upon us by the captain of our good ship, was to the South Shetlands and the Bellingshausen Sea, or else by the South Orkneys into the Weddell Sea, we planned to sail west to the Ross Sea, which Captain Scott had explored and described, and from which the brave Ernest Shackleton had returned only the previous autumn. More was known about this region than any other portion of the coast of Antarctica, and though that more was not much, yet it served as some insurance of the safety of the ship, which we felt we had no right to imperil. Captain Pardo had fully agreed with us after studying the charts and our planned itinerary; and so it was westward that we took our course out of the Strait next morning.

Our journey half round the globe was attended by fortune. The little *Yelcho* steamed cheerily along through gale and gleam, climbing up and down those seas of the Southern Ocean that run unbroken round the world. Juana, who had fought bulls and the far more dangerous cows on her family's *estancia*, called the ship '*la vaca valiente*', because she always returned to the charge. Once we got over being seasick we all enjoyed the sea voyage, though oppressed at times by the kindly but officious protectiveness of the captain and his officers, who felt that we were only 'safe' when huddled up in the three tiny cabins which they had chivalrously vacated for our use.

We saw our first iceberg much farther south than we had looked for it, and saluted it with Veuve Clicquot at dinner. The next day we entered the ice pack, the belt of floes and bergs, broken loose from the land ice and winter-frozen seas of Antarctica, which drifts northward in the spring. Fortune still smiled on us: our little steamer, incapable, with her unreinforced metal hull, of forcing a way into the ice, picked her way from lane to lane without hesitation, and on the third day we were through the pack, in which ships have sometimes struggled for weeks and been obliged to turn back at last. Ahead of us now lay the dark grey waters of the Ross Sea, and beyond that, on the horizon, the remote glimmer, the cloud-reflected whiteness of the Great Ice Barrier.

Entering the Ross Sea a little east of Longitude West 160°, we came in sight of the Barrier at the place where Captain Scott's party, finding a bight in the vast wall of ice, had gone ashore and sent up their hydrogen-gas balloon for reconnaissance and photography. The towering face of the Barrier, its sheer cliffs and azure and violet water-worn caves, all were as described, but the location had changed: instead of a narrow bight there was a considerable bay, full of the beautiful and terrific orca whales playing and spouting in the sunshine of that brilliant southern spring.

Evidently masses of ice many acres in extent had broken away from the Barrier (which—at least for most of its vast extent—does not rest on land but floats on water) since the *Discovery*'s passage in 1902. This put our plan to set up camp on the Barrier itself in a new light; and while we were discussing alternatives, we asked Captain Pardo to take the ship west along the Barrier face towards Ross Island and McMurdo Sound. As the sea was clear of ice and quite calm, he was happy to do so, and, when we sighted the smoke plume of Mount Erebus, to share in our celebration—another half case of Veuve Clicquot.

The *Yelcho* anchored in Arrival Bay, and we went ashore in the ship's boat. I cannot describe my emotions when I set foot on the earth, on that earth, the barren, cold gravel at the foot of the long volcanic slope. I felt elation, impatience, gratitude, awe, familiarity. I felt that I was home at last. Eight Adélie penguins immediately came to greet us with many exclamations of interest not unmixed with disapproval. 'Where on earth have you been? What took you so long? The Hut is around this way. Please come this way. Mind the rocks!' They insisted on our going to visit Hut Point, where the large structure built by Captain Scott's party stood, looking just as in the photographs and drawings that illustrate his book. The area about it, however, was disgusting—a kind of graveyard of seal skins, seal bones, penguin bones, and rubbish, presided over by the mad, screaming skua gulls. Our escorts waddled past the slaughterhouse in all tranquillity, and one showed me personally to the door, though it would not go in.

The interior of the hut was less offensive, but very dreary. Boxes of supplies had been stacked up into a kind of room within the room; it did not look as I had imagined it when the *Discovery* party put on their melodramas and minstrel shows in the long winter night. (Much later, we learned that Sir Ernest had rearranged it a good deal when he was there just a year before us.) It was dirty, and had about it a mean disorder. A pound tin of tea was standing open. Empty meat tins lay about; biscuits were spilled on the floor; a lot of dog turds were underfoot—frozen, of course, but not a great deal improved by that. No doubt the last occupants had had to leave in a hurry, perhaps even in a blizzard. All the same, they could have closed the tea tin. But housekeeping, the art of the infinite, is no game for amateurs.

Teresa proposed that we use the hut as our camp. Zoe counterproposed that we set fire to it. We finally shut the door and left it as we had found it. The penguins appeared to approve, and cheered us all the way to the boat.

McMurdo Sound was free of ice, and Captain Pardo now proposed to take us off Ross Island and across to Victoria Land, where we might camp at the foot of the Western Mountains, on dry and solid earth. But those mountains, with their storm-darkened peaks and hanging cirques and glaciers, looked as awful as Captain Scott had found them on his western journey, and none of us felt much inclined to seek shelter among them.

Aboard the ship that night we decided to go back and set up our base as we had originally planned, on the Barrier itself. For all available reports indicated that the clear way south was across the level Barrier surface until one could ascend one of the confluent glaciers to the high plateau which appears to form the whole interior of the continent. Captain Pardo argued strongly against this plan, asking what would become of us if the Barrier 'calved'—if our particular acre of ice broke away and started to drift northward. 'Well,' said Zoe, 'then you won't have to come so far to meet us.' But he was so persuasive on this theme that he persuaded himself into leaving one of the *Yelcho*'s boats with us when we camped, as a means of escape. We found it useful for fishing, later on.

My first steps on Antarctic soil, my only visit to Ross Island, had not been pleasure unalloyed. I thought of the words of the English poet:

> *Though every prospect pleases,*
> *And only Man is vile.*

But then, the backside of heroism is often rather sad; women and servants know that. They know also that the heroism may be no less real for that. But achievement is smaller than men think. What is large is the sky, the earth, the sea, the soul. I looked back as the ship sailed east again that evening. We were well into September now, with ten hours or more of daylight. The spring sunset lingered on the twelve-thousand-foot peak of Erebus and shone rosy gold on her long plume of steam. The steam from our own small funnel faded blue on the twilit water as we crept along under the towering pale wall of ice.

On our return to 'Orca Bay'—Sir Ernest, we learned years later, had named it the Bay of Whales—we found a sheltered nook where the Barrier edge was low enough to provide fairly easy access from the ship. The *Yelcho* put out her ice anchor, and the next long, hard days were spent in unloading our supplies and setting up our camp on the ice, a half kilometre in from the edge: a task in which the *Yelcho*'s crew lent us invaluable aid and interminable advice. We took all the aid gratefully, and most of the advice with salt.

The weather so far had been extraordinarily mild for spring

in this latitude; the temperature had not yet gone below −20°
Fahrenheit, and there was only one blizzard while we were
setting up camp. But Captain Scott had spoken feelingly of
the bitter south winds on the Barrier, and we had planned
accordingly. Exposed as our camp was to every wind, we built
no rigid structures above ground. We set up tents to shelter in
while we dug out a series of cubicles in the ice itself, lined
them with hay insulation and pine boarding, and roofed them
with canvas over bamboo poles, covered with snow for weight
and insulation. The big central room was instantly named
Buenos Aires by our Argentineans, to whom the centre,
wherever one is, is always Buenos Aires. The heating and
cooking stove was in Buenos Aires. The storage tunnels and
the privy (called Punta Arenas) got some back heat from the
stove. The sleeping cubicles opened off Buenos Aires, and
were very small, mere tubes into which one crawled feet first;
they were lined deeply with hay and soon warmed by one's
body warmth. The sailors called them 'coffins' and 'worm-
holes', and looked with horror on our burrows in the ice. But
our little warren or prairie-dog village served us well,
permitting us as much warmth and privacy as one could
reasonably expect under the circumstances. If the *Yelcho* was
unable to get through the ice in February, and we had to spend
the winter in Antarctica, we certainly could do so, though on
very limited rations. For this coming summer, our base—
Sudamérica del Sur, South South America, but we generally
called it the Base—was intended merely as a place to sleep, to
store our provisions, and to give shelter from blizzards.

To Berta and Eva, however, it was more than that. They
were its chief architect-designers, its most ingenious builder-
excavators, and its most diligent and contented occupants,
forever inventing an improvement in ventilation, or learning
how to make skylights, or revealing to us a new addition to
our suite of rooms, dug in the living ice. It was thanks to
them that our stores were stowed so handily, that our stove

drew and heated so efficiently, and that Buenos Aires, where nine people cooked, ate, worked, conversed, argued, grumbled, painted, played the guitar and banjo, and kept the Expedition's library of books and maps, was a marvel of comfort and convenience. We lived there in real amity; and if you simply had to be alone for a while, you crawled into your sleeping hole head first.

Berta went a little farther. When she had done all she could to make South South America livable, she dug out one more cell just under the ice surface, leaving a nearly transparent sheet of ice like a greenhouse roof; and there, alone, she worked at sculptures. They were beautiful forms, some like a blending of the reclining human figure with the subtle curves and volumes of the Weddell seal, others like the fantastic shapes of ice cornices and ice caves. Perhaps they are there still, under the snow, in the bubble in the Great Barrier. There where she made them they might last as long as stone. But she could not bring them north. That is the penalty for carving in water.

Captain Pardo was reluctant to leave us, but his orders did not permit him to hang about the Ross Sea indefinitely, and so at last, with many earnest injunctions to us to stay put—make no journeys—take no risks—beware of frostbite—don't use edge tools—look out for cracks in the ice—and a heartfelt promise to return to Orca Bay on the twentieth of February, or as near that date as wind and ice would permit, the good man bade us farewell, and his crew shouted us a great goodbye cheer as they weighed anchor. That evening, in the long orange twilight of October, we saw the topmast of the *Yelcho* go down the north horizon, over the edge of the world, leaving us to ice, and silence, and the Pole.

That night we began to plan the Southern Journey.

The ensuing month passed in short practice trips and depot-laying. The life we had led at home, though in its own way strenuous, had not fitted any of us for the kind of strain met with in sledge-hauling at ten or twenty degrees below freezing.

We all needed as much working-out as possible before we dared undertake a long haul.

My longest exploratory trip, made with Dolores and Carlota, was south-west towards Mount Markham, and it was a nightmare—blizzards and pressure ice all the way out, crevasses and no view of the mountains when we got there, and white weather and sastrugi all the way back. The trip was useful, however, in that we could begin to estimate our capacities; and also in that we had started out with a very heavy load of provisions, which we depoted at 100 and 130 miles SSW of Base. Thereafter other parties pushed on farther, till we had a line of snow cairns and depots right down to Latitude 83° 43', where Juana and Zoe, on an exploring trip, had found a kind of stone gateway opening on a great glacier leading south. We established these depots to avoid, if possible, the hunger that had bedevilled Captain Scott's Southern Party, and the consequent misery and weakness. And we also established to our own satisfaction—intense satisfaction— that we were sledge-haulers at least as good as Captain Scott's husky dogs. Of course we could not have expected to pull as much or as fast as his men. That we did so was because we were favoured by much better weather than Captain Scott's party ever met on the Barrier; and also the quantity and quality of our food made a very considerable difference. I am sure that the fifteen per cent of dried fruits in our pemmican helped prevent scurvy; and the potatoes, frozen and dried according to an ancient Andean Indian method, were very nourishing yet very light and compact—perfect sledging rations. In any case, it was with considerable confidence in our capacities that we made ready at last for the Southern Journey.

The Southern Party consisted of two sledge teams: Juana, Dolores, and myself; Carlota, Pepita, and Zoe. The support team of Berta, Eva, and Teresa set out before us with a heavy load of supplies, going right up onto the glacier to prospect routes and leave depots of supplies for our return journey.

We followed five days behind them, and met them returning between Depot Ercilla and Depot Miranda (see map). That 'night'—of course there was no real darkness—we were all nine together in the heart of the level plain of ice. It was the fifteenth of November, Dolores's birthday. We celebrated by putting eight ounces of pisco in the hot chocolate, and became very merry. We sang. It is strange now to remember how thin our voices sounded in that great silence. It was overcast, white weather, without shadows and without visible horizon or any feature to break the level; there was nothing to see at all. We had come to that white place on the map, that void, and there we flew and sang like sparrows.

After sleep and a good breakfast the Base Party continued north, and the Southern Party sledged on. The sky cleared presently. High up, thin clouds passed over very rapidly from south-west to north-east, but down on the Barrier it was calm and just cold enough, five or ten degrees below freezing, to give a firm surface for hauling.

On the level ice we never pulled less than eleven miles, seventeen kilometres, a day, and generally fifteen or sixteen miles, twenty-five kilometres. (Our instruments, being British made, were calibrated in feet, miles, degrees Fahrenheit, etc., but we often converted miles to kilometres because the larger numbers sounded more encouraging.) At the time we left South America, we knew only that Mr Shackleton had mounted another expedition to the Antarctic in 1908, had tried to attain the Pole but failed, and had returned to England in June of the current year, 1909. No coherent report of his explorations had yet reached South America when we left; we did not know what route he had gone, or how far he had got. But we were not altogether taken by surprise when, far across the featureless white plain, tiny beneath the mountain peaks and the strange silent flight of the rainbow-fringed cloud wisps, we saw a fluttering dot of black. We turned west from our course to visit it: a snow heap nearly buried by the winter's storms—a flag on a bamboo pole, a mere shred of threadbare cloth—an empty oilcan—and a few footprints standing some inches above the ice. In some conditions of weather the snow compressed under one's weight remains when the surrounding soft snow melts or is scoured away by the wind; and so these reversed footprints had been left standing all these months, like rows of cobbler's lasts—a queer sight.

We met no other such traces on our way. In general I believe our course was somewhat east of Mr Shackleton's. Juana, our surveyor, had trained herself well and was faithful and methodical in her sightings and readings, but our equipment was minimal—a theodolite on tripod legs, a sextant with artificial horizon, two compasses, and chronometers. We had only the wheel meter on the sledge to give distance actually travelled.

In any case, it was the day after passing Mr Shackleton's waymark that I first saw clearly the great glacier among the mountains to the south-west, which was to give us a pathway from the sea level of the Barrier up to the altiplano, ten thousand feet above. The approach was magnificent: a gateway formed by immense vertical domes and pillars of rock. Zoe and Juana had called the vast ice river that flowed through that gateway the Florence Nightingale Glacier, wishing to honour the British, who had been the inspiration and guide of our expedition; that very brave and very peculiar lady seemed to represent so much that is best, and strangest, in the island race. On maps, of course, this glacier bears the name Mr Shackleton gave it, the Beardmore.

The ascent of the Nightingale was not easy. The way was open at first, and well marked by our support party, but after some days we came among terrible crevasses, a maze of hidden cracks, from a foot to thirty feet wide and from thirty to a thousand feet deep. Step by step we went, and step by step, and the way always upward now. We were fifteen days on the glacier. At first the weather was hot, up to 20° F., and the hot nights without darkness were wretchedly uncomfortable in our small tents. And all of us suffered more or less from snowblindness just at the time when we wanted clear eyesight to pick our way among the ridges and crevasses of the tortured ice, and to see the wonders about and before us. For at every day's advance more great, nameless peaks came into view in the west and south-west, summit beyond summit, range beyond range, stark rock and snow in the unending noon.

We gave names to these peaks, not very seriously, since we did not expect our discoveries to come to the attention of geographers. Zoe had a gift for naming, and it is thanks to her that certain sketch maps in various suburban South American attics bear such curious features as 'Bolívar's Big Nose', 'I Am General Rosas', 'The Cloudmaker', 'Whose Toe?' and 'Throne of Our Lady of the Southern Cross'. And when at last we got up onto the altiplano, the great interior plateau, it was Zoe who called it the pampa, and maintained that we walked there among vast herds of invisible cattle, transparent cattle pastured on the spindrift snow, their gauchos the restless, merciless winds. We were by then all a little crazy with exhaustion and the great altitude—twelve thousand feet— and the cold and the wind blowing and the luminous circles and crosses surrounding the suns, for often there were three or four suns in the sky, up there.

That is not a place where people have any business to be. We should have turned back; but since we had worked so hard to get there, it seemed that we should go on, at least for a while.

A blizzard came with very low temperatures, so we had to stay in the tents, in our sleeping bags, for thirty hours, a rest we all needed; though it was warmth we needed most, and there was no warmth on that terrible plain anywhere at all but in our veins. We huddled close together all that time. The ice we lay on is two miles thick.

It cleared suddenly and became, for the plateau, good

weather: twelve below zero and the wind not very strong. We three crawled out of our tent and met the others crawling out of theirs. Carlota told us then that her group wished to turn back. Pepita had been feeling very ill; even after the rest during the blizzard, her temperature would not rise above 94°. Carlota was having trouble breathing. Zoe was perfectly fit, but much preferred staying with her friends and lending them a hand in difficulties to pushing on towards the Pole. So we put the four ounces of pisco which we had been keeping for Christmas into the breakfast cocoa, and dug out our tents, and loaded our sledges, and parted there in the white daylight on the bitter plain.

Our sledge was fairly light by now. We pulled on to the south. Juana calculated our position daily. On the twenty-second of December, 1909, we reached the South Pole. The weather was, as always, very cruel. Nothing of any kind marked the dreary whiteness. We discussed leaving some kind of mark or monument, a snow cairn, a tent pole and flag; but there seemed no particular reason to do so. Anything we could do, anything we were, was insignificant, in that awful place. We put up the tent for shelter for an hour and made a cup of tea, and then struck '90° Camp'. Dolores, standing patient as ever in her sledging harness, looked at the snow; it was so hard frozen that it showed no trace of our footprints coming, and she said, 'Which way?'

'North,' said Juana.

It was a joke, because at that particular place there is no other direction. But we did not laugh. Our lips were cracked with frostbite and hurt too much to let us laugh. So we started back, and the wind at our backs pushed us along, and dulled the knife edges of the waves of frozen snow.

All that week the blizzard wind pursued us like a pack of mad dogs. I cannot describe it. I wished we had not gone to the Pole. I think I wish it even now. But I was glad even then that we had left no sign there, for some man longing to be first might come some day, and find it, and know then what a fool he had been, and break his heart.

We talked, when we could talk, of catching up to Carlota's party, since they might be going slower than we. In fact they had used their tent as a sail to catch the following wind and had got far ahead of us. But in many places they had built snow cairns or left some sign for us; once Zoe had written on the lee side of a ten-foot sastrugi, just as children write on the sand of the beach at Miraflores, 'This Way Out!' The wind blowing over the frozen ridge had left the words perfectly distinct.

In the very hour that we began to descend the glacier, the weather turned warmer, and the mad dogs were left to howl forever tethered to the Pole. The distance that had taken us fifteen days going up we covered in only eight days going down. But the good weather that had aided us descending the Nightingale became a curse down on the Barrier ice, where we had looked forward to a kind of royal progress from depot to depot, eating our fill and taking our time for the last three hundred-odd miles. In a tight place on the glacier I lost my goggles—I was swinging from my harness at the time in a crevasse—and then Juana had broken hers when we had to do some rock climbing coming down to the Gateway. After two days in bright sunlight with only one pair of snow goggles to pass amongst us, we were all suffering badly from snowblindness. It became acutely painful to keep lookout for landmarks or depot flags, to take sightings, even to study the compass, which had to be laid down on the snow to steady the needle. At Concolorcorvo Depot, where there was a particularly good supply of food and fuel, we gave up, crawled into our sleeping bags with bandaged eyes, and slowly boiled alive like lobsters in the tent exposed to the relentless sun. The voices of Berta and Zoe were the sweetest sound I ever heard. A little concerned about us, they had skied south to meet us. They led us home to Base.

We recovered quite swiftly, but the altiplano left its mark. When she was very little, Rosita asked if a dog 'had bitted Mama's toes'. I told her Yes, a great, white, mad dog named Blizzard! My Rosita and my Juanito heard many stories when they were little, about that fearful dog and how it howled, and the transparent cattle of the invisible gauchos, and a river of ice eight thousand feet high called Nightingale, and how Cousin Juana drank a cup of tea standing on the bottom of the world under seven suns, and other fairy tales.

We were in for one severe shock when we reached Base at last. Teresa was pregnant. I must admit that my first response to the poor girl's big belly and sheepish look was anger—rage—fury. That one of us should have concealed anything, and such a thing, from the others! But Teresa had done nothing of the sort. Only those who had concealed from her what she most needed to know were to blame. Brought up by servants, with four years' schooling in a convent, and married at sixteen, the poor girl was still so ignorant at twenty years of age that she had thought it was 'the cold weather' that made her miss her periods. Even this was not entirely stupid, for all of us on the Southern Journey had seen our periods change or stop altogether as we experienced increasing cold, hunger, and fatigue. Teresa's appetite had begun to draw general attention; and then she had begun, as she said pathetically, 'to get fat'. The others were worried at the thought of all the sledge-hauling she had done, but she flourished, and the only problem was her positively insatiable appetite. As well as could be determined from her shy references to her last night on the hacienda with her husband, the baby was due at just about the same time as the *Yelcho*, the twentieth of February. But we had not been back from the Southern Journey two weeks when, on February 14, she went into labour.

Several of us had borne children and had helped with deliveries, and anyhow most of what needs to be done is fairly self-evident; but a first labour can be long and trying, and we were all anxious, while Teresa was frightened out of her wits. She kept calling for her José till she was as hoarse as a skua. Zoe lost all patience at last and said, 'By God, Teresa, if you say "José!" once more I hope you have a penguin!' But what she had, after twenty long hours, was a pretty little red-faced girl.

Many were the suggestions for that child's name from her eight proud midwife-aunts: Polita, Penguina, McMurdo, Victoria.... But Teresa announced, after she had had a good sleep and a large serving of pemmican, 'I shall name her Rosa—Rosa del Sur', Rose of the South. That night we drank the last two bottles of Veuve Clicquot (having finished the pisco at 88° 30' South) in toasts to our little Rose.

On the nineteenth of February, a day early, my Juana came down into Buenos Aires in a hurry. 'The ship,' she said, 'the ship has come,' and she burst into tears—she who had never wept in all our weeks of pain and weariness on the long haul.

Of the return voyage there is nothing to tell. We came back safe.

In 1912 all the world learned that the brave Norwegian Amundsen had reached the South Pole; and then, much later, came the accounts of how Captain Scott and his men had come there after him, but did not come home again.

Just this year, Juana and I wrote to the captain of the *Yelcho*, for the newspapers have been full of the story of his gallant dash to rescue Sir Ernest Shackleton's men from Elephant Island, and we wished to congratulate him, and once more to thank him. Never one word has he breathed of our secret. He is a man of honour, Luis Pardo.

I add this last note in 1929. Over the years we have lost touch with one another. It is very difficult for women to meet, when they live so far apart as we do. Since Juana died, I have seen none of my old sledge-mates, though sometimes we write. Our little Rosa del Sur died of the scarlet fever when she was five years old. Teresa had many other children. Carlota took the veil in Santiago ten years ago. We are old women now, with old husbands, and grown children, and grandchildren who might some day like to read about the Expedition. Even if they are rather ashamed of having such a crazy grandmother, they may enjoy sharing in the secret. But they must not let Mr Amundsen know! He would be terribly embarrassed and disappointed. There is no need for him or anyone else outside the family to know. We left no footprints, even.

In Amundsen's Tent

John Martin Leahy

'Inside the tent, in a little bag, I left a letter, addressed to H.M. the King, giving information of what he (sic) *had accomplished. . . . Besides this letter, I wrote a short epistle to Captain Scott, who, I assumed, would be the first to find the tent.'*

Captain Amundsen: The South Pole.

'We have just arrived at this tent, 2 miles from our camp, therefore about 1½ miles from the pole. In the tent we find a record of five Norwegians having been here, as follows:

> *Roald Amundsen*
> *Olav Olavson Bjaaland*
> *Hilmer Hanssen*
> *Sverre H. Hassel*
> *Oscar Wisting*

16 Dec. 1911.

'Left a note to say I had visited the tent with companions.'

Captain Scott: his last journal.

'Travellers,' says Richard A. Proctor, 'are sometimes said to tell marvellous stories; but it is a noteworthy fact that, in nine cases out of ten, the marvellous stories of travellers have been confirmed.'

Certainly no traveller ever set down a more marvellous story than that of Robert Drumgold. This record I am at last giving to the world, with my humble apologies to the spirit of the hapless explorer for withholding it so long. But the truth is that Eastman, Dahlstrom and I thought it the work of a mind deranged; little wonder, forsooth, if his mind had given way, what with the fearful sufferings which he

110

had gone through and the horror of that fate which was closing in upon him.

What was it, that *thing* (if thing it was) which came to him, the sole survivor of the party which had reached the Southern Pole, thrust itself into the tent and, issuing, left but the severed head of Drumgold there?

Our explanation at the time, and until recently, was that Drumgold had been set upon by his dogs and devoured. Why, though, the flesh had not been stripped from the head was to us an utter mystery. But that was only one of the many things that were utter mysteries.

But now we know—or feel certain—that this explanation was as far from the truth as that desolate, ice-mantled spot where he met his end is from the smiling, flower-spangled regions of the tropics.

Yes, we thought that the mind of poor Robert Drumgold had given way, that the horror in Amundsen's tent and that thing which came to Drumgold there in his own—we thought all was madness only. Hence our suppression of this part of the Drumgold manuscript. We feared that the publication of so extraordinary a record might cast a cloud of doubt upon the real achievements of the Sutherland expedition.

But of late our ideas and beliefs have undergone a change that is nothing less than a metamorphosis. This metamorphosis, it is scarcely necessary to say, was due to the startling discoveries made in the region of the Southern Pole by the late Captain Stanley Livingstone, as confirmed and extended by the expedition conducted by Darwin Frontenac. Captain Livingstone, we now learn, kept his real discovery, what with the doubts and derision which met him on his return to the world, a secret from every living soul but two—Darwin Frontenac and Bond McQuestion. It is but now, on the return of Frontenac, that we learn how truly wonderful and amazing were those discoveries made by the ill-starred captain. And yet, despite the success of the Frontenac expedition, it must be admitted that the mystery down there in the Antarctic is enhanced rather than dissipated. Darwin Frontenac and his companions saw much; but we know that there are things and beings down there that they did not see. The Antarctic—or, rather, part of it—has thus suddenly become the most interesting and certainly the most fearful area on this globe of ours.

So another marvellous story told—or, rather, only partly told—by a traveller has been confirmed. And here are Eastman and I preparing to go once more to the Antarctic to confirm, as we hope, another story—one eerie and fearful as any ever conceived by any romanticist.

And to think that it was ourselves, Eastman, Dahlstrom and I, who made the discovery! Yes, it was we who entered the tent, found there the head of Robert Drumgold and the pages whereon he had scrawled his story of mystery and horror. To think that we stood there, in the very spot where it had been and thought the story but as the baseless fabric of some madman's vision!

How vividly it all rises before me again—the white expanse glaring, blinding in the untempered light of the Antarctic sun, the dogs straining in the harness, the cases on the sleds, long and black like coffins; our sudden halt as Eastman fetched up in his tracks, pointed and said, 'Hello! What's that?'

A half-mile or so off to the left, some object broke the blinding white of the plains.

'*Nunatak*, I suppose,' was my answer.

'Looks to me like a cairn or a tent,' Dahlstrom said.

'How on earth,' I queried, 'could a tent have got down here in 87° 30' south? We are far from the route of either Amundsen or Scott.'

'H'm,' said Eastman, shoving his amber-coloured glasses up onto his forehead that he might get a better look, 'I wonder—Jupiter Ammon, Nels,' he added, glancing at

Dahlstrom, 'I believe that you are right.'

'It certainly,' Dahlstrom nodded, 'looks like a cairn or a tent to me. I don't think it's a *nunatak*.'

'Well,' said I, 'it would not be difficult to put it to the proof.'

'And that, my hearties,' exclaimed Eastman, 'is just what we'll do! We'll soon see what it is—whether it is a cairn, a tent, or only a *nunatak*.'

The next moment we were in motion, heading straight for that mysterious object there in the midst of the eternal desolation of snow and ice.

'Look there!' Eastman, who was leading the way, suddenly shouted. 'See that? It *is* a tent!'

A few moments, and I saw that it was indeed so. But who had pitched it there? What were we to find within it?

I could never describe those thoughts and feelings which were ours as we approached that spot. The snow lay piled about the tent to a depth of four feet or more. Nearby, a splintered ski protruded from the surface—and that was all.

And the stillness! The air, at the moment, was without the slightest movement. No sounds but those made by our movements, and those of the dogs, and our own breathing, broke that awful silence of death.

'Poor devils!' said Eastman at last. 'One thing, they certainly pitched their tent well.'

The tent was supported by a single pole, set in the middle. To this pole three guy-lines were fastened, one of them as taut as the day its stake had been driven into the surface. But this was not all: a half-dozen lines, or more, were attached to the sides of the tent. There it had stood for we knew not how long, bidding defiance to the fierce winds of that terrible region.

Dahlstrom and I each got a spade and began to remove the snow. The entrance we found unfastened but completely blocked by a couple of provision-cases (empty) and a piece of canvas. 'How on earth,' I exclaimed, 'did those things get into that position?'

'The wind,' said Dahlstrom. 'And, if the entrance had not been blocked, there wouldn't have been any tent here now; the wind would have split and destroyed it long ago.'

'H'm,' mused Eastman. 'The wind did it, Nels—blocked the place like that? I wonder.'

The next moment we had cleared the entrance. I thrust my head through the opening. Strangely enough, very little snow had drifted in. The tent was dark green, a circumstance which rendered the light within somewhat weird and ghastly—or perhaps my imagination contributed not a little to that effect.

'What do you see, Bill?' asked Eastman. 'What's inside?'

My answer was a cry, and the next instant I had sprung back from the entrance.

'What is it, Bill?' Eastman exclaimed. 'Great heaven, what is it, man?'

'A head!' I told him.

'A head?'

'A human head!'

He and Dahlstrom stooped and peered in. 'What is the meaning of this?' Eastman cried. 'A severed human head!'

Dahlstrom dashed a mittened hand across his eyes.

'Are we dreaming?' he exclaimed.

''Tis no dream, Nels,' returned our leader. 'I wish to heaven it was. A head! A human head!'

'Is there nothing more?' I asked.

'Nothing. No body, not even stripped bone—only that severed head. Could the dogs—'

'Yes?' queried Dahlstrom.

'Could the dogs have done this?'

'Dogs!' Dahlstrom said. 'This is not the work of dogs.'

We entered and stood looking down upon that grisly remnant of mortality.

'It wasn't dogs,' said Dahlstrom.

'Not dogs?' Eastman queried. 'What other explanation is there—except cannibalism?'

Cannibalism! A shudder went through my heart. I may as well say at once, however, that our discovery of a good supply of pemmican and biscuit on the sled, at that moment completely hidden by the snow, was to show us that that fearful explanation was not the true one. The dogs! That was it, that was the explanation—even though what the victim himself had set down told us a very different story. Yes, the explorer had been set upon by his dogs and devoured. But there were things that militated against that theory. Why had the animals left that head—in the frozen eyes (they were blue eyes) and upon the frozen features of which was a look of horror that sends a shudder through my very soul even now? Why, the head did not have even the mark of a single fang, though it appeared to have been *chewed* from the trunk. Dahlstrom, however, was of the opinion that it had been *hacked* off.

And there, in the man's story, in the story of Robert Drumgold, we found another mystery—a mystery as insoluble (if it was true) as the presence here of his severed head. There the story was, scrawled in lead-pencil across the pages of his journal. But what were we to make of a record—the concluding pages of it, that is—so strange and so dreadful?

But enough of this, of what we thought and of what we wondered. The journal itself lies before me, and I now proceed to set down the story of Robert Drumgold in his own words. Not a word, not a comma shall be deleted, inserted or changed.

Let it begin with his entry for January the 3rd, at the end of which day the little party was only fifteen miles (geographical) from the Pole.

Here it is.

Jan. 3.—Lat. of our camp 89° 45' 10". Only fifteen miles more, and the Pole is ours—unless Amundsen or Scott has beaten us to it, or both. But it will be ours just the same, even though the glory of discovery is found to be another's. What shall we find there?

All are in fine spirits. Even the dogs seem to know that this is the consummation of some great achievement. And a thing that is a mystery to us is the interest they have shown this day in the region before us. Did we halt, there they were gazing and gazing straight south and sometimes sniffing and sniffing. What does it mean?

Yes, in fine spirits all—dogs as well as we three men. Everything is auspicious. The weather for the last three days has been simply glorious. Not once, in this time, has the temperature been below minus 5. As I write this, the thermometer shows one degree above. The blue of the sky is like that of which painters dream, and, in that blue, tower cloud formations, violet-tinged in the shadows, that are beautiful beyond all description. If it were possible to forget the fact that nothing stands between ourselves and a horrible death save the meagre supply of food on the sleds, one could think he was in some fairyland—a glorious fairyland of white and blue and violet.

A fairyland? Why has that thought so often occurred to me? Why have I so often likened this desolate, terrible region to fairyland? Terrible? Yes, to human beings it is terrible—frightful beyond all words. But, though so unutterably terrible to men, it may not be so in reality. After all, are all things, even of this earth of ours, to say nothing of the universe, made for man—this being (a god-like spirit in the body of a quasi-ape) who, set in the midst of wonders, leers and slavers in madness and hate and wallows in the muck of a thousand lusts? May there not be other beings—yes, even on this very earth of ours—more wonderful—yes, and more terrible too—than he?

Heaven knows, more than once, in this desolation of snow and ice, I have seemed to feel their presence in the air about us—nameless entities, disembodied, *watching* things.

Little wonder, forsooth, that I have again and again thought of these strange words of one of America's greatest scientists Alexander Winchell:

> *Nor is incorporated rational existence conditioned on warm blood, nor on any temperature which does not change the forms of matter of which the organism may be composed. There may be intelligences corporealised after some concept not involving the processes of ingestion, assimilation and reproduction. Such bodies would not require daily food and warmth. They might be lost in the abysses of the ocean, or laid up on a stormy cliff through the tempests of an arctic winter, or plunged in a volcano for a hundred years, and yet retain consciousness and thought.*

All this Winchell tells us is conceivable, and he adds:

> *Bodies are merely the local fitting of intelligence to particular modifications of universal matter and force.*

And these entities, nameless things whose presence I seem to feel at times—are they benignant beings or things more fearful than even the madness of the human brain ever has fashioned?

But, then, I must stop this. If Sutherland or Travers were to read what I have set down here, they would think that I was losing my senses or would declare me already insane. And yet, as there is a heaven above us, it seems that I do actually believe that this frightful place knows the presence of beings other than ourselves and our dogs—things which we cannot see but which are watching us.

Enough of this.

Only fifteen miles from the Pole. Now for a sleep and on to our goal in the morning. Morning! There is no morning here, but day unending. The sun now rides as high at midnight as it does at midday. Of course, there is a change in altitude, but it is so slight as to be imperceptible without an instrument.

But the Pole! Tomorrow the Pole! What will we find there? Only an unbroken expanse of white, or—

Jan. 4.—The mystery and horror of this day—oh, how could I ever set that down? Sometimes, so fearful were those hours through which we have just passed, I even find myself wondering if it wasn't all only a dream. A dream! I would to heaven that it had been but a dream! As for the end—I must keep such thoughts out of my head.

Got under way at an early hour. Weather more wondrous than ever. Sky an azure that would have sent a painter into ecstasies. Cloud formations indescribably beautiful and grand. The going, however, was pretty difficult. The place a great plain stretching away with a monotonous uniformity of surface as far as the eye could reach. A plain never trod by human foot before? At length, when our dead reckoning showed that we were drawing near to the Pole, we had the answer to that. Then it was that the keen eyes of Travers detected some object rising above the blinding white of the snow.

On the instant Sutherland had thrust his amber glasses up onto his forehead and had his binoculars to his eyes.

'Cairn!' he exclaimed, and his voice sounded hollow and very strange. 'A cairn or a—*tent*. Boys, they have beaten us to the Pole!'

He handed the glasses to Travers and leaned, as though a sudden weariness had settled upon him, against the provision-cases on his sled.

'Forestalled!' said he. 'Forestalled!'

I felt very sorry for our brave leader in those, his moments of terrible disappointment, but for the life of me I did not know what to say. And so I said nothing.

At that moment a cloud concealed the sun, and the place where we stood was suddenly involved in a gloom that was deep and awful. So sudden and pronounced, indeed, was the change that we gazed about us with curious and wondering looks. Far off to the right and to the left, the plain blazed white and blinding. Soon, however, the last gleam of sunshine had vanished from off it. I raised my look up to the heavens. Here and there edges of cloud were touched as though with the light of wrathful golden fire. Even then, however, that light was fading. A few minutes, and the last angry gleam of the sun had vanished.

The gloom seemed to deepen about us every moment. A curious haze was concealing the blue expanse of the sky overhead. There was not the slightest movement in the gloomy and weird atmosphere. The silence was heavy, awful, the silence of the abode of utter desolation and of death.

'What on earth are we in for now?' said Travers.

Sutherland moved from his sled and stood gazing about into the eerie gloom.

'Queer change, this!' said he. 'It would have delighted the heart of Doré.'

'It means a blizzard, most likely,' I observed. 'Hadn't we better make camp before it strikes us? No telling what a blizzard may be like in this awful spot.'

'Blizzard?' said Sutherland. 'I don't think it means a blizzard, Bob. No telling, though. Mighty queer change, certainly. And how different the place looks now, in this strange gloom! It is surely weird and terrible—that is, it certainly looks weird and terrible.'

He turned his look to Travers.

'Well, Bill,' he asked, 'what did you make of it?'

He waved a hand in the direction of that mysterious object the sight of which had so suddenly brought us to a halt. I say in the direction of the object, for the thing itself was no longer to be seen.

'I believe it is a tent,' Travers told him.

'Well,' said our leader, 'we can soon find out what it is—cairn or tent, for one or the other it must certainly be.'

The next instant the heavy, awful silence was broken by the sharp crack of his whip.

'Mush on, you poor brutes!' he cried. 'On we go to see what is over there. Here we are at the South Pole. Let us see who has beaten us to it.'

But the dogs didn't want to go on, which did not surprise me at all, because, for some time now, they had been showing signs of some strange, inexplicable uneasiness. What had got into the creatures, anyway? For a time we puzzled over it; then we *knew*, though the explanation was still an utter mystery to us. They were *afraid*. Afraid? An inadequate word, indeed. It was fear, stark, terrible, that had entered the poor brutes. But whence had come this inexplicable fear? That also we soon knew. The thing they feared, whatever it was, was in that very direction in which we were headed!

A cairn, a tent? What did this thing mean?

'What on earth is the matter with the critters?' exclaimed Travers. 'Can it be that—'

'It's for us to find out what it means,' said Sutherland.

Again we got in motion. The place was still involved in that strange, weird gloom. The silence was still that awful silence of desolation and of death.

Slowly but steadily we moved forward, urging on the reluctant, fearful animals with our whips.

At last Sutherland, who was leading, cried out that he saw it. He halted, peering forward into the gloom, and we urged our teams up alongside his.

'It must be a tent,' he said.

And a tent we found it to be—a small one supported by a single bamboo and well guyed in all directions. Made of drab-coloured gaberdine. To the top of the tent pole another had been lashed. From this, motionless in the still air, hung the remains of a small Norwegian flag and, underneath it, a pennant with the word 'Fram' upon it. Amundsen's tent!

What should we find inside it? And what was the meaning of that—the strange way it bulged out on one side?

The entrance was securely laced. The tent, it was certain,

had been here for a year, all through the long Antarctic night; and yet, to our astonishment, but little snow was piled up about it, and most of this was drift. The explanation of this must, I suppose, be that, before the air currents have reached the Pole, almost all the snow has been deposited from them.

For some minutes we just stood there, and many, and some of them dreadful enough, were the thoughts that came and went. Through the long Antarctic night! What strange things this tent could tell us had it been vouchsafed the power of words! But strange things it might tell us, nevertheless. For what was that inside, making the tent bulge out in so unaccountable a manner? I moved forward to feel of it there with my mittened hand, but, for some reason that I cannot explain, of a sudden I drew back. At that instant one of the dogs whined—the sound so strange and the terror of the animal so unmistakable that I shuddered and felt a chill pass through my heart. Others of the dogs began to whine in that mysterious manner, and all shrank back cowering from the tent.

'What does it mean?' said Travers, his voice sunk almost to a whisper. 'Look at them. It is as though they are imploring us to—keep away.'

'To keep away,' echoed Sutherland, his look leaving the dogs and fixing itself once more on the tent.

'Their senses,' said Travers, 'are keener than ours. They already know what we can't know until we see it.'

'See it!' Sutherland exclaimed. 'I wonder. Boys, what are we going to see when we look into that tent? Poor fellows! They reached the Pole. But did they ever leave it? Are we going to find them in there dead?'

'Dead?' said Travers with a sudden start. 'The dogs would never act that way if 'twas only a corpse inside. And, besides, if that theory was true, wouldn't the sleds be here to tell the story? Yet look around. The level uniformity of the place shows that no sled lies buried here.'

'That is true,' said our leader. 'What *can* it mean? What *could* make that tent bulge out like that? Well, here is the mystery before us, and all we have to do is unlace the entrance and look inside to solve it.'

He stepped to the entrance, followed by Travers and me, and began to unlace it. At that instant an icy current of air struck the place and the pennant above our heads flapped with a dull and ominous sound. One of the dogs, too, thrust his muzzle skyward, and a deep and long-drawn howl arose. And while the mournful, savage sound yet filled the air, a strange thing happened.

Through a sudden rent in that gloomy curtain of cloud, the sun sent a golden, awful light down upon the spot where we stood. It was but a shaft of light, only three or four hundred feet wide, though miles in length, and there we stood in the very middle of it, the plain on each side involved in that weird gloom, now denser and more eerie than ever in contrast to that sword of golden fire which thus so suddenly had been flung down across the snow.

'Queer place this!' said Travers. 'Just like a beam lying across a stage in a theatre.'

Travers' smile was a most apposite one, more so than he perhaps ever dreamed himself. That place was a stage, our light the wrathful fire of the Antarctic sun, ourselves the actors in a scene stranger than any ever beheld in the mimic world.

For some moments, so strange was it all, we stood there looking about us in wonder and perhaps each one of us in not a little secret awe.

'Queer place, all right!' said Sutherland. 'But—'

He laughed a hollow, sardonic laugh. Up above, the pennant flapped and flapped again, the sound of it hollow and ghostly. Again rose the long-drawn, mournful, fiercely sad howl of the wolf-dog.

'But,' added our leader, 'we don't want to be imagining things, you know.'

'Of course not,' said Travers.

'Of course not,' I echoed.

A little space, and the entrance was open and Sutherland had thrust head and shoulders through it.

I don't know how long it was that he stood there like that. Perhaps it was only a few seconds, but to Travers and me it seemed rather long.

'What is it?' Travers exclaimed at last. 'What do you see?' The answer was a scream—the horror of that sound I can never forget—and Sutherland came staggering back and, I believe, would have fallen had we not sprung and caught him.

'What is it?' cried Travers. 'In God's name, Sutherland, what did you see?'

Sutherland beat the side of his head with his hand, and his look was wild and horrible.

'What is it?' I exclaimed. 'What did you see in there?'

'I can't tell you—I can't! Oh, oh, I wish that I had never seen it! Don't look! Boys, don't look, into that tent—unless you are prepared to welcome madness, or worse.'

'What gibberish is this?' Travers demanded, gazing at our leader in utter astonishment. 'Come, come, man! Buck up. Get a grip on yourself. Let's have an end to this nonsense. Why should the sight of a dead man, or dead men, affect you in this mad fashion?'

'Dead men?' Sutherland laughed, the sound wild, maniacal.

'Dead men? If 'twas only that! Is this the South Pole? Is this the earth, or are we in a nightmare on some other planet?'

'For heaven's sake,' cried Travers, 'come out of it! What's got into you? Don't let your nerves go like this.'

'A dead man?' queried our leader, peering into the face of Travers. 'You think I saw a dead man? I wish it was only a dead man. Thank God, you two didn't look!'

On the instant Travers had turned.

'Well,' said he, 'I am going to look!'

But Sutherland cried out, screamed, sprang after him and tried to drag him back.

'It would mean horror and perhaps madness!' cried Sutherland. 'Look at me. Do you want to be like me?'

'No!' Travers returned. 'But I am going to see what is in that tent.'

He struggled to break free, but Sutherland clung to him in a frenzy of madness.

'Help me, Bob!' Sutherland cried.

'Hold him back, or we'll all go insane.'

But I did not help him to hold Travers back, for, of course, it was my belief that Sutherland himself was insane. Nor did Sutherland hold Travers. With a sudden wrench, Travers was free. The next instant he had thrust head and shoulders through the entrance of the tent.

Sutherland groaned and watched him with eyes full of unutterable horror.

I moved toward the entrance, but Sutherland flung himself at me with such violence that I was sent over into the snow. I sprang to my feet full of anger and amazement.

'What the hell,' I cried, 'is the matter with you, anyway? Have you gone crazy?'

The answer was a groan, horrible beyond all words of man but that sound did not come from Sutherland. I turned. Travers was staggering away from the entrance, a hand pressed over his face, sounds that I could never describe breaking from deep in his throat. Sutherland, as the man came staggering up to him, thrust forth an arm and touched Travers lightly on the shoulder. The effect was instantaneous and frightful. Travers sprang aside as though a serpent had struck at him, screamed and screamed yet again.

'There, there!' said Sutherland gently. 'I told you not to do it. I tried to make you understand, but—but you thought that I was mad.'

'It can't belong to this earth!' moaned Travers.

'No,' said Sutherland. 'That horror was never born on this planet of ours. And the inhabitants of earth, though they do not know it, can thank God Almighty for that.'

'But it is *here*!' Travers exclaimed. 'How did it come to this awful place? And where did it come from?'

'Well,' consoled Sutherland, 'it is dead—it must be dead.'

'Dead? How do we know that it is dead? And don't forget this: it didn't come here alone!'

Sutherland started. At that moment the sunlight vanished, and everything was once more involved in gloom.

'What do you mean?' Sutherland asked. 'Not alone? How do you know that it did not come alone?'

'Why, it is there *inside* the tent; but the entrance was laced—from the *outside*!'

'Fool, fool that I am!' cried Sutherland a little fiercely. 'Why didn't I think of that? Not alone! Of course it was not alone!'

He gazed about into the gloom, and I knew the nameless fear and horror that chilled him to the very heart, for they chilled me to my very own.

Of a sudden arose again that mournful, savage howl of the wolf-dog. We three men started as though it was the voice of some ghoul from hell's most dreadful corner.

'Shut up, you brute!' gritted Travers. 'Shut up, or I'll brain you!'

Whether it was Travers' threat or not, I do not know; but that howl sank, ceased almost on the instant. Again the silence of desolation and of death lay upon the spot. But above the tent the pennant stirred and rustled, the sound of it, I thought, like the slithering of some repulsive serpent.

'What did you see in there?' I asked them.

'Bob—Bob,' said Sutherland, 'don't ask us that.'

'The thing itself,' said I, turning, 'can't be any worse than this mystery and nightmare of imagination.'

But the two of them threw themselves before me and barred my way.

'No!' said Sutherland firmly. 'You must not look into that tent, Bob. You must not see that—that—I don't know what to call it. Trust us; believe us, Bob! 'Tis for your sake that we say that you must not do it. We, Travers and I, can never be the same men again—the brains, the souls of us can never be what they were before we saw *that*!'

'Very well,' I acquiesced. 'I can't help saying, though, that the whole thing seems to me like the dream of a madman.'

'That,' said Sutherland, 'is a small matter indeed. Insane? Believe that it is the dream of a madman. Believe that we are insane. Believe that you are insane yourself. Believe anything you like. Only *don't look*!'

'Very well,' I told them. 'I won't look. I give in. You two have made a coward of me.'

'A coward?' said Sutherland. 'Don't talk nonsense, Bob. There are some things that a man should never know; there are some things that a man should never see; that horror there in Amundsen's tent is—both!'

'But you said that it is dead.'

Travers groaned. Sutherland laughed a little wildly.

'Trust us,' said the latter; 'believe us, Bob. 'Tis for your sake, not for our own. For that is too late now. We have seen it, and you have not.'

For some minutes we stood there by the tent, in that weird gloom, then turned to leave the cursed spot. I said that undoubtedly Amundsen had left some records inside, that possibly Scott had reached the Pole, and visited the tent, and that we ought to secure any such mementoes. Sutherland and Travers nodded, but each declared that he would not put his head through that entrance again for all the wealth of Ormus and of Ind—or words to that effect. We must, they said, get away from the awful place—get back to the world of men with our fearful message.

'You won't tell me what you saw,' I said, 'and yet you want to get back so that you can tell it to the world.'

'We aren't going to tell the world what we saw,' answered Sutherland. 'In the first place, we couldn't, and, in the second place, if we could, not a living soul would believe us. But we can warn people, for that thing in there did not come alone. Where is the other one—or the others?'

'Dead, too, let us hope!' I exclaimed.

'Amen!' said Sutherland. 'But maybe, as Bill says, it isn't dead. Probably—'

Sutherland paused, and a wild, indescribable look came into his eyes.

'Maybe it—*can't die*!'

'Probably,' said I nonchalantly, yet with secret disgust and with poignant sorrow.

What was the use? What good would it do to try to reason with a couple of madmen? Yes, we must get away from this spot, or they would have me insane, too. And the long road back? Could we ever make it now? And what *had* they seen? What unimaginable horror was there behind that thin wall of gaberdine? Well, whatever it was, it was real. Of that I could not entertain the slightest doubt. Real? Real enough to wreck, virtually instantaneously, the strong brains of two strong men. But—were my poor companions really mad, after all?

'Or maybe,' Sutherland was saying, 'the other one, or the others, went back to Venus or Mars or Sirius or Algol, or hell itself, or wherever they came from, to get more of their kind. If that is so, heaven have pity on poor humanity! And, if it or they are still here on this earth, then sooner or later—it may be a dozen years, it may be a century—but sooner or later the world will know it, know it to its woe and to its horror. For they, if living, or if gone for others, will come again.'

'I was thinking—' began Travers, his eyes fixed on the tent.

'Yes?' Sutherland queried.

'—that,' Travers told him, 'it might be a good plan to empty the rifle into that thing. Maybe it isn't dead; maybe it can't die—maybe it only *changes*. Probably it is just hibernating, so to speak.'

'If so,' I laughed, 'it will probably hibernate till doomsday.'

But neither one of my companions laughed.

'Or,' said Travers, 'it may be a demon, a ghost materialised. I can't say incarnated.'

'A ghost materialised!' I exclaimed. 'Well, may not every man or woman be just that? Heaven knows, many a one acts like a demon or a fiend incarnate.'

'They may be,' nodded Sutherland. 'But that hypothesis doesn't help us any here.'

'It may help things some,' said Travers, starting toward his sled.

A moment or two, and he had got out the rifle.

'I thought,' said he, 'that nothing could ever take me back to that entrance. But the hope that I may—'

Sutherland groaned.

'It isn't earthly, Bill,' he said hoarsely. 'It's a nightmare. I think we had better go now.'

Travers was going—straight toward the tent.

'Come back, Bill!' groaned Sutherland. 'Come back! Let us go while we can.'

But Travers did not come back. Slowly he moved forward, rifle thrust out before him, finger on the trigger. He reached the tent, hesitated a moment, then thrust the rifle barrel through. As fast as he could work trigger and lever, he emptied the weapon into the tent—into that horror inside it.

He whirled and came back as though in fear the tent was about to spew forth behind him all the legions of foulest hell.

What was that? The blood seemed to freeze in my veins and heart as there arose from out the tent a sound—a sound low and throbbing—a sound that no man ever had heard on this earth—one that I hope no man will ever hear again.

A panic, a madness seized upon us, upon men and dogs alike, and away we fled from that cursed place.

The sound ceased. But again we heard it. It was more fearful, more unearthly, soul-maddening, hellish than before.

'Look?' cried Sutherland. 'Oh, my God, *look at that*!'

The tent was barely visible now. A moment or two, and the curtain of gloom would conceal it. At first I could not imagine what had made Sutherland cry out like that. Then I saw it in that very moment before the gloom hid it from view. The tent was moving! It swayed, jerked like some shapeless monster in the throes of death, like some nameless thing seen in the horror of nightmare or limned on the brain of utter madness itself.

And that is what happened there; that is what we saw. I have set it down at some length and to the best of my ability under the truly awful circumstances in which I am placed. In these hastily scrawled pages is recorded an experience that, I believe, is not surpassed by the wildest to be found in the pages of the most imaginative romanticist. Whether the record is destined ever to reach the world, ever to be scanned by the eye of another—only the future can answer that.

I will try to hope for the best. I cannot blink the fact, however, that things are pretty bad for us. It is not only this sinister, nameless mystery from which we are fleeing—though heaven knows that is horrible enough—but it is the *minds* of my companions. And, added to that, is the fear for my own. But there, I must get myself in hand. After all, as Sutherland said, I didn't see it. I must not give way. We must somehow get our story to the world, though we may have for our reward only the mockery of the world's unbelief, its scoffing—the world, against which is now moving, gathering, a menace more dreadful than any that ever moved in the fevered brain of any prophet of woe and blood and disaster.

We are a dozen miles or so from the Pole now. In that mad dash away from that tent of horror, we lost our bearings and for a time, I fear, went panicky. The strange, eerie gloom denser than ever. Then came a fall of fine snow-crystals, which rendered things worse than ever. Just when about to give up in despair, chanced upon one of our beacons. This gave us our bearings, and we pressed on to this spot.

Travers has just thrust his head into the tent to tell us that he is sure he saw something moving off in the gloom. Something moving! This must be looked into.

(If Robert Drumgold could only have left as full a record of those days which followed as he had of that fearful 4th of January! No man can ever know what the three explorers went through in their struggle to escape that doom from which there was no escape—a doom the mystery and horror of which perhaps surpass in gruesomeness what the most dreadful Gothic imagination ever conceived in its utterest abandonment to delirium and madness.)

Jan. 5.—Travers *had* seen something, for we, the three of us, saw it again today. Was it that horror, that thing not of this earth, which they saw in Amundsen's tent? We don't know what it is. All we know is that it is something that moves. God have pity on us all—and on every man and woman and child on this earth of ours if this thing is what we fear!

6th.—Made 25 mi. today—20 yesterday. Did not see it today. *But heard it.* Seemed near—once, in fact, as though right over our heads. But that must have been imagination. Effect on dogs most terrible. Poor brutes! It is as horrible to them as it is to us. Sometimes I think even more. Why is it following us?

7th.—Two of dogs gone this morning. One or another of us on guard all 'night'. Nothing seen, not a sound heard, yet the animals have vanished. Did they desert us? We say that is what happened but each man of us knows that none of us believes it. Made 18 mi. Fear that Travers is going mad.

8th.—Travers gone! He took the watch last night at 12, relieving Sutherland. That was the last seen of Travers—the last that we shall ever see. No tracks—not a sign in the snow. Travers, poor Travers, gone! Who will be the next?

Jan. 9.—Saw it again! Why does it let us see it like this—sometimes? Is it that horror in Amundsen's tent? Sutherland declares that it is not—that it is something even more hellish. But then S. is mad now—mad—mad—mad. If I wasn't sane, I could think that it all was only imagination. *But I saw it!*

Jan. 11.—Think it is the 11th but not sure. I can no longer be sure of anything—save that I am alone and that it is watching me. Don't know how I know, for I cannot see it. But I do know—it is watching me. It is always watching. And sometime it will come and get me—as it got Travers and Sutherland and half of the dogs.

Yes, today must be the 11th. For it was yesterday—surely it was only yesterday—that it took Sutherland. I didn't see it take him, for a fog had come up, and Sutherland—he would go on in the fog—was so slow in following that the vapour hid him from view. At last when he didn't come, I went back. But S. was gone—man, dogs, sled, everything was gone. Poor Sutherland! But then he was mad. Probably that was why it took him. Has it spared me because I am yet sane? S. had the rifle. Always he clung to that rifle—as though a bullet could save him from what we saw! My only weapon is an axe. But what good is an axe?

Jan. 13.—Maybe it is the 14th. I don't know. What does it matter? Saw it *three* times today. Each time it was closer. Dogs still whining about tent. There—that horrible hellish sound again. Dogs still now. That sound again. But I dare not look out. The axe.

Hours later. Can't write any more.

Silence. Voices—I seem to hear voices. But that sound again.

Coming nearer. At entrance now—now—

The Barrier Silence

Edward Wilson

The Silence was deep with a breath like sleep
      As our sledge runners slid on the snow,
And the fate-full fall of our fur-clad feet
      Struck mute like a silent blow
On a questioning 'hush', as the settling crust
      Shrank shivering over the floe;
And the sledge in its track sent a whisper back
      Which was lost in a white fog-bow.

And this was the thought that the Silence wrought
      As it scorched and froze us through,
Though secrets hidden are all forbidden
      Till God means man to know,
We might be the men God meant should know
      The heart of the Barrier snow,
      In the heat of the sun, and the glow
      And the glare from the glistening floe,
As it scorched and froze us through and through
      With the bite of the drifting snow.

Wilson's Diary
(*for Josie and Ian*)

Dorothy Porter

Cri de coeur
   is simply
      strength of character
whimpering to itself
   on sea-ice
      that is yielding
         to the spine
            of a killer whale—

the water
   is a palaeontologist's
      paradise,
frozen fossils
   surfacing
      to add nostalgia
   to a century
      that likes defrosting
         extinct things,
   the water is quite fascinating
      and will kill you
         damn quick!

When the wind drops
   the sea will come for you
      stiff, shuffling, white
         like an Edgar Allan Poe
         bride
whose hands are cold

whose memory
    is frightfully good—

Have I made myself perfectly clear?

   Yes sir!!

   Toast, fires, chat
         and fagging
           at Eton
are behind your resolve
     not to look
       to shiver
       to care
ah, the soul is a plateau
      a plateau
        dignified
              bare—

not a hymn
    of shameless tears
    flooding out
     the conduits
      of glistening
       infatuation

well said!

And no sea snakes
    to taunt us here
nothing twisting
    us about
     with beauty
just this avenue of icebergs
    mauve, pink, gold!

ice crystals
    the sham jewels
        of Purgatory!

Hell's Versailles!
can you cope?

If I come South
    (come South!
    come South!)
it's because
    I've fallen in love
and love
    is a trance,
        a marching order!
Let my heart crack
    like a ship destroyed
            in pack ice
let my soul
    perish
    like a sledger pulling
    across an infinite glacier
let my eyes
    blister
        in the blizzard
        of God.

The Photographer in the Antarctic

Chris Orsman

Whatever his talk of 'gathering it in'
—those pouting expeditions

with cameras, kinematograph—
he returns again and again

to the same scenes: caves, crevasses,
the colonies and rookeries

of our rude neighbours.
It's no wonder that he acquires

a mastery of ice subjects,
or grows fit manhauling his sledge

although it constrains him
to local subjects on our coast.

At first he makes no selection
but photographs what he finds;

he grows literal and adept,
serving a subtle proof that things

have been seen for the first time.
A clarity of new creation

soon gives way to 'art'
—the selective inward eye,

to things that frame a field of vision,
standing figures, mast and spar.

The ship repeats itself,
all grow accustomed

to posing by their sledges.
They stand as polar silhouettes

while distinctive backgrounds
move in and out of focus

and efface themselves
against the oncoming storm.

*

That youthful century on the ice
made new by the kinematograph:

here's the Owner with a football,
smiling shyly as he emerges

from the doorway of the hut;
the others are learning their rhythm,

skimming the ground in balaclavas.
This early footage is played hard

with a graceful optimism.
Men smile, stamp, breathe

into their permanent images,
along with the groomed ponies.

A portrait of tethered men
breaking through the snow crust

and brought to their knees
seems more comic than ominous.

Lastly, here are the motor-sledges
careering to the horizon,

and the pony-sledges, too,
off at a gallop to the Pole

—shooed off, waved off, and soon
hopelessly out of range.

The Ice Fleet Sails

Chris Orsman

The march reminded me of a regatta
or a somewhat disorganised fleet
with ships of very unequal speed.
2 November 1911

The ice fleet sails out
under the steam of breathing ponies

and men—over the sea ice,
skirting islands and the black

rock of the bays, keeping pace
unequally, stringing out

into the self-effacing, white
modernist horizon.

Small objects are greatly
exaggerated—tempers,

the back of a boot.
The dogs are instructed

in shouts of Russian,
the only language they understand.

*

The motor-sledges have died on us;
we found the tell-tale scribble

on the snow—benzine and motor oil.
We came across the first

bleeding from a cylinder,
it had fired its own *coup de grâce*.

I got my kinematograph
bearing on the scene

as the next sledge rolled
in an unearthly manner.

So, the dream of great help
from the machines is at an end.

*

The prediction of blizzards becomes an almost
accurate art—they bare a finger to the wind

and study cloud forms as they pass.
The atmosphere presses down on them;

someone remembers Turner's *Snowstorm*
and speaks, haltingly, out of turn.

Then that great painting is upon them,
in which nothing comes to rest: great bands

of snow and cloud arch over the explorers,
deflected by the light, unhinging

their belief in balance and stability.
The beasts, on whom so much depends,

are hit as usual when the blizzard falls;
under failing light they build snow walls.

Impressions on the March

Robert Falcon Scott

The seductive folds of the sleeping-bag.

The hiss of the primus and the fragrant steam of the cooker issuing from the tent ventilator.

The small green tent and the great white road.

The whine of a dog and the neigh of our steeds.

The driving cloud of powdered snow.

The crunch of footsteps which break the surface crust.

The wind-blown furrows.

The blue arch beneath the smoky cloud.

The crisp ring of the ponies' hoofs and the swish of the following sledge.

The droning conversation of the march as driver encourages or chides his horse.

The patter of dog pads.

The gentle flutter of our canvas shelter.

Its deep booming sound under the full force of a blizzard.

The drift snow like finest flour penetrating every hole and corner—flickering up beneath one's head covering, pricking sharply as a sand blast.

The sun with blurred image peeping shyly through the wreathing drift giving pale shadowless light.

The eternal silence of the great white desert. Cloudy columns of snow drift advancing from the south, pale yellow wraiths, heralding the coming storm, blotting out one by one the sharp-cut lines of the land.

The blizzard, Nature's protest—the crevasse, Nature's pitfall—that grim trap for the unwary—no hunter could conceal his snare so perfectly—the light rippled snow bridge gives no hint or sign of the hidden danger, its position unguessable till man or beast is floundering, clawing and struggling for foothold on the brink.

The vast silence broken only by the mellow sounds of the marching column.

2 February 1911

Antarctica
(for Richard Ryan)

Derek Mahon

'I am just going outside and may be some time.'
The others nod, pretending not to know.
At the heart of the ridiculous, the sublime.

He leaves them reading and begins to climb,
Goading his ghost into the howling snow;
He is just going outside and may be some time.

The tent recedes beneath its crust of rime
And frostbite is replaced by vertigo:
At the heart of the ridiculous, the sublime.

Need we consider it some sort of crime,
This numb self-sacrifice of the weakest? No,
He is just going outside and may be some time—

In fact, for ever. Solitary enzyme,
Though the night yield no glimmer there will glow,
At the heart of the ridiculous, the sublime.

He takes leave of the earthly pantomime
Quietly, knowing it is time to go.
'I am just going outside and may be some time.'
At the heart of the ridiculous, the sublime.

Edward Wilson

Glyn Maxwell

A dream of English watercolourists
all spread out on the hills: the sky is blue.
No breeze, nothing creative, not the least
exploratory dab. Then the same view

clouds and differs. Hills on the horizon
breed and open till the light has all
its colours boiling and there's only Wilson,
sketching in a blizzard, with his whole

blood sausage fist about a charcoal point,
grasping forever things in their last form
before the whiteness. A late English saint
has only eggs to save, himself to warm,

picturing Oriana. Lost winds
tug at the sketchbook. Shaded round, the eyes
Scott has to look at till tomorrow ends
are unenquiring and as blue as skies.

from
The Fire on the Snow

Douglas Stewart

THE ANNOUNCER

I am to break into the conversation
With a word that tastes like snow to say;
I am to interrupt the contemplation
Of the familiar headlines of the day—
Horses, divorces, politics, murders—
With a word cold to hear or look at,
Colder to speak. These are my orders,

And who am I to deny or question
A voice that says to speak of ice
And to speak of death. I have made the suggestion
That a free man should have his choice,
That the Pole keep its cold and the dead stay dead;
I have no wish to bring to supper
The blizzard to sing, the dead to be fed.

But the reply comes: The world is spun
Between two giant hands of ice,
And on any peak of living won
From hardest hours, the blizzards hiss,
And the reward set for the blindest faith
In the fixed needle directing us
Is to reach the Pole; and the Pole is death.

I say what I have to say: 'Death',
The word that drops in the room like rain
Making the live coals gasp for breath

146

And blackening slowly among the brain
When a man is sitting up late, alone.
I say what I have to: 'Death in the South;
Flesh that is snow; ice that was bone.'

I see what I have to see: Scott,
Oates, Evans, Wilson, Bowers,
Whose bodies lie, too cold to rot,
Where the aurora leaps and towers
Colouring the Antarctic sky with terror,
Like their own memorial marbles, like
Their own reflections trapped in a mirror.

My instructor, summoning the dead men's voices
And the sight of their undecaying bodies,
Does not pretend that here he rejoices
Or has much comfort to bring to the ladies.
He says, 'Let the dead men tell what they know,
Let them come to us now, these five men struggling
Like dark tough flames on the snow.'

* * *

THE ANNOUNCER

This journey is one man's dream
As it is one man's burden
And the man is Scott, the leader.
The others do what they're bidden,
Bearing their share of the load,
But cannot tell what it means.
Evans, who understood least,
Was the first to die, a man
Lost in a nightmare, lost
In the fog of another man's dream.

Only the dreamer is living.
And now when grief is gone
Is the hour of peace and release,
For the dream is clear again.
Calm as an albatross
The sunlight rides the gale
Or dives at the shoals of ice
In a flash like a flock of gulls,
And the heart leaps and rejoices
For the dreamer knows he is living.

He knows he is living his dream
On the pure plane of action
Where the white, sparkling scene,
Almost his own creation,
Is stamped with his own design
Of marching and halting, marching,
And the sledge's long snowy sigh
In the stream of their movement, lurching
Like a boulder down to the sea,
Just as he planned in his dream.

The dreamer knows he is master,
As every dreamer has been
Who ruled men's minds or bodies
Who had no will of their own.
Nothing the future bodes
Or the past has done can hurt
The hour when the dreamer walks
Alive in the dream of his heart.
Who will quench the delight that wakes
When the master knows he is master?

That delight is a moment's delight, it will die at
the moment of knowing

That a man lies dead on the snow and another
    man's steps are slowing
And the barren plain has no end and the iron
    wind is blowing.

* * *

THE ANNOUNCER

Rollers of blizzard
Roar and break
In foam on the tent.
The tide of the South
White, tremendous,
Roars on the tent,
Roars in the ears
Of drowning men.

It is evil, evil to lie awake in the night
And listen to the snow, more sinister than rain,
Pelt at the walls; evil to lie awake
And watch the mottled wet green walls of the tent
Crumple like water in the booming tide of the wind.
Bedraggled, sopping clothes, personal things
Are seaweed, flotsam, relics of another life,
Relics of a life hardly to be remembered now
By the men who, falling asleep, look like the drowned,
Lost beyond hope in the roaring tide of the storm.

BOWERS. Listen to it. Listen to the wind. Still snowing.
    It had to stop to-day. It's still snowing.
SCOTT. I know, Birdie. Once or twice in the night I thought
    It was dying out. There'd be a moment of calm
    And then it would shriek again.
BOWERS.   Perhaps it will drop.
SCOTT. It sounds so solid. A wall of white outside
    Nothing can break, not the sun, nor you nor Wilson.

149

WILSON. It's a clumsy way of killing us. We should be flattered
That the whole Antarctic has to lash itself to a fury
To kill three men.
                    It's taken its time,
Weeks and weeks since the Pole when it marked us down;
But it knows what it's doing now, it's making certain.
BOWERS. That's a mad way to talk. And it's madness, too,
To take this lying down. There must be some way
Out, the storm must ease, something must happen;
We can't lie here and wait and not do anything.
SCOTT. What will you do? March in a blizzard?
BOWERS.   I won't
Lie here and wait for the end like a rotting log.
I will march in the blizzard if that's what it comes to!
I'll die in the track.
SCOTT.   While we are here there's a chance.
Even to-morrow we may be able to march,
But a man doesn't do much marching once he is dead
And any man who tackles that blizzard will die.
BOWERS. We planned yesterday to march to-day. To-day
You say we'll march to-morrow. We'll never march.
We'll be so weak to-morrow with cold and hunger
We couldn't walk a mile. I suppose you're right,
It's death outside; but how can you bear this waiting,
How can you bear it?
WILSON.   There's nothing else we can do
But bear it and not be weak. I want to march,
I want to act as much as you do, but action
Is weakness now, and strength is all in acceptance,
Strength is in patience. We've had our share of action
And like the old people I've watched, whose hands
And voices tremble like water, we must learn to be patient
To keep our hands still and our voices calm,
True witnesses of the wells of darkness we are
Under these broken shallows.

                    It maddens me most
That all this elaborate setting of snow and wind
Was needed for such a simple thing as our passing;
But that's the curse of the body. Everything's cumbrous,
An axe of wind and snow and a block of ice.
But at least there is dignity
In waiting quietly. I've thought of death as a lake,
Nothing but calm acceptance of whatever light
The sun or the moon or God like the gleam of sunrise
Burns on the waters.

BOWERS. It's our deaths you're talking about, our deaths.
You can lie there calmly in your sleeping-bag
And talk about us as if you were speaking of strangers,
Or as if we were dead already and couldn't hear you.
Look, here's my hand. I can move it. Here's
My voice, I can speak to you. I'm alive. We're all alive,
We can talk, move, we have thoughts, there are people
    who love us.
Three dead bodies frozen in a tent
That's what we'll be. My God, think of the silence,
Think of the silence. Do you wonder I want to get out?

                    THE ANNOUNCER

    The man of action
    Shall have satisfaction,
    The man of peace
    A leaf's release,
    The leader's ambition
    Its consummation;
    For death is leaping,
    And calm escaping,
    And the final shaping:
    And death is nothing
    But stopping breathing.

                        151

The men sleep, too tired any more for thinking,
Like stones that know nothing of green or blue or gold
Or black as the turning seasons cry their colours.
Hunger and cold are less to their grey silence
Than lichens to rocks, or the sunny river water
To the deaf pebbles as it sings and shines and dances.
But sleep is suddenly haunted, worse than waking
With the white horror of snow on remembered fields
Devouring the grass, and remembered faces devoured,
And remembered bodies lost among winter dusk.
They wake again and find it is snowing still.
It will snow till the end of the world and snow in hell.

SCOTT. If we had a shovel handy, Wilson, I'd ask you
To shovel away the snow that's inside my head,
That's where it's falling now. My brain's a snowdrift.
Somewhere deep down there's a fire. I can almost see it,
Red under masses of snow.
WILSON.   While you were sleeping
A fire went out in the tent: Bowers is dead.
About an hour ago.
SCOTT.   Bowers! He can't be.
WILSON. He is. That was the last wild flare, that vigour
Yesterday, wanting to march. He broke his heart
With impatience, as if he had hurled his mind, as he wanted
To hurl his body, against this wall of blizzard.
SCOTT. How did he die? Was it easy?
WILSON.   No, not easy.
SCOTT. Poor fellow, poor fellow.
WILSON.   Yes,
But it's over now. And what a life he has had,
How brave and cheerful he was, such a fighter always.
SCOTT. I have said so in my diary. It will be found
And people will know some day that Bowers was a hero
And Oates walked to death like a god and Evans was strong.

They'll know, too, how much your friendship has meant.
It's good to hear your voice. How dark the tent is.
WILSON. Everything's dark; but talking is like a candle.
SCOTT. I've been thinking the whole trip over. I'm sure for myself,
And perhaps for the others, too, that it's been worthwhile.
I'd hoped to live. I wanted to teach my son
That life when it's lived like this, hard and heroic,
Is something so joyful no one could understand it
Unless he was willing to dare it. No bird and no beast
That lives an unthinking life can know such delight.
It's reserved for the saint, the martyr; perhaps for the soldier
On the peak of death: and women tortured by cancer.
I am glad we have lived so bitterly and die so hard;
And if only they find what I've written, perhaps our story
Will say what I wanted to say; that a man must learn
To endure agony, to endure and endure again
Until agony itself is beaten out into joy.

Facing this certain death these last two days,
Writing these farewell letters to friends and the world,
I have seen our lives as a drowning man would see them,
I have seen them whole, and there's nothing I would change.
Do you remember it all, remember living?
WILSON. I remember the ship going out, so much more daring
Than the gulls that so quickly scudded back to the port.
SCOTT. I remember before that, vaguely, England. It seems
A blue mist, and hollows where leaves were green
And everyone was kind, you could touch their hands.
That was years ago. I remember more clearly
New Zealand, that garden at Christchurch, how sharply blue
The peaks of the Kaikouras stabbed the horizon,
And the Avon looked so tranquil among its willows,
And the city was quiet. But that was years ago.
I remember the ship, yes; shouting and the gulls,
And in such a little while no gulls or shouting,

153

But the sea darkening and looking lonely. Wilson,
Remember those days in the pack, the sun on the ice
And the men's voices clear as bells as they sang,
Clear as bells.

WILSON. The ice was dazzling white and the sea was blue,
A very dark blue, and all the sailors were singing.
I remember the winter, the comradeship in the hut,
But it faded out. We were cold. Those long dark days
When nobody spoke and we felt like dreams and shadows.

SCOTT. One night I walked to the cliffs alone, and the moon
Was pure and burning on those frozen spires and crags,
So that they leapt like flames. The ice was blazing.
And the hut, when I came back, was a red island,
A ship at sea, a fire of human beings,
Warm and secure. But that was years ago.
I remember the march to the Pole beginning; sledges,
Dogs, ponies, the happy cavalcade,
The long swinging easy marches, the feeling
Of songs and banners.
I remember the black flag that told us about Amundsen,
That fatal day.

WILSON.   We shouldn't have cared.

SCOTT.   But we did,
And the Pole was ghosts and ruins, and the snow on our
    mouths
Was ashes, ashes. And Evans crumbled away,
And the Soldier after him.
                    How am I justified,
Wilson, how am I justified for Oates and Evans,
And Bowers . . . and you?

WILSON.   All of us chose to do it,
Our own will brought us, our death on the ice
Was foreseen by each of us; accepted. Let your mind be at peace.
I have seen this death as the common fate made clearer,
And cleaner, too, this simple struggle on the ice.

We dreamed, we so nearly triumphed, we were defeated
As every man in some great or humble way
Dreams, and nearly triumphs, and is always defeated,
And then, as we did, triumphs again in endurance.
Triumph is nothing; defeat is nothing; life is
Endurance; and afterwards, death. And whatever death is,
The endurance remains like a fire, a sculpture, a mountain
To hearten our children. I tell you,
Such a struggle as ours is living; it lives after death
Purely, like flame, a thing burning and perfect.
SCOTT. There was something else. I can't remember now;
I am tired. Death is very near me.
                              Wilson,
There is something else, something to do with me.
Moonlight on ice. Wilson—
                  Wilson!
                          Agony.
Two dead men; and a dying man remembering.
The burning snow, the crags towering like flame.

The Pole
Drama in One Act

Vladimir Nabokov

CAST OF CHARACTERS
Captain Scott
Fleming
Kingsley
Johnson

'He was a very gallant gentleman' (from Scott's notebook)

Interior of a tent. Four figures: Captain Scott, dubbed 'Chief,' and Fleming semi-reclining; Kingsley and Johnson asleep, totally bundled up. All four have their legs in fur bags.

FLEMING.
    Only twelve miles to go—yet we must wait. . . .
    What a snowstorm . . . it roves, it tears. . . . Still writing,
    Chief?
CAPT. SCOTT. *(leafing through his diary)*
            Yes, it must be done. . . . It's forty-four
    days now since we departed from the Pole,
    and it is the fifth day that we have been
    held captive by the storm inside this tent,
    and have no food. . . .
JOHNSON. *(sleepily)*   Oh. . . .
CAPT. SCOTT.   You're awake? How are
    you feeling?
JOHNSON.   Not too bad. . . . It's curious. . . .
    It seems as if I'm split into two parts—
    one is myself, strong, lucid . . . while the other's

156

scorbutic, drowsy . . . a real sleepyhead. . . .

CAPT. SCOTT.

How about a little water?

JOHNSON.   No, no thanks. . . .
Another thing: I had a dream when I
was little—I still remember—that my feet,
when I looked down, had turned into the feet of
an elephant. *(laughs)*
                                             I guess my dream's come true now.
How's Kingsley?

CAPT. SCOTT.   Bad, I gather—he was raving . . .
but now he's still.

JOHNSON.   When we are all back home
we'll organise a banquet . . . what a banquet—
we'll have a turkey and, above all, speeches,
speeches. . . .

CAPT. SCOTT.   I know—you could pass for a turkey
yourself, when you get really good and drunk!
Eh, Johnson?
                                             He's already asleep . . .

FLEMING.   Just think—
twelve miles between us and the coast, the inlet,
where, tilting to one side its hoary masts,
amid blue icebergs waits our ship! I can
see it so clearly! . . .

CAPT. SCOTT.   Well, what can we do,
Fleming? Our luck ran out. That's all. . . .

FLEMING.   And only
twelve miles to go! Chief, I don't know—what do
you think: after the blizzard has abated,
could we, dragging the sick on sleds behind
us, make it back? . . .

CAPT. SCOTT.   I doubt it . . .

FLEMING.   Right. And if . . .
If they weren't there?

CAPT. SCOTT.   Forget that. . . . Who knows all
the things one can conceive of. . . . Would you check
the time, my friend.

FLEMING.   You're right, Chief. . . . It is six
past one. . . .

CAPT. SCOTT.   Oh, well—we can hold out until
nightfall. . . . You realise, Fleming—after all,
they're looking for us, coming from the coast
to meet us. . . . Maybe they will stumble on us. . . .
Meanwhile let's sleep. . . . It will be easier. . . .

FLEMING.
I don't feel sleepy.

CAPT. SCOTT.   In that case, you'll wake me—
say—in an hour. Or else I might just lapse,
just lapse. . . . Oh well, you understand. . . .

FLEMING.   Aye, aye, Chief. *(pause)*
All three asleep. . . . Lucky for them. . . . To whom, then,
can I explain that I am strong and avid,
that I could gobble up not twelve but hundreds
of miles, so stubborn is the life within me.
My hunger and the icy wind have forced
all of my strength into one burning, bursting
mote. . . . And there is nothing in the world
a mote like that cannot achieve. . . .
(pause)   Johnson,
what is it? Do you need some help?

JOHNSON.   I'll manage,
don't worry. . . . I'm going outside, Fleming. . . .

FLEMING.   Where?

JOHNSON.
Oh, I just want to have a look if there
is anything in sight. I may well be
some time. . . .

FLEMING.   Take care—don't lose your bearings in
the blizzard. . . .

Gone. . . . A miracle that he's
still capable of walking, with his feet
already rotting. . . .

(pause)   What a storm! The whole
tent shudders from the snowy din. . . .

KINGSLEY. *(delirious)*   Oh, Jessie,
my darling—It's so beautiful. . . . We've seen
the Pole, and I have brought you back a penguin.
Here, Jessie—you just take a look how smoo-
smoo-smooth he is . . . and how he waddles. . . . Jessie,
you're honeysuckle. . . . *(laughs)*

CAPT. SCOTT.   What's that? Who's there?
What happened?

FLEMING.   Nothing, Chief. Everything's quiet. . . .
Except for Kingsley—he's delirious. . . .

CAPT. SCOTT.
I had a kind of radiant, fearful dream. . . .
Where's Johnson?

FLEMING.   Gone, to have a look if there
are rescuers in sight.

CAPT. SCOTT.   How long ago?

FLEMING.
By now, I'd say it's twenty minutes.

CAPT. SCOTT.   Fleming,
you really shouldn't have let him go outside. . . .
However. . . . Hurry, hurry, help me up—
we're going out.

FLEMING.   I'm sorry, Chief—I thought . . .

CAPT. SCOTT.
No, it is not your fault.

FLEMING.   Lucky man. . . . I have
no one to be delirious about. . . .
The Captain has a wife and little son
in London. Kingsley has a fiancée,
almost a widow. . . . Johnson, I don't know—

I think his mother. . . . What a notion to
go walking. Funny chap, that Johnson, really.
To him life is a mixture of exploit
and prank. . . . He knows no doubts, his soul is straight as
the shadow of a post on level snow. . . .
A lucky man. . . . While I must be a coward. . . .
Danger enticed me, but aren't women enticed
like that by an abyss? My life's not been
much good. . . . I've been a ship's boy and a diver,
hurled my harpoon upon uncharted seas. Oh,
those years of seafaring, of wandering,
of longing. . . . Few have been the peaceful nights,
the happy days I've had from life . . . and yet. . . .

KINGSLEY. *(delirious)*
Come on, come on! That's it, nice going! Hurry!
Don't dawdle, shoot—shoot at the goal! . . . Our Father,
Which art . . . *(mumbles)*

FLEMING.   And yet I've an unbearable
desire to live. . . . Yes, to pursue a ball,
a woman, or the sun or—still more simply—
to eat, to eat a lot, to tear the plump
sardines in golden oil out of their tin. . . .
I want to live so much, it maddens me,
it hurts—to live somehow. . . .
  Look at that snow!

(They go out together.)
(pause)

KINGSLEY. *(alone, delirious)*
Don't push—I can do it myself. . . . Stop it,
I don't need to be pushed . . . . *(raises himself up)*
       Chief, Fleming, Johnson!
Hey, Chief! . . . No one. . . . Ah yes, I understand—
all three of them are gone. They must have thought

that I was dead already. . . . They have left me,
they have set out. . . .

     No! It must be a joke!
Wait, please come back. . . . I have something to tell you. . . .
I want to tell. . . . So—this is what death means: a
glass entrance . . . water . . . water . . . it's all clear.

(pause)
(Capt. Scott and Fleming return.)

CAPT. SCOTT.

 How silly—I can't use my feet.

       Oh, thanks. . . .
 No matter. Not much chance of finding Johnson
 in any case. . . . You realise what he's done?

FLEMING.

 Of course. . . . He weakened, fell—called, helplessly,
 perhaps. . . . All this is very frightening. . . . *(goes back
 into the depths of the tent)*

CAPT. SCOTT. *(aside)*

 That's wrong—he did not call. He only thought
 that, being sick, he was a burden to
 the rest, and so he left. . . . It was so simple,
 so valorous. . . . My bag is like a rock—
 I can't get into it. . . .

FLEMING.   Chief, this is dreadful—

 Kingsley is dead. . . . Look at him. . . .

CAPT. SCOTT.   My poor Eric!

 Why did I have to bring him with me? He was
 the youngest one of us. . . . Remember how
 he cried when he discovered, at the Pole, the
 Norwegian flag? . . . The body can stay here—
 don't touch it. . . .

(pause)

FLEMING. We are left alone now, Chief. . . .
CAPT. SCOTT.
But not for long, my friend, but not for long. . . .
FLEMING.
The blizzard's dying down. . . .
CAPT. SCOTT. You know, I was just
thinking—Columbus, for example. . . . True,
he suffered, but, in recompense, discovered
such splendid lands, while we have suffered to
discover only ruinous white deserts—
and still, you know, it had to be. . . .
FLEMING. Well, Chief,
what if we tried to make a go for it?
Only twelve miles, and we'll be saved. . . .
CAPT. SCOTT. No, Fleming—
I can't get up . . .
FLEMING. We have a sled. . . .
CAPT. SCOTT. You'd never
make it with me—I'm heavy. I am better
off here. It's peaceful. And so is my soul—
like Sunday in a Scottish townlet . . . feet
just hurt a little—and often they're a wee
bit tedious, our slow Sundays. . . . Pity we
don't have a chess set—we could have. . . .
FLEMING. Yes, pity . . .
CAPT. SCOTT.
Now listen, Fleming—you go by yourself. . . .
FLEMING.
And leave you here alone? Weak as you are. . . .
You said yourself you might not last the night. . . .
CAPT. SCOTT.
Go on alone. It's what I want. . . .
FLEMING. But how. . . .
CAPT. SCOTT.
I'll last, I'll last. . . . You will have enough time

162

to send them for me when you reach the inlet.
Go on! Perhaps you'll even meet our men
along the way. I want you to—go on. . . . I
demand it. . . .

FLEMING.   Yes, then I shall go, I think. . . .

CAPT. SCOTT.
Go on. . . . What will you take along?

FLEMING.   The sled
I do not need. . . . I'll only take these skis, and
a stick. . . .

CAPT. SCOTT.   No, wait—you take another pair. . . . .
It seems to me the heel strap on that ski
is weak. . . .
            Farewell. . . . Give me your hand. . . . If you—
no, never mind. . . .

FLEMING.   My compass. . . . Damn, it's broken. . . .

CAPT. SCOTT.
Here's mine—you take it. . . .

FLEMING.   Right. . . .
                        I guess I'm ready. . . .
All right. Good-bye, Chief. I'll be coming back
with help. No later than tomorrow night. . . .
Be careful not to fall asleep. . . .

CAPT. SCOTT   Farewell. . . . *(Fleming leaves.)*
Yes, he will make it. . . . It's twelve miles. . . . Besides,
the blizzard's dying down. . . . *(pause)*
                        I need to pray. . . .
My diary—here it is, my humble, faithful
prayer book. . . . Think I'll start in the middle. . . . . *(reads)*
    'Fifteenth
November: moon is blazing like a bonfire;
and Venus seems a little Japanese
lantern. . . .' *(turns page)*
                'Bravo for Kingsley. Always looks like
he's playing—sturdy and light-footed. . . . Problems

163

with our poor dogs: Gypsy's gone blind, and Grouse
has vanished: fell into a seal hole, I
imagine. . . .'
                              'Christmas Eve: today the sky was
lit up by an aurora borealis. . . .' *(turns page)*
'Eighth February: the Pole. Norwegian flag
is sticking from the snow. . . . We have been beaten.
I'm very sorry for my loyal companions.
And now we must go back.' *(turns page)* 'Eighteenth of
    March:
we're straying. Sleds keep getting stuck. And Kingsley
is going downhill.' 'The twentieth: the last of
the cocoa and meat powder. . . . Johnson's feet
aren't well. He's very cheerful, very lucid.
We still go on discussing, he and I,
what we'll do afterwards, on our return.'
Well, . . . Now I must add only that—too bad
the pencil's broken. . . .
                              I suppose it is
the most appropriate ending. . . .
                              Lord, I'm ready.
My life, just like the needle of a compass,
has quivered and has pointed to the Pole—and
Thou art that Pole. . . .
                              My skis have left their tracks
upon your boundless snows. There's nothing else.
That's all there is. *(pause)*
                              And in a city park,
back home in London, with some toy or other,
all bathed in sunshine, and with naked knees. . . .
They'll tell him later on. . . . *(pause)*
                              Everything's quiet.
I picture Fleming on the vast, smooth plain—
he walks and walks, moving his skis ahead
so steadily—one, two . . . he's disappearing. . . .

And I'm no longer hungry. . . . Such great weakness,
such quietude is rippling through my body. . . . *(pause)*
It's probably delirium. . . . I hear. . . .
I hear. . . . Can it really be possible?
They've found us, here they come . . . our men . . . our
    men. . . .
Keep calm, Captain, keep calm. . . . No, it is not
delirium, not the wind. I clearly hear
snow creaking, movement, steps upon the snow.
Keep calm . . . must rise . . . must meet them. . . . Who is
    there?

FLEMING.
  It's Fleming. . . .

CAPT. SCOTT.   Ah, the blizzard has died down—
  hasn't it? . . .

FLEMING.
    Yes, it's cleared up. The wind has stopped. *(sits down)*
  The outside of our tent is all aglitter,
  powdered with snow. . . .

CAPT. SCOTT.   Say, do you have a knife?
  My pencil's broken. Thanks, this will do fine.
  I have to make an entry that you're back.

FLEMING.
  And you can add that Johnson isn't.

CAPT. SCOTT.   It's
  one and the same. . . . *(pause)*

FLEMING.   Our tent will not be hard
  to notice, it shines so. . . .
                  Oh, by the way,
  about Johnson: I came across his body.
  He'd dug into the snow, face down, his hood
  thrown back. . . .

CAPT. SCOTT.   It seems a pity, but I do
  not think I can write more. . . . Now, listen—can
  you tell me for what reason you came back. . . .

FLEMING.

    I simply couldn't help it. . . . He was lying
so well. His death had been so comfortable.
And now I shall remain here. . . .

CAPT. SCOTT.   Fleming, you
remember how, as children, we would read
about Sinbad's adventures—you remember?

FLEMING.

    I do, yes.

CAPT. SCOTT.

        People are fond of fables, aren't they?
Thus, you and I, alone, amid the snows,
so far away. . . . I think that England. . . .

CURTAIN

Ice House

Anne Michaels

Wherever we cry,
it's far from home.

*

At Sandwich, our son pointed
persistently to sea.
I followed his infant gaze,
expecting a bird or a boat
but there was nothing.
How unnerving,
as if he could see you
on the horizon,
knew where you were
exactly:
at the edge of the world.

*

You unloaded the ship at Lyttelton
and repacked her:

'thirty-five dogs
five tons of dog food
fifteen ponies
thirty-two tons of pony fodder
three motor-sledges
four hundred and sixty tons of coal
collapsible huts

an acetylene plant
thirty-five thousand cigars
one guinea pig
one fantail pigeon
three rabbits
one cat with its own hammock, blanket and pillow
one hundred and sixty-two carcasses of mutton and
an ice house'

*

Men returned from war
without faces, with noses lost
discretely as antique statues,
accurately as if eaten
by frostbite.
In clay I shaped their
flesh, sometimes
retrieving a likeness
from photographs.
Then the surgeons copied
nose, ears, jaw
with molten wax and metal plates
and horsehair stitches;
with borrowed cartilage,
from the soldiers' own ribs,
leftovers stored under the skin
of the abdomen. I held the men down
until the morphia
slid into them.
I was only sick
afterwards.

Working the clay, I remembered
mornings in Rodin's studio,
his drawerfuls of tiny hands and feet,

like a mechanic's tool box.
I imagined my mother in her blindness
before she died, touching my face,
as if still she could
build me with her body.

At night, in the studio
I took your face in my hands and your fine
arms and long legs, your small waist,
and loved you into stone.

The men returned from France
to Ellerman's Hospital.
Their courage
was beautiful.
I understood the work at once:
To use scar tissue to advantage.
To construct through art,
one's face to the world.
Sculpt what's missing.

*

You reached furthest south,
then you went further.

In neither of those forsaken places
did you forsake us.

*

At Lyttelton the hills unrolled,
a Japanese scroll painting;
we opened the landscape with our bare feet.

So much learned by observation.
We took in brainfuls of New Zealand air
on the blue climb over the falls.

Our last night together we slept
not in the big house but
in the Kinseys' garden.
Belonging only
to each other.
Guests of the earth.

*

Mid-sea, a month out of range
of the wireless;
on my way to you. Floating
between landfalls,
between one hemisphere and another.
Between the words
'wife' and 'widow'.

*

Newspapers, politicians
scavenged your journals.

But your words
never lost their way.

*

We mourn in a place no one knows;
it's right that our grief be unseen.

I love you as if you'll return
after years of absence.
As if we'd invented
moonlight.

*

Still I dream
of your arrival.

Diary Extracts from Scott's Voyage to Discover the West Pole

James Brown

— 'The sea is a woman who never grows old.'
The crew sing to keep their spirits up.
Yet song cannot silence our disappointment
at being forestalled to the Pole by a bear.
Although this Pooh is, of course, a stout English bear.

— The sea can never be judged too quickly.
It is never as it appears / as it reappears.
Gosh.

— We ate our last pony today—'Bolger'.
I shot the brave little beast myself.
Oh but he was lost and lame with no sea legs.

— Sun, salt, and more sun.
How the green waves boil!
How I long for ice and a cool breeze.

— I see the future as uncertain
with my deteriorating humour.
Yet our struggles are already immortal.
Knock Knock we say.
Amundsen who?

— Food is short.
The tractors were not a good idea.

— This tropical heat does not agree with us.
  We have become argumentative.
  I am constantly having to cite the Concise Oxford.

— The most wondrous wave formations today!
  Like sastrugi. But in this humidity
  our photographic apparatus fails to function.

— We have lost Oates. We had gathered on deck
  during a particularly bad bout of calenture.
  He simply stepped over the rail to pick flowers.

— All hope is fading.
  The sea is just there, it shines and shines.

— For God's sake look after our people.

Scott of the Sahara

Monty Python

On Tuesday Chris Conger took a BBC film unit to the location where Twentieth Century Vole are shooting their latest epic 'Scott of the Antarctic'.

Chris Conger standing with back to pier and a few holidaymakers behind him.

CONGER. (GRAHAM) Sea, sand and sunshine make Paignton the queen of the English Riviera. But for the next six months this sleepy Devonshire resort will be transformed into the blizzard-swept wastes of the South Pole. For today shooting starts on the epic 'Scott of the Antarctic', produced by Gerry Schlick. *(walks over to Schlick)*

SCHLICK. (ERIC) *(American)* Hello.

CONGER. Gerry, you chose Paignton as the location for Scott.

SCHLICK. Right, right.

CONGER. Isn't it a bit of a drawback that there's no snow here?

SCHLICK. Well, we have 28,000 cubic feet of Wintrex, which is a new white foam rubber which actually on screen looks more like snow than snow . . .

Cut to shot of people nailing and sticking white foam rubber over things. It looks terrible. Others are painting the sand with white paint.

SCHLICK. . . . and 1,600 cubic US furlongs of white paint, with a special snow finish.

CONGER. And I believe Kirk Vilb is playing the title role.

SCHLICK. That is correct. We were very thrilled and honoured when Kirk agreed to play the part of Lieutenant Scott *(cut to Kirk Vilb who is wearing furs open at the chest;*

173

he is having a chest wig stuck on and icing sugar squeezed on to his nose and eyebrows) because a star of his magnitude can pick and choose, but he read the title and just flipped. *(cut back to Gerry Schlick and Chris Conger)* And directing we have a very fine young British director, James McRettin, who's been collaborating on the screenplay, of course Jimmy . . .

McRettin rushes into foreground. He is in no way like J. McGrath.

McRETTIN. (JOHN) Oh, there you are. Hello. Hello. No problem. Have a drink. Have a drink. Great. Hello. Marvellous. Marvellous. Hello. Rewrite. Oh this is really great. I mean, it's really saying something, don't you think?

CONGER. Have you started shooting yet?

McRETTIN. Yes, yes. Great. Perfect. No, no, we haven't started yet. No. But great—great.

CONGER. What is the first scene that you shoot this morning?

McRETTIN. Great. Terrific. Oh it's great. No problem. We'll sort it out on the floor. Sort it out on the floor. No problem. This film is basically pro-humanity and anti-bad things and it rips aside the hypocritical façade of our society's gin and tonic and leaves a lot of sacred cows rolling around in agony, have a drink, have a drink.

CONGER. But which *scene* are we shooting first, Jimmy?

McRETTIN. Yes, great. Oh, marvellous. *(calls)* Which scene are we shooting first? What? *(to Conger)* It's scene one. Scene one. It's in the middle of the movie. Well, it is now. I rewrote it. *(calls)* I thought we cut that? Didn't we cut that?

SCHLICK. No, we didn't.

McRETTIN. We didn't. Oh great. That's even better. I'll put it back in. Rewrite. *(calling)* Scene one's back in everyone. Scene one's back in. Great. Great. *(to Conger)* This is the scene—outside the tent—it's all bloody marvellous.

174

It makes you want to throw up.

Cut to Schlick and Conger on the beach.

SCHLICK. Now in this scene Lieutenant Scott returns to camp in the early morning after walking the huskies to have brunch with the rest of his team. *(cut to shot of tent with Bowers, who is black, and Oates, sitting outside)* Oates, played by your very own lovely Terence Lemming, who is an English cockney officer seconded to the US Navy, and Bowers played by Seymour Fortescue, the Olympic pole vaulter.

Film: Scott comes up to them. He has two large boxes strapped to his feet to make him look tall.

OATES. (TERRY J) Hi, Lieutenant.

SCOTT. (MICHAEL) Hi, Oatesy. Sure is a beautiful day already.

McRETTIN. *(rushing in)* Great, great.

SCOTT. What? What are you saying?

McRETTIN. I was just saying great, great. Cue Evans.

Sexy girl with long blond hair comes into shot with short pink fur coat. She walks up to Scott who towers four feet above her as she is walking in a trench.

SCHLICK. And this is Vanilla Hoare as Miss Evans.

CONGER. Miss Evans?

SCHLICK. Right.

Miss Evans is now beneath Scott at knee height.

SCOTT. Good morning, Miss Evans.

EVANS. (CAROL) Oh, I've forgotten my line.

McRETTIN. What's her line? What's her line?

Girl runs in with script.

GIRL. It's 'Good morning, Captain Scott'.

EVANS. Oh, yeah. 'Good morning, Captain Sc' . . . oh, I'm just not happy with that line. Could I just say 'Hi Scottie'?

McRETTIN. Great. Great. Rewrite. Cue.

EVANS. Hi Scarrie! Oh, sorry. Hi Stocky! Oh—I'm sorry again. Oh, Jim. I'm just unhappy with this line. Hey, can I do

175

it all sort of kooky, like this? *(goes berserk waving hands)* Hi Scottie!

McRETTIN. Great! We'll shoot it.

SCOTT. Are you sure that's right?

McRETTIN. Oh, it's great.

Gerry Schlick walks into the shot.

SCHLICK. Jim.

McRETTIN. Jim! Jim! Oh, me!

SCHLICK. Jim, I feel we may be running into some problems here in the area of height.

McRETTIN. Great! Where are they?

SCHLICK. Where are who?

McRETTIN. I don't know. I was getting confused.

SCHLICK. Jim, I feel here, that Scott may be too tall in the area of height with reference to Vanilla who is too near the ground in the area of being too short at this time.

McRETTIN. Great . . . Oh, I know. I'm going to dig a pit for Scott and put a box in Vanilla's trench.

SCOTT. Say, why don't I take the boxes off and Vanilla get up out of the trench.

McRETTIN. It wouldn't work . . . It's even better! Great. Rewrite!

EVANS. What was that?

McRETTIN. Oh, it's easy. I've worked it out. Scott takes his boxes off and you don't stand in the trench.

EVANS. I say my lines *out* of the trench?

McRETTIN. Even better. Great.

EVANS. But I've never acted out of a trench. I might fall over. It's dangerous.

McRETTIN. Oh well, could you just try it?

EVANS. Look, you crumb bum, I'm a star. Star, star, star. I don't get a million dollars to act *out* of a trench. I played Miss St John the Baptist in a trench, *(she walks along in the trench and we see that she has two boxes strapped to her feet)* and I played Miss Napoleon Bonaparte in a

176

trench, and I played Miss Alexander Fleming in a furrow so if you want this scene played out of a trench, well you just get yourself a goddamn stuntman. *(walks off)* I played Miss Galileo in a groove and I played Mrs Jesus Christ in a geological syncline, so don't . . .

McRETTIN. Great. Great everyone. Lunch now. Lunch. It's all in the can. Good morning's work.

SCHLICK. But you haven't done a shot.

McRETTIN. Just keeping morale up. *(tries to take a drink from his viewfinder)*
The same: afternoon.

SCHLICK. Now this afternoon we're going to shoot the scene where Scott gets off the boat on to the ice floe and he sees the lion and he fights it and kills it and the blood goes pssssssssshhh in slow motion.

CONGER. But there aren't any lions in the Antarctic.

SCHLICK. What?

CONGER. There aren't any lions in the Antarctic.

SCHLICK. You're right. There are no lions in the Antarctic. That's ridiculous; whoever heard of a lion in the Antarctic. Right. Lose the lion.

McRETTIN. Got to keep the lion. It's great!

SCHLICK. Lose the lion.

McRETTIN. Great. We're losing the lion. Rewrite. Lose the lion everyone. That's fantastic.

SCOTT. What's this about our losing the lion?

SCHLICK. Well, Kirk, we thought perhaps we might lose the fight with the lion a little bit, Kirk, angel.

SCOTT. *(loudly)* Why?

SCHLICK. Well, Kirkie, doll, there are no lions in the Antarctic, baby.

SCOTT. *(shouts)* I get to fight the lion.

SCHLICK. It'd be silly.

SCOTT. Listen, I gotta fight the lion. That's what that guy Scott's all about. I know. I've studied him already.

SCHLICK. But why couldn't you fight a penguin?

McRETTIN. Great! *(falls over)*

SCOTT. Fight a rotten penguin?

SCHLICK. It needn't be a little penguin. It can be the biggest penguin you've ever seen. An electric penguin, twenty feet high, with long green tentacles that sting people, and you can stab it in the wings and the blood can go spurting pssssshhhh in slow motion.

SCOTT. The lion is in the contract.

SCHLICK. He fights the lion.

McRETTIN. Even better. Great. Have a drink. Lose the penguin. Stand by to shoot. *(falls over)*

SCHLICK. Where do they have lions?

CONGER. Africa.

SCHLICK. That's it. Scott's in Africa. As many lions as we need.

McRETTIN. Great!

SCHLICK. He's looking for a pole no one else knows about. That ties in with the sand. Right. Paint the sand yellow again. Okay, let's get this show on the road. 'Scott of the Sahara.'

Cut instantly to sky.

CAPTION: 'SCOTT OF THE SAHARA'

VOICE OVER. (MICHAEL) Booming out of the pages of history comes a story of three men and one woman whose courage shocked a generation.

Blinding sun. Pan down to Paignton beach. Scott, Evans, Oates and Bowers wearing furs crossing sand on snow shoes. With sledge pulled by motley selection of mongrel dogs, badly disguised as huskies.

VOICE OVER. From the same team that brought you . . . *(the names come out superimposed)* 'Lawrence of Glamorgan' . . . 'Bridge Over the River Trent' . . . 'The Mad Woman of Biggleswade' . . . and 'Krakatoa, East of Leamington' . . . comes the story of three people and a woman united

178

by fate who set out in search of the fabled Pole of the Sahara and found . . . themselves. See . . . Lieutenant Scott's death struggle with a crazed desert lion.

The four are walking along. Suddenly they stop, stare, and react in horror. Scott steps to the front to defend the others. Intercut, non-matching stock shot of lion running out of jungle and leaping at camera. Scott waits poised and is then struck by completely rigid stuffed lion. Montage of shots of him wrestling, firstly with the stuffed lion, then with an actor in a tatty lion suit. The lion picks up a chair, fends Scott off, smashes it over his head. Finally Scott kicks the lion on the shin. The lion leaps around on one leg and picks up a knife. Scott points, the lion looks, Scott kicks the knife out of the lion's paw. He advances on the lion, and socks him on the jaw. The lion collapses in slow motion. After a pause, phoney blood spurts out.

VOICE OVER. See Ensign Oates' frank adult death struggle with the spine-chilling giant electric penguin . . .

Oates looks up in horror, a shadow crosses him. Reverse shot of model penguin (quite small, about a foot) which lights up and looks electric. The penguin is close to the camera in the foreground and appears huge. Oates looks around desperately then starts to undress. Shot of penguin throwing tentacle. Half-nude Oates struggles with it. Intercut a lot of phoney reverses. Oates by now clad only in posing briefs sees a stone. He picks up the stone, then camera zooms into above-navel shot; he removes his briefs, puts the stone in the briefs, twirls it like a sling, and releases stone. The penguin is hit on beak, and falls over backwards.

VOICE OVER. . . . See Miss Evans pursued by the man-eating roll-top writing desk.

Miss Evans is running along screaming. Shot of desk chasing her (phoney desk with man inside). The roll

top goes up and down, emitting roars, and displaying
fearsome white teeth inside. As Evans runs, her clothing
gets torn on each of the three cactuses. These are well
spaced apart so that there is a lot of trouble to get near
them. When she is practically nude, she runs out of
shot revealing the announcer.

ANNOUNCER. (JOHN) And now for something completely
different.

Crean. Night Watch

Melinda Mueller

What would make Crean blush
would make a butcher's dog drop its bone.

Coming back from Captain Scott's
last voyage, well, we sailed
into Oamaru in dead of night
and stood off till dawn, hailed

though we were by the lighthouse—*What ship?*
What ship?—wanting to prevent
the news from getting out till the families
could be cabled, as was only decent.

A funeral ship we were, that time.
Nor will I forget the sight
of what we found inside that tent.
Yet back I've come in spite

of all. One thing, I'd like to stand
at the Pole. I was that close
I could have shouted at it, and when
Scott turned us back and chose

the other team for the last push,
I'm not ashamed to say
it was a blow brought me to tears.
We watched them march away

181

and thought them a sure bet. And so
they were—to reach the Pole.
It's the coming home was more than they
could do, God rest their souls.

Sledging up the Beardmore Glacier,
I once saw the team ahead
lifted by mirage, their doubles hung
in air above their heads

as if the Ice breathed out a mirror.
In the Ice you see your mates
for what they're worth—see yourself,
what's more, and love or hate

what shows there. I knew a man
came South with brown eyes
and went back home with blue ones,
their colour frozen by the Ice.

More than how you look, 'tis what
you see that changes most.
The first time I saw trees again,
they looked to me like green ghosts.

What The Ice Gets
23–29 October 1915

Melinda Mueller

Out of whose womb came the ice?
And the hoary frost of heaven, who hath gendered it?
The waters are hid as with a stone,
And the face of the deep is frozen.

Two floes catch hold of the ship, one to port,
the other starboard. A third floe grinding aft
tears out her sternpost. The salt sea pours in.
McNeish wades into the engine room
and starts a cofferdam to stanch the bleeding.
Behind him Rickinson and Kerr shovel
fuel into the engines—coal, blubber, wood—
anything to get her fires up and drive
the steam pumps. But the steam pumps can't keep pace
and the hand pumps are choked with ice. Worsley,
Greenstreet, and Hudson clamber below decks
to clear them, scrambling through darkness over
lurching coal. Ice-cold water surges round
their legs, and in their ears explodes a din
of cracking beams, like rifle shots. The men
go on watch and watch, four hours at the pumps
or swinging pickaxes to break the Ice
that grips her keel. Four hours uneasy rest,
then back to pumps and axes. 'Every muscle
aches, revolting at the agony of toil.'
For three days they keep at it with scant sleep.
McNeish still works in water to his waist,
he and Hurley caulking the dam with strips

of blanket. The engineers keep steam up,
though beside them the thick bulkheads heave in
and out as the Ice shifts, 'giving the awful
impression that the ship gasps for breath'.
The air resounds with shrieks of rending wood,
whingeing yowls of dogs and roaring Pressure.
Eight emperor penguins approach the ship,
stretch their throats and keen like banshees. McLeod,
who's refused to eat penguin meat because
they are drowned sailors' souls, turns to Macklin:
'Hear that? We'll none of us get home again.'
Shackleton gropes up the deck and sees how
the ship's been bent like a bow in the rack
of ice. He orders stores and boats lowered
to the floes. Worsley tears out charts and maps
from the ship's books, choosing every landfall
they might need to reach, or could. Green—well Green's
a cook, so he cooks dinner. Then the fires
are all let down so the engines won't blow
when the sea floods in. Some men make a chute
of canvas and toss the dogs into it
to slide them to the Ice. Wild picks his way
fore and aft, finding the men off-watch who've
dropped asleep exhausted. 'She's going, boys.
It's time to get off.' The decks break upward
as they climb overboard. Her stretched rigging
sings in the wind. Higher and higher notes.

On the floe they try to sleep. But all night
'you hear the Ice being ground into her.
You almost feel it is your own ribs
being crushed. It seems the end of everything.'
Eerie groans and shouts, jigs, ululations
from a mosque, keenings, long chords too low
to hear but that shake the heart from its chest

like leaves out of a tree—grisly music
wrung from the ship by the Ice that breaks her.
The Boss and Wild stand on watch while the rest
lie in their tents. They jury-rig a stove
and in the morning boil up hot milk
for all hands. All hands accept without remark.
Wild plants a fist on either hip and says,
'If any of you gentlemen also
wants his boots blacked, kindly leave them outside
your doors.'

      Nearby the *Endurance* lies
mangled in the Ice, all her fine bones
broken. White shards driven through her sides
hold her up, 'sullen dark against the sky'.
Shackleton musters the crew. 'Well, boys. Ship
and stores have gone. So now we'll go home.'
Crean takes the youngest pups and the ship's cat
behind a hummock of ice and shoots them.
The food won't stretch past working dogs and men.

from
At the Mountains of Madness
H.P. Lovecraft

Many people will probably judge us callous as well as mad
for thinking about the northward tunnel and the abyss so
soon after our sombre discovery, and I am not prepared to
say that we would have immediately revived such thoughts
but for a specific circumstance which broke in upon us and
set up a whole new train of speculations. We had replaced
the tarpaulin over poor Gedney and were standing in a kind
of mute bewilderment when the sounds finally reached our
consciousness—the first sounds we had heard since descending
out of the open where the mountain wind whined faintly from
its unearthly heights. Well known and mundane though they
were, their presence in this remote world of death was more
unexpected and unnerving than any grotesque or fabulous
tones could possibly have been—since they gave a fresh
upsetting to all our notions of cosmic harmony.

Had it been some trace of that bizarre musical piping over
a wide range which Lake's dissection report had led us to
expect in those others—and which, indeed, our overwrought
fancies had been reading into every wind-howl we had heard
since coming on the camp horror—it would have had a kind
of hellish congruity with the aeon-dead region around us. A
voice from other epochs belongs in a graveyard of other
epochs. As it was, however, the noise shattered all our
profoundly seated adjustments—all our tacit acceptance of
the inner antarctic as a waste as utterly and irrevocably void
of every vestige of normal life as the sterile disc of the moon.
What we heard was not the fabulous note of any buried
blasphemy of elder earth from whose supernal toughness an
age-denied polar sun had evoked a monstrous response.

186

Instead, it was a thing so mockingly normal and so unerringly familiarised by our sea days off Victoria Land and our camp days at McMurdo Sound that we shuddered to think of it here, where such things ought not to be. To be brief—it was simply the raucous squawking of a penguin.

The muffled sound floated from subglacial recesses nearly opposite to the corridor whence we had come—regions manifestly in the direction of that other tunnel to the vast abyss. The presence of a living water bird in such a direction— in a world whose surface was one of age-long and uniform lifelessness—could lead to only one conclusion; hence our first thought was to verify the objective reality of the sound. It was, indeed, repeated; and seemed at times to come from more than one throat. Seeking its source, we entered an archway from which much debris had been cleared; resuming our trailblazing—with an added paper supply taken with curious repugnance from one of the tarpaulin bundles on the sledges—when we left daylight behind.

As the glaciated floor gave place to a litter of detritus, we plainly discerned some curious dragging tracks; and once Danforth found a distinct print of a sort whose description would be only too superfluous. The course indicated by the penguin cries was precisely what our map and compass prescribed as an approach to the more northerly tunnel-mouth, and we were glad to find that a bridgeless thoroughfare on the ground and basement levels seemed open. The tunnel, according to the chart, ought to start from the basement of a large pyramidal structure which we seemed vaguely to recall from our aerial survey as remarkably well preserved. Along our path the single torch shewed a customary profusion of carvings, but we did not pause to examine any of these.

Suddenly a bulky white shape loomed up ahead of us, and we flashed on the second torch. It is odd how wholly this new quest had turned our minds from earlier fears of what might lurk near. Those other ones, having left their supplies in the great circular place, must have planned to return after their scouting trip toward or into the abyss; yet we had now discarded all caution concerning them as completely as if they had never existed. This white, waddling thing was fully six feet high, yet we seemed to realise at once that it was not one of those others. They were larger and dark, and according to the sculptures their motion over land surfaces was a swift, assured matter despite the queerness of their sea-born tentacle equipment. But to say that the white thing did not profoundly frighten us would be vain. We were indeed clutched for an instant by a primitive dread almost sharper than the worst of our reasoned fears regarding those others. Then came a flash of anticlimax as the white shape sidled into a lateral archway to our left to join two others of its kind which had summoned it in raucous tones. For it was only a penguin—albeit of a huge, unknown species larger than the greatest of the known king penguins, and monstrous in its combined albinism and virtual eyelessness.

When we had followed the thing into the archway and turned both our torches on the indifferent and unheeding group of three, we saw that they were all eyeless albinos of the same unknown and gigantic species. Their size reminded us of some of the archaic penguins depicted in the Old Ones' sculptures, and it did not take us long to conclude that they were descended from the same stock—undoubtedly surviving through a retreat to some warmer inner region whose perpetual blackness had destroyed their pigmentation and atrophied their eyes to mere useless slits. That their present habitat was the vast abyss we sought, was not for a moment to be doubted; and this evidence of the gulf's continued warmth and habitability filled us with the most curious and subtly perturbing fancies.

We wondered, too, what had caused these three birds to venture out of their usual domain. The state and silence of the great dead city made it clear that it had at no time been an habitual seasonal rookery, whilst the manifest indifference of the trio to our presence made it seem odd that any passing party of those others should have startled them. Was it possible that those others had taken some aggressive action or tried to increase their meat supply? We doubted whether that pungent odour which the dogs had hated could cause an equal antipathy in these penguins; since their ancestors had obviously lived on excellent terms with the Old Ones—an amicable relationship which must have survived in the abyss below as long as any of the Old Ones remained. Regretting—in a flare up of the old spirit of pure science—that we could not photograph these anomalous creatures, we shortly left them to their squawking and pushed on toward the abyss whose openness was now so positively proved to us, and whose exact direction occasional penguin tracks made clear.

Not long afterward a steep descent in a long, low, doorless, and peculiarly sculptureless corridor led us to believe that we were approaching the tunnel-mouth at last. We had passed two more penguins, and heard others immediately ahead. Then the corridor ended in a prodigious open space which made us gasp involuntarily—a perfect inverted hemisphere, obviously deep underground; fully a hundred feet in diameter and fifty feet high, with low archways opening around all parts of the circumference but one, and that one yawning cavernously with a black arched aperture which broke the symmetry of the vault to a height of nearly fifteen feet. It was the entrance to the great abyss.

In this vast hemisphere, whose concave roof was impressively though decadently carved to a likeness of the primordial celestial dome, a few albino penguins waddled—aliens there, but indifferent and unseeing. The black tunnel yawned indefinitely off at a steep descending grade, its aperture adorned with grotesquely chiselled jambs and lintel. From that cryptical mouth we fancied a current of slightly warmer air and perhaps even a suspicion of vapour proceeded; and we wondered what living entities other than penguins the limitless void below, and the contiguous honeycombings of the land and the titan mountains, might conceal. We wondered, too, whether the trace of mountain-top smoke at first suspected by poor Lake, as well as the odd haze we had ourselves perceived around the rampart-crowned peak, might not be caused by the tortuous-channelled rising of some such vapour from the unfathomed regions of earth's core.

Entering the tunnel, we saw that its outline was—at least at the start—about fifteen feet each way; sides, floor, and arched roof composed of the usual megalithic masonry. The sides were sparsely decorated with cartouches of conventional designs in a late, decadent style; and all the construction and carving were marvellously well preserved. The floor was quite clear, except for a slight detritus bearing outgoing penguin tracks and the inward tracks of those others. The farther one advanced, the warmer it became; so that we were soon unbuttoning our heavy garments. We wondered whether there were any actually igneous manifestations below, and whether the waters of that sunless sea were hot. After a short distance the masonry gave place to solid rock, though the tunnel kept the same proportions and presented the same aspect of carved regularity. Occasionally its varying grade became so steep that grooves were cut in the floor. Several times we noted the mouths of small lateral galleries not recorded in our diagrams; none of them such as to complicate the problem of our return, and all of them welcome as possible refuges in case we met unwelcome entities on their way back from the abyss. The nameless scent of such things was very distinct. Doubtless it was suicidally foolish to venture into that tunnel under the known conditions, but the lure of the unplumbed is stronger in certain persons than most suspect—indeed, it was just such a lure which had brought us to this unearthly polar waste in the first place. We saw several penguins as we passed along, and speculated on the distance we would have to traverse.

190

The carvings had led us to expect a steep downhill walk of about a mile to the abyss, but our previous wanderings had shewn us that matters of scale were not wholly to be depended on.

After about a quarter of a mile that nameless scent became greatly accentuated, and we kept very careful track of the various lateral openings we passed. There was no visible vapour as at the mouth, but this was doubtless due to the lack of contrasting cooler air. The temperature was rapidly ascending, and we were not surprised to come upon a careless heap of material shudderingly familiar to us. It was composed of furs and tent cloth taken from Lake's camp, and we did not pause to study the bizarre forms into which the fabrics had been slashed. Slightly beyond this point we noticed a decided increase in the size and number of the side galleries, and concluded that the densely honeycombed region beneath the higher foothills must now have been reached. The nameless scent was now curiously mixed with another and scarcely less offensive odour—of what nature we could not guess, though we thought of decaying organisms and perhaps unknown subterrene fungi. Then came a startling expansion of the tunnel for which the carvings had not prepared us—a broadening and rising into a lofty, natural-looking elliptical cavern with a level floor; some seventy-five feet long and fifty broad, and with many immense side-passages leading away into cryptical darkness.

Though this cavern was natural in appearance, an inspection with both torches suggested that it had been formed by the artificial destruction of several walls between adjacent honeycombings. The walls were rough, and the high vaulted roof was thick with stalactites; but the solid rock floor had been smoothed off, and was free from all debris, detritus, or even dust to a positively abnormal extent. Except for the avenue through which we had come, this was true of the floors of all the great galleries opening off from it; and the singularity of the condition was such as to set us vainly puzzling. The curious new foetor which had supplemented the nameless scent was excessively pungent here; so much so that it destroyed all trace of the other. Something about this whole place, with its polished and almost glistening floor, struck us as more vaguely baffling and horrible than any of the monstrous things we had previously encountered.

The regularity of the passage immediately ahead, as well as the larger proportion of penguin-droppings there, prevented all confusion as to the right course amidst this plethora of equally great cave-mouths. Nevertheless we resolved to resume our paper trailblazing if any further complexity should develop; for dust tracks, of course, could no longer be expected. Upon resuming our direct progress we cast a beam of torchlight over the tunnel walls—and stopped short in amazement at the supremely radical change which had come over the carvings in this part of the passage. We realised, of course, the great decadence of the Old Ones' sculpture at the time of the tunnelling; and had indeed noticed the inferior workmanship of the arabesques in the stretches behind us. But now, in this deeper section beyond the cavern, there was a sudden difference wholly transcending explanation—a difference in basic nature as well as in mere quality, and involving so profound and calamitous a degradation of skill that nothing in the hitherto observed rate of decline could have led one to expect it.

This new and degenerate work was coarse, bold, and wholly lacking in delicacy of detail. It was countersunk with exaggerated depth in bands following the same general line as the sparse cartouches of the earlier sections, but the height of the reliefs did not reach the level of the general surface. Danforth had the idea that it was a second carving—a sort of palimpsest formed after the obliteration of a previous design. In nature it was wholly decorative and conventional; and consisted of crude spirals and angles roughly following the quintile mathematical tradition of the Old Ones, yet seeming more like a parody than a perpetuation of that tradition. We could not get it out of our minds that some subtly but profoundly alien element had been added to the aesthetic feeling behind the technique—an alien element, Danforth guessed, that was responsible for the manifestly laborious substitution. It was like, yet disturbingly unlike, what we had come to recognise as the Old Ones' art; and I was persistently reminded of such hybrid things as the ungainly Palmyrene sculptures fashioned in the Roman manner. That others had recently noticed this belt of carving was hinted by the presence of a used torch battery on the floor in front of one of the most characteristic designs.

Since we could not afford to spend any considerable time in study, we resumed our advance after a cursory look; though frequently casting beams over the walls to see if any further decorative changes developed. Nothing of the sort was perceived, though the carvings were in places rather sparse because of the numerous mouths of smooth-floored lateral tunnels. We saw and heard fewer penguins, but thought we caught a vague suspicion of an infinitely distant chorus of them somewhere deep within the earth. The new and inexplicable odour was abominably strong, and we could detect scarcely a sign of that other nameless scent. Puffs of visible vapour ahead bespoke increasing contrasts in temperature, and the relative nearness of the sunless sea cliffs of the great abyss. Then, quite unexpectedly, we saw certain obstructions on the polished floor ahead—obstructions which were quite definitely not penguins—and turned on our second torch after making sure that the objects were quite stationary.

193

Still another time have I come to a place where it is very difficult to proceed. I ought to be hardened by this stage; but there are some experiences and intimations which scar too deeply to permit of healing, and leave only such an added sensitiveness that memory reinspires all the original horror. We saw, as I have said, certain obstructions on the polished floor ahead; and I may add that our nostrils were assailed almost simultaneously by a very curious intensification of the strange prevailing foetor, now quite plainly mixed with the nameless stench of those others which had gone before us. The light of the second torch left no doubt of what the obstructions were, and we dared approach them only because we could see, even from a distance, that they were quite as past all harming power as had been the six similar specimens unearthed from the monstrous star-mounded graves at poor Lake's camp.

They were, indeed, as lacking in completeness as most of those we had unearthed—though it grew plain from the thick, dark-green pool gathering around them that their incompleteness was of infinitely greater recency. There seemed to be only four of them, whereas Lake's bulletins would have suggested no less than eight as forming the group which had preceded us. To find them in this state was wholly unexpected, and we wondered what sort of monstrous struggle had occurred down here in the dark.

Penguins, attacked in a body, retaliate savagely with their beaks; and our ears now made certain the existence of a rookery far beyond. Had those others disturbed such a place and aroused murderous pursuit? The obstructions did not suggest it, for penguin beaks against the tough tissues Lake had dissected could hardly account for the terrible damage our approaching glance was beginning to make out. Besides, the huge blind birds we had seen appeared to be singularly peaceful.

Had there, then, been a struggle among those others, and

were the absent four responsible? If so, where were they? Were they close at hand and likely to form an immediate menace to us? We glanced anxiously at some of the smooth-floored lateral passages as we continued our slow and frankly reluctant approach. Whatever the conflict was, it had clearly been that which had frightened the penguins into their unaccustomed wandering. It must, then, have arisen near that faintly heard rookery in the incalculable gulf beyond, since there were no signs that any birds had normally dwelt here. Perhaps, we reflected, there had been a hideous running fight, with the weaker party seeking to get back to the cached sledges when their pursuers finished them. One could picture the daemoniac fray between namelessly monstrous entities as it surged out of the black abyss with great clouds of frantic penguins squawking and scurrying ahead.

I say that we approached those sprawling and incomplete obstructions slowly and reluctantly. Would to Heaven we had never approached them at all, but had run back at top speed out of that blasphemous tunnel with the greasily smooth floors and the degenerate murals aping and mocking the things they had superseded—run back, before we had seen what we did see, and before our minds were burned with something which will never let us breathe easily again!

Both of our torches were turned on the prostrate objects, so that we soon realised the dominant factor in their incompleteness. Mauled, compressed, twisted, and ruptured as they were, their chief common injury was total decapitation. From each one the tentacled starfish head had been removed; and as we drew near we saw that the manner of removal looked more like some hellish tearing or suction than like any ordinary form of cleavage. Their noisome dark-green ichor formed a large, spreading pool; but its stench was half overshadowed by the newer and stranger stench, here more pungent than at any other point along our route. Only when we had come very close to the sprawling obstructions could we trace that

195

second, unexplainable foetor to any immediate source—and the instant we did so Danforth, remembering certain very vivid sculptures of the Old Ones' history in the Permian age 150 million years ago, gave vent to a nerve-tortured cry which echoed hysterically through that vaulted and archaic passage with the evil, palimpsest carvings.

I came only just short of echoing his cry myself; for I had seen those primal sculptures, too, and had shudderingly admired the way the nameless artist had suggested that hideous slime coating found on certain incomplete and prostrate Old Ones—those whom the frightful shoggoths had characteristically slain and sucked to a ghastly headlessness in the great war of resubjugation. They were infamous, nightmare sculptures even when telling of age-old, bygone things; for shoggoths and their work ought not to be seen by human beings or portrayed by any beings. The mad author of the *Necronomicon* had nervously tried to swear that none had been bred on this planet, and that only drugged dreamers had ever conceived them. Formless protoplasm able to mock and reflect all forms and organs and processes—viscous agglutinations of bubbling cells—rubbery fifteen-foot spheroids infinitely plastic and ductile—slaves of suggestion, builders of cities—more and more sullen, more and more intelligent, more and more amphibious, more and more imitative—Great God! What madness made even those blasphemous Old Ones willing to use and to carve such things?

And now, when Danforth and I saw the freshly glistening and reflectively iridescent black slime which clung thickly to those headless bodies and stank obscenely with that new unknown odour whose cause only a diseased fancy could envisage—clung to those bodies and sparkled less voluminously on a smooth part of the accursedly resculptured wall *in a series of grouped dots*—we understood the quality of cosmic fear to its uttermost depths. It was not fear of those four missing others—for all too well did we suspect they would do no harm again. Poor devils! After all, they were not evil things of their kind. They were the men of another age and another order of being. Nature had played a hellish jest on them—as it will on any others that human madness, callousness, or cruelty may hereafter drag up in that hideously dead or sleeping polar waste—and this was their tragic homecoming.

They had not been even savages—for what indeed had they done? That awful awakening in the cold of an unknown epoch—perhaps an attack by the furry, frantically barking quadrupeds, and a dazed defence against them and the equally frantic white simians with the queer wrappings and paraphernalia . . . poor Lake, poor Gedney . . . and poor Old Ones! Scientists to the last—what had they done that we would not have done in their place? God, what intelligence and persistence! What a facing of the incredible, just as those carven kinsmen and forbears had faced things only a little less incredible! Radiates, vegetables, monstrosities, star-spawn—whatever they had been, they were men!

They had crossed the icy peaks on whose templed slopes they had once worshipped and roamed among the tree ferns. They had found their dead city brooding under its curse, and had read its carven latter days as we had done. They had tried to reach their living fellows in fabled depths of blackness they had never seen—and what had they found? All this flashed in unison through the thoughts of Danforth and me as we looked from those headless, slime-coated shapes to the loathsome palimpsest sculptures and the diabolical dot groups of fresh slime on the wall beside them—looked and understood what must have triumphed and survived down there in the Cyclopean water city of that nighted, penguin-fringed abyss, whence even now a sinister curling mist had begun to belch pallidly as if in answer to Danforth's hysterical scream.

The shock of recognising that monstrous slime and headlessness had frozen us into mute, motionless statues, and it is only through later conversations that we have learned of the complete identity of our thoughts at that moment. It seemed aeons that we stood there, but actually it could not have been more than ten or fifteen seconds. That hateful, pallid mist curled forward as if veritably driven by some remoter advancing bulk—and then came a sound which upset much of what we had just decided, and in so doing broke the spell and enabled us to run like mad past squawking, confused penguins over our former trail back to the city, along ice-sunken megalithic corridors to the great open circle, and up that archaic spiral ramp in a frenzied automatic plunge for the sane outer air and light of day.

The new sound, as I have intimated, upset much that we had decided; because it was what poor Lake's dissection had led us to attribute to those we had judged dead. It was, Danforth later told me, precisely what he had caught in infinitely muffled form when at that spot beyond the alley-corner above the glacial level; and it certainly had a shocking resemblance to the wind-pipings we had both heard around the lofty mountain caves. At the risk of seeming puerile I will add another thing, too; if only because of the surprising way Danforth's impressions chimed with mine. Of course common reading is what prepared us both to make the interpretation, though Danforth has hinted at queer notions about unsuspected and forbidden sources to which Poe may have had access when writing his *Arthur Gordon Pym* a century ago. It will be remembered that in that fantastic tale there is a word of unknown but terrible and prodigious significance connected with the antarctic and screamed eternally by the gigantic, spectrally snowy birds of that malign region's core. '*Tekeli-li! Tekeli-li!*' That, I may admit, is exactly what we thought we heard conveyed by that sudden sound behind the advancing white mist—that insidious musical piping over a singularly wide range.

We were in full flight before three notes or syllables had

been uttered, though we knew that the swiftness of the Old Ones would enable any scream-roused and pursuing survivor of the slaughter to overtake us in a moment if it really wished to do so. We had a vague hope, however, that non-aggressive conduct and a display of kindred reason might cause such a being to spare us in case of capture; if only from scientific curiosity. After all, if such an one had nothing to fear for itself it would have no motive in harming us. Concealment being futile at this juncture, we used our torch for a running glance behind, and perceived that the mist was thinning. Would we see, at last, a complete and living specimen of those others? Again came that insidious musical piping—'*Tekeli-li! Tekeli-li!*'

Then, noting that we were actually gaining on our pursuer, it occurred to us that the entity might be wounded. We could take no chances, however, since it was very obviously approaching in answer to Danforth's scream rather than in flight from any other entity. The timing was too close to admit of doubt. Of the whereabouts of that less conceivable and less mentionable nightmare—that foetid, unglimpsed mountain of slime-spewing protoplasm whose race had conquered the abyss and sent land pioneers to recarve and squirm through the burrows of the hills—we could form no guess; and it cost us a genuine pang to leave this probably crippled Old One—perhaps a lone survivor—to the peril of recapture and a nameless fate.

Thank Heaven we did not slacken our run. The curling mist had thickened again, and was driving ahead with increased speed; whilst the straying penguins in our rear were squawking and screaming and displaying signs of a panic really surprising in view of their relatively minor confusion when we had passed them. Once more came that sinister, wide-ranged piping—'*Tekeli-li! Tekeli-li!*' We had been wrong. The thing was not wounded, but had merely paused on encountering the bodies of its fallen kindred and the hellish slime inscription above them. We could never know what that daemon message was—but those burials at Lake's camp had shewn how much importance the beings attached to their dead. Our recklessly used torch now revealed ahead of us the large open cavern where various ways converged, and we were glad to be leaving those morbid palimpsest sculptures—almost felt even when scarcely seen—behind.

Another thought which the advent of the cave inspired was the possibility of losing our pursuer at this bewildering focus of large galleries. There were several of the blind albino penguins in the open space, and it seemed clear that their fear of the oncoming entity was extreme to the point of unaccountability. If at that point we dimmed our torch to the very lowest limit of travelling need, keeping it strictly in front of us, the frightened squawking motions of the huge birds in the mist might muffle our footfalls, screen our true course, and somehow set up a false lead. Amidst the churning, spiralling fog the littered and unglistening floor of the main tunnel beyond this point, as differing from the other morbidly polished burrows, could hardly form a highly distinguishing feature; even, so far as we could conjecture, for those indicated special senses which made the Old Ones partly though imperfectly independent of light in emergencies. In fact, we were somewhat apprehensive lest we go astray ourselves in our haste. For we had, of course, decided to keep straight on toward the dead city; since the consequences of loss in those unknown foothill honeycombings would be unthinkable.

The fact that we survived and emerged is sufficient proof that the thing did take a wrong gallery whilst we providentially hit on the right one. The penguins alone could not have saved us, but in conjunction with the mist they seem to have done so. Only a benign fate kept the curling vapours thick enough at the right moment, for they were constantly shifting and threatening to vanish. Indeed, they did lift for a second just before we emerged from the nauseously resculptured tunnel into the cave; so that we actually caught one first and only half-glimpse of the oncoming entity as we cast a final, desperately fearful glance backward before dimming the torch and mixing with the penguins in the hope of dodging pursuit. If the fate which screened us was benign, that which gave us the half-glimpse was infinitely the opposite; for to that flash of semi-vision can be traced a full half of the horror which has ever since haunted us.

Our exact motive in looking back again was perhaps no more than the immemorial instinct of the pursued to gauge the nature and course of its pursuer; or perhaps it was an automatic attempt to answer a subconscious question raised by one of our senses. In the midst of our flight, with all our faculties centred on the problem of escape, we were in no condition to observe and analyse details; yet even so our latent brain cells must have wondered at the message brought them by our nostrils. Afterward we realised what it was—that our retreat from the foetid slime coating on those headless obstructions, and the coincident approach of the pursuing entity, had not brought us the exchange of stenches which logic called for. In the neighbourhood of the prostrate things that new and lately unexplainable foetor had been wholly dominant; but by this time it ought to have largely given place to the nameless stench associated with those others. This it had not done—for instead, the newer and less bearable smell was now virtually undiluted, and growing more and more poisonously insistent each second.

So we glanced back—simultaneously, it would appear; though no doubt the incipient motion of one prompted the imitation of the other. As we did so we flashed both torches full strength at the momentarily thinned mist; either from sheer primitive anxiety to see all we could, or in a less primitive but equally unconscious effort to dazzle the entity before we dimmed our light and dodged among the frantic penguins of the labyrinth-centre ahead. Unhappy act! Not Orpheus himself, or Lot's wife, paid much more dearly for a backward glance. And again came that shocking, wide-ranged piping—*'Tekeli-li! Tekeli-li!'*

I might as well be frank—even if I cannot bear to be quite direct—in stating what we saw; though at the time we felt that it was not to be admitted even to each other. The words reaching the reader can never even suggest the awfulness of the sight itself. It crippled our consciousness so completely that I wonder we had the residual sense to dim our torches as planned, and to strike the right tunnel toward the dead city. Instinct alone must have carried us through—perhaps better than reason could have done; though if that was what saved us, we paid a high price. Of reason we certainly had little enough left. Danforth was totally unstrung, and the first thing I remember of the rest of the journey was hearing him light-headedly chant an hysterical formula in which I alone of mankind could have found anything but insane irrelevance. It reverberated in falsetto echoes among the squawks of the penguins; reverberated through the vaultings ahead, and—thank God—through the now empty vaultings behind. He could not have begun it at once—else we would not have been alive and blindly racing. I shudder to think of what a shade of difference in his nervous reactions might have brought.

'South Station Under—Washington Under—Park Street Under—Kendall—Central—Harvard. . . .' The poor fellow was chanting the familiar stations of the Boston-Cambridge tunnel that burrowed through our peaceful native soil thousands of miles away in New England, yet to me the ritual had neither irrelevance nor home-feeling. It had only horror, because I knew unerringly the monstrous, nefandous analogy that had suggested it. We had expected, upon looking back, to see a terrible and incredible moving entity if the mists were thin enough; but of that entity we had formed a clear idea. What we did see—for the mists were indeed all too malignly thinned—was something altogether different, and immeasurably more hideous and detestable. It was the utter, objective embodiment of the fantastic novelist's 'thing that should not be'; and its nearest comprehensible analogue is a vast, onrushing subway train as one sees it from a station platform—the great black front looming colossally out of infinite subterraneous distance, constellated with strangely coloured lights and filling the prodigious burrow as a piston fills a cylinder.

But we were not on a station platform. We were on the track ahead as the nightmare plastic column of foetid black iridescence oozed tightly onward through its fifteen-foot sinus; gathering unholy speed and driving before it a spiral, rethickening cloud of the pallid abyss-vapour. It was a terrible, indescribable thing vaster than any subway train—a shapeless congeries of protoplasmic bubbles, faintly self-luminous, and with myriads of temporary eyes forming and unforming as pustules of greenish light all over the tunnel-filling front that bore down upon us, crushing the frantic penguins and slithering over the glistening floor that it and its kind had swept so evilly free of all litter. Still came that eldritch, mocking cry—'*Tekeli-li! Tekeli-li!*' And at last we remembered that the daemoniac shoggoths—given life, thought, and plastic organ patterns solely by the Old Ones, and having no language save that which the dot-groups expressed—*had likewise no voice save the imitated accents of their bygone masters.*

Danforth and I have recollections of emerging into the great sculptured hemisphere and of threading our back trail through the Cyclopean rooms and corridors of the dead city; yet these are purely dream-fragments involving no memory of volition, details, or physical exertion. It was as if we floated in a nebulous world or dimension without time, causation, or orientation. The grey half-daylight of the vast circular space sobered us somewhat; but we did not go near those cached sledges or look again at poor Gedney and the dog. They have a strange and titanic mausoleum, and I hope the end of this planet will find them still undisturbed.

It was while struggling up the colossal spiral incline that we first felt the terrible fatigue and short breath which our race through the thin plateau air had produced; but not even fear of collapse could make us pause before reaching the normal outer realm of sun and sky. There was something vaguely appropriate about our departure from those buried epochs; for as we wound our panting way up the sixty-foot cylinder of primal masonry we glimpsed beside us a continuous procession of heroic sculptures in the dead race's early and undecayed technique—a farewell from the Old Ones, written fifty million years ago.

Finally scrambling out at the top, we found ourselves on a great mound of tumbled blocks; with the curved walls of higher stonework rising westward, and the brooding peaks of the great mountains shewing beyond the more crumbled structures toward the east. The low antarctic sun of midnight peered redly from the southern horizon through rifts in the jagged ruins, and the terrible age and deadness of the nightmare city seemed all the starker by contrast with such relatively known and accustomed things as the features of the polar landscape. The sky above was a churning and opalescent mass of tenuous ice-vapours, and the cold clutched at our vitals. Wearily resting the outfit-bags to which we had instinctively clung throughout our desperate flight, we rebuttoned our heavy garments for the stumbling climb down the mound and the walk through the aeon-old stone maze to the foothills where our aeroplane waited. Of what had set us fleeing from that darkness of earth's secret and archaic gulfs we said nothing at all.

In less than a quarter of an hour we had found the steep grade to the foothills—the probable ancient terrace—by which we had descended, and could see the dark bulk of our great plane amidst the sparse ruins on the rising slope ahead. Half way uphill toward our goal we paused for a momentary breathing spell, and turned to look again at the fantastic palaeogean tangle of incredible stone shapes below us—once more outlined mystically against an unknown west. As we did so we saw that the sky beyond had lost its morning haziness; the restless ice-vapours having moved up to the zenith, where their mocking outlines seemed on the point of settling into some bizarre pattern which they feared to make quite definite or conclusive.

There now lay revealed on the ultimate white horizon behind the grotesque city a dim, elfin line of pinnacled violet whose needle-pointed heights loomed dreamlike against the beckoning rose-colour of the western sky. Up toward this shimmering rim sloped the ancient table-land, the depressed course of the bygone river traversing it as an irregular ribbon of shadow. For a second we gasped in admiration of the scene's unearthly cosmic beauty, and then vague horror began to creep into our souls. For this far violet line could be nothing else than the terrible mountains of the forbidden land—highest of earth's peaks and focus of earth's evil; harbourers of nameless horrors and Archaean secrets; shunned and prayed to by those who feared to carve their meaning; untrodden by any living thing of earth, but visited by the sinister lightnings and sending strange beams across the plains in the polar night—beyond doubt the unknown archetype of that dreaded Kadath in the Cold Waste beyond abhorrent Leng, whereof unholy primal legends hint evasively. We were the first human beings ever to see them—and I hope to God we may be the last.

If the sculptured maps and pictures in that prehuman city had told truly, these cryptic violet mountains could not be much less than 300 miles away; yet none the less sharply did their dim elfin essence jut above that remote and snowy rim, like the serrated edge of a monstrous alien planet about to rise into unaccustomed heavens. Their height, then, must have been tremendous beyond all comparison—carrying them up into tenuous atmospheric strata peopled by such gaseous wraiths as rash flyers have barely lived to whisper of after unexplainable falls. Looking at them, I thought nervously of certain sculptured hints of what the great bygone river had washed down into the city from their accursed slopes—and wondered how much sense and how much folly had lain in the fears of those Old Ones who carved them so reticently. I recalled how their northerly end must come near the coast at Queen Mary Land, where even at that moment Sir Douglas Mawson's expedition was doubtless working less than a thousand miles away; and hoped that no evil fate would give Sir Douglas and his men a glimpse of what might lie beyond the protecting coastal range. Such thoughts formed a measure of my overwrought condition at the time—and Danforth seemed to be even worse.

Yet long before we had passed the great star-shaped ruin and reached our plane our fears had become transferred to the lesser but vast enough range whose recrossing lay ahead of us. From these foothills the black, ruin-crusted slopes reared up starkly and hideously against the east, again reminding us of those strange Asian paintings of Nicholas Roerich; and when we thought of the damnable honeycombs inside them, and of the frightful amorphous entities that might have pushed their foetidly squirming way even to the topmost hollow pinnacles, we could not face without panic the prospect of again sailing by those suggestive skyward cave-mouths where the wind made sounds like an evil musical piping over a wide range. To make matters worse, we saw distinct traces of local mist around several of the summits—as poor Lake must have done when he made that early mistake about volcanism—and thought shiveringly of that kindred mist from which we had just escaped; of that, and of the blasphemous, horror-fostering abyss whence all such vapours came.

All was well with the plane, and we clumsily hauled on our heavy flying furs. Danforth got the engine started without trouble, and we made a very smooth take-off over the nightmare city. Below us the primal Cyclopean masonry spread out as it had done when first we saw it—so short, yet infinitely long, a time ago—and we began rising and turning to test the wind for our crossing through the pass. At a very high level there must have been great disturbance, since the ice-dust clouds of the zenith were doing all sorts of fantastic things; but at 24,000 feet, the height we needed for the pass, we found navigation quite practicable. As we drew close to the jutting peaks the wind's strange piping again became manifest, and I could see Danforth's hands trembling at the controls. Rank amateur though I was, I thought at that moment that I might be a better navigator than he in effecting the dangerous crossing between pinnacles; and when I made motions to change seats and take over his duties he did not protest. I tried to keep all my skill and self-possession about me, and stared at the sector of reddish farther sky betwixt the walls of the pass—resolutely refusing to pay attention to the puffs of mountain-top vapour, and wishing that I had wax-stopped ears like Ulysses' men off the Sirens' coast to keep that disturbing wind-piping from my consciousness.

But Danforth, released from his piloting and keyed up to a dangerous nervous pitch, could not keep quiet. I felt him turning and wriggling about as he looked back at the terrible receding city, ahead at the cave-riddled, cube-barnacled peaks, sidewise at the bleak sea of snowy, rampart-strown foothills, and upward at the seething, grotesquely clouded sky. It was then, just as I was trying to steer safely through the pass, that his mad shrieking brought us so close to disaster by shattering my tight hold on myself and causing me to fumble helplessly with the controls for a moment. A second afterward my resolution triumphed and we made the crossing safely—yet I am afraid that Danforth will never be the same again.

I have said that Danforth refused to tell me what final horror made him scream out so insanely—a horror which, I feel sadly sure, is mainly responsible for his present breakdown. We had snatches of shouted conversation above the wind's piping and the engine's buzzing as we reached the safe side of the range and swooped slowly down toward the camp, but that had mostly to do with the pledges of secrecy we had made as we prepared to leave the nightmare city. Certain things, we had agreed, were not for people to know and discuss lightly—and I would not speak of them now but for the need of heading off that Starkweather-Moore Expedition, and others, at any cost. It is absolutely necessary, for the peace and safety of mankind, that some of earth's dark, dead corners and unplumbed depths be let alone; lest sleeping abnormalities wake to resurgent life, and blasphemously surviving nightmares squirm and splash out of their black lairs to newer and wider conquests.

All that Danforth has ever hinted is that the final horror was a mirage. It was not, he declares, anything connected with the cubes and caves of echoing, vaporous, wormily honeycombed mountains of madness which we crossed; but a single fantastic, daemoniac glimpse, among the churning zenith-clouds, of what lay back of those other violet westward mountains which the Old Ones had shunned and feared. It is very probable that the thing was a sheer delusion born of the previous stresses we had passed through, and of the actual though unrecognised mirage of the dead transmontane city experienced near Lake's camp the day before; but it was so real to Danforth that he suffers from it still.

He has on rare occasions whispered disjointed and irresponsible things about 'the black pit', 'the carven rim', 'the proto-shoggoths', 'the windowless solids with five dimensions', 'the nameless cylinder', 'the elder pharos', 'Yog-Sothoth', 'the primal white jelly', 'the colour out of space', 'the wings', 'the eyes in darkness', 'the moon-ladder', 'the original, the eternal, the undying', and other bizarre conceptions; but when he is fully himself he repudiates all this and attributes it to his curious and macabre reading of earlier years. Danforth, indeed, is known to be among the few who have ever dared go completely through that worm-riddled copy of the *Necronomicon* kept under lock and key in the college library.

The higher sky, as we crossed the range, was surely vaporous and disturbed enough; and although I did not see the zenith I can well imagine that its swirls of ice-dust may have taken strange forms. Imagination, knowing how vividly distant scenes can sometimes be reflected, refracted, and magnified by such layers of restless cloud, might easily have supplied the rest—and, of course, Danforth did not hint any of these specific horrors till after his memory had had a chance to draw on his bygone reading. He could never have seen so much in one instantaneous glance.

At the time, his shrieks were confined to the repetition of a single mad word of all too obvious source:

'Tekeli-li! Tekeli-li!'

Byrd in Antarctica

Henry Hart

The last voices flapped into the radio's gusts of static.
June sun thinned to blue ash on the ice cap's rim.

What was it that entered his shack dug deep in ice,
whittling his bones to quills, tightening his skin to a drum?

Even the cold that gelled oil in lamps,
broke breath in splinters before it fell

could not freeze it out. Against its power
his flashlights paled.

In his sleeping bag he hallucinated wings
and woke in a damp moult.

Was it fumes from the stove pooling on his ceiling
or just the blackness of Ross Barrier

as sunlight fizzled from the horizon
on its snuffed wick?

He heard continents shift beneath him,
plates of ice quake,

afterward nothing,
not even the clock beating its ribs.

Above, planets froze in their circuits.
The moon hardened to a sliver of ice.

Then, out of nowhere, sparks scribbled
a filigree around stars.

The void
erupted in auroras.

Now he was flying,
his bones light as wings,

his poisonous shack
an insignificant crystal.

Years later, among the many faces,
he kept returning to that moment

when the sky's origin
wrote itself out in flames,

when he soared
toward magnetic lights.

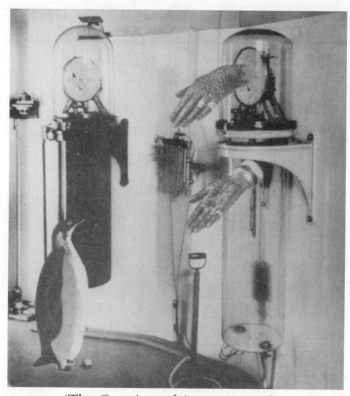

'The Creation of Antarctic Light'
—Ern Malley

from

The Amazing Adventures of Kavalier and Clay

Michael Chabon

Joe woke in the Hangar to the smell of a burning cheroot and found himself gazing up at the oft-patched wing of the Condor.

'Lucky you,' said Shannenhouse. He snapped shut his lighter and exhaled. He was sitting on a canvas folding stool beside Joe, legs spread wide in best cowboy manner. Shannenhouse was from a raw town called Tustin in California and cultivated cowboy habits that sat unlikely on his slight frame, with his professorial mien. He had fair thinning hair and rimless spectacles and hands that, while horny and scarred, remained delicate. He tried to be taciturn but was given to lecturing. He tried to be stern and friendless but was an inveterate kibitzer. He was the old man of Kelvinator Station, an eight-kills ace from the first war who had spent the twenties flying in the Sierras and in the Alaskan bush. He had enlisted after Pearl and was as disappointed as any of them by his assignment to Kelvinator. He had not seriously hoped to fight again, but he had been doing interesting work all his life and was looking for more. Since their arrival at Kelvinator—the official, classified name was Naval Station SD-A2(R)—the weather had been so bad that he had been up in the air only twice, once on a recon mission that was aborted after twenty minutes in the teeth of a blizzard, and once on an unauthorised, failed jaunt to try to find the base of the first Byrd expedition, or of the last Scott expedition, or of the first Amundsen expedition, or the site of *something* that had happened in this waste for which the adjective 'godforsaken' appeared to have been coined. He was nominally a first lieutenant, but nobody stood on ceremony or rank at Kelvinator Station. They were all obedient to the dictates of survival, and no further discipline was really necessary. Joe himself was a radioman second-class, but nobody ever called him anything but Sparks, Dit, or, most often, Dopey.

The smoke of the cigar smelled very good to Joe. It had an unantarctic flavour of autumn and fire and dirt. There was something lurking inside him that the smell of the burning cheroot seemed to keep at bay. He reached for Shannenhouse's hand, raising an eyebrow. Shannenhouse passed the cheroot to Joe, and Joe sat up to take it in his teeth. He saw that he was tucked into a sleeping bag on the floor of the Hangar, his upper body propped on a pile of blankets. He leaned back on one elbow and took a long drag, inhaling the strong black stuff into his lungs. This was a mistake. His coughing spasm was long and racking, and the pain in his chest and head reminded him abruptly of the dead men and the dogs in the tunnels with their lungs full of some kind of agent or germ. He lay back down again, forehead stitched with sweat.

'Oh, shit,' he said.

'Indeed,' Shannenhouse said.

'Johnny, you can't go down in there, okay, you promise? They all—'

'Now you tell me.'

Joe tried to sit up, scattering ash down the blankets. 'You didn't go down in there?'

'You were not awake to warn me, remember?' Shannenhouse reclaimed his cigar as if in reproach, and shoved Joe back down to the floor. He gave his head a shake, trying to clear away a memory that clung. 'Jesus. That.' Normally his voice was fluting and animated by a scholarly verve, but now it came out cowboy flat, dry and flat as Joe imagined Tustin, California, to be. 'That is the worst thing I have ever seen.'

A good deal of Shannenhouse's talk over the months had been of awful things he had seen, tales rife with burning men, arterial fountains of blood spraying from the armless shoulders of fellows who strayed into the whirl of propellers, hunters half-devoured by bears dragging their stumps into camp in the morning.

'Oh, shit,' Joe said again.

Shannenhouse nodded. 'The worst thing I have ever seen.'

'Johnny, I beg you not to say this again.'

'Sorry, Joe.'

'Where were *you*, anyway? Why didn't you . . .'

'I was out here.' The Hangar, though buried in the snow of Marie Byrd Land like all the other buildings of Kelvinator Station, was not connected to the rest by tunnel, again because of the heavy weather that had come so viciously and early this year. 'I had the watch, I came out here just to have a look at her.' He jerked a thumb toward the aging Condor. 'I do not know what Kelly thought he was doing, but the wire—'

'We have to raise Gitmo, we have to tell them.'

'I tried to raise them,' Shannenhouse said. 'The radio is out. Could not raise shit.'

Joe felt panic lurch up inside him now, as it had on the day he fell through the haycock, in a clatter of skis and bindings, the wind knocked from his lungs, mouth packed with snow, a cold blade of ice jabbing for his heart.

'The radio is out? Johnny, why is the radio out?' In his panic, the melodramatic notion, worthy of one of Sammy's plots, that Shannenhouse was a German spy and had killed them all streaked through his thoughts. '*What is going on?*'

'Relax, Dopey, all right? Please do not lose your shit.' He passed the cheroot back to Joe.

'Johnny,' Joe said, as calmly as he could, letting out smoke, 'I feel that I am going to lose my shit.'

'Look here, the fellows are dead and the radio is out, but there is no connection between the two. One has nothing to do with the other, like everything else in life. It was not some Nazi superweapon. Jesus Christ. It was the fucking stove.'

'The stove?'

'It was carbon monoxide from Wayne.' The Antarctic Waldorf was heated by a gasoline stove, affectionately known as Wayne because of the legend FT. WAYNE IRON WORKS INDIANA USA stamped on its side. The naming madness that came over men when they arrived here in the unmapped blankness seeped quickly into every corner of their lives. They named the radios, the latrine, they named their hangovers and cuts on their fingers. 'I went up and checked the ventilators in the roof. Packed with snow. Same thing with Dog-town. I told Captain they were poorly made. Maybe I did not. The thought did occur to me at the time we were laying them in.'

'They all died,' Joe said, the statement rising at the end with just the faintest hopeful intimation of a doubt.

Shannenhouse nodded. 'Everyone but you and your boy-friend, maybe I guess because you were lying at the very end of the tunnel from the door. Now, as far as the radio goes, who the fuck knows. Magnetism. Sunspots. It will come back.'

'What do you mean, my boyfriend?'

'The mutt. Mussels.'

'Oyster?'

Shannenhouse nodded again. 'He is all right. I tied him up in the Mess Hall for the night.'

'What?' Joe started to his feet, but Shannenhouse reached out and forced him back, not gently.

'Lie down, Dopey. I shut down the damn stove, I dug out the ventilators. Your dog will be all right.'

So Joe lay down, and Shannenhouse leaned back against the wall of the Hangar and looked up at his airplane. They passed the cigar back and forth. In a little while, it was going to be time for them to discuss their chances, and plan for their survival until they could be rescued. They had food to last two dozen men two years, plenty of fuel for the gener

ators. The Mess Hall would provide sleeping quarters suitably free of the spectacle of frozen corpses. Compared to the early heroes of the continent, starving and dying in their caribou-skin tents, gnawing a raw hunk of frozen seal, they were in clover. Even if the navy couldn't get a ship or a plane in until spring, they would have more than enough of what they needed to make it through. But somehow the idea that death had reached down through all that snow and ice into their tunnels and cozy rooms and in a single night—in an hour—killed all of their fellows and all but one of the dogs, made their survival, for all their ample provisions and matériel, seem less than assured.

Both of the men had felt all along, on certain evenings as they hurried from the transmitter tower or the Hangar back toward the hatch that led to safety and warmth, a stirring at the fringes of the station, a presence, something struggling to be born out of the winds, the darkness, the looming towers and jagged teeth of the ice. The hair on the back of the neck stood erect and you ran, in spite of yourself, ribs ringing with panic, certain as a child running up the cellar stairs that something very bad was after you. Antarctica was beautiful— even Joe, who loathed it with every fibre of his being as the symbol, the embodiment, the blank unmeaning heart of his impotence in this war, had felt the thrill and grandeur of the Ice. But it was trying, at every moment you remained on it, to kill you. They could not let their guard down for a moment; they had all known that from the start. Now it seemed to Joe and the pilot as if the evil intent of the place, the glittering ripples of dust gathering in the darkness, would find a way to get them no matter how warm their berth or full their bellies, no matter how many layers of wool and hide and fur they put between them and it. Survival, at that moment, seemed beyond the reach or agency of their plans.

'I don't like having the dogs in here, messing up my airplane,' said Shannenhouse, studying the struts of the Condor's left wing with an approving frown. 'You know that.'

The winter drove them mad. It drove every man mad who had ever lived through it; there was only ever the question of degree. The sun disappeared, and you could not leave the tunnels, and everything and everyone you loved was ten thousand miles away. At best, a man suffered from strange lapses in judgment and perception, finding himself at the mirror about to comb his hair with a mechanical pencil, stepping into his undershirt, boiling up a pot of concentrated orange juice for tea. Most men felt a sudden blaze of recovery in their hearts at the first glimpse of a pale hem of sunlight on the horizon in mid-September. But there were stories, apocryphal, perhaps, but far from dubious, of men in past expeditions who sank so deeply into the drift of their own melancholy that they were lost forever. And few among the wives and families of the men who returned from a winter on the Ice would have said that what they got back was identical to what they had sent down there.

In the case of John Wesley Shannenhouse, the winter madness was merely a kind of modulation, a deepening of his long-standing involvement with his Curtiss-Wright AT-32. The Condor seaplane was ten years old, and had been hard used by the navy before finding her present billet. She had seen action and taken fire, hunting steamship pirates on the Yangtze in the mid-thirties. She had flown thousands of cargo runs in and out of Honduras, Cuba, Mexico, and Hawaii, and enough of the plane and her engines had been replaced over the years, according to the dictates of local expediency, parts shortages, and mechanics' ingenuity and neglect, from the tiniest bolts and wire clasps to one of the big Wright Cyclone engines and entire sections of the fuselage and wings, that it was a metaphysical question long pondered by Shannenhouse that winter whether she could fairly be said to be the same plane that had rolled out of Glenn Curtiss's plant in San Diego in 1934.

As the winter wore on, the question so vexed him—Joe was certainly well sick of it, and of Shannenhouse and his stinking cheroots—that he decided the only way to gain surcease would be to replace every replaceable part, making himself the guarantor of the Condor's identity. The navy had provided Kelly and Bloch, the dead mechanics, with an entire tractor-load of spare parts, and a machine shop equipped with a toolmaker's lathe, a milling machine, a drill press, an oxyacetylene welding outfit, a miniature blacksmith's shop, and eight different kinds of power saw from jig to joiner. Shannenhouse found that simply by dint of drinking sixty-five to eighty cups of coffee a day (with everyone dead, there was certainly no need to stint) he could reduce his sleep requirements to half their former seven hours, at least. When he did sleep, it was in the Condor, wrapped in several sleeping bags (it was cold in the Hangar). He moved in a dozen crates of canned food and took to cooking his meals in there, too, crouching over a Primus stove as if huddled out on the Ice.

First he rebuilt the engines, machining new parts where he found the originals worn or their replacements substandard or borrowed from some alien breed of plane. Then he went to work on the frame of the aircraft, milling new struts and ribs, replacing every screw and grommet. When Joe finally lost track of Shannenhouse's labours, the pilot had embarked on the long and difficult job of doping, repairing the airplane's canvas sheathing with a sickly-sweet bubbling compound he cooked up on the same stove he used to make his dinner. It was tough work for one man, but he refused Joe's halfhearted offer of help as if it had been a proposal that they share wives.

'Get your own airplane,' he said. His beard stuck straight out from his chin, bristling and orange-blond and seven inches long. His eyes were pink and glittering from the dope, he was thickly covered in a reddish pelt of reindeer fur from his

219

sleeping bag, and he stank more than any human Joe had ever smelled (though there would come worse), as if he had been dipped in some ungodly confection of Camembert and rancid gasoline brewed up in a spit-filled cuspidor. He punctuated this remark by hurling a crescent wrench, which missed Joe's head by two inches and gouged a deep hole out of the wall beside him. Joe quickly climbed back up through the hatch and went topside. He did not see Shannenhouse again for nearly three weeks.

He had his own madness to contend with.

Radio service at Naval Station SD-A2(R) had been restored seventeen hours after the Waldorf disaster. Joe did not sleep during that entire period, making a fresh attempt every ten minutes, and finally managed to raise Mission Command at Guantánamo Bay at 0700 GMT and inform them, transmitting in code, painfully slowly without Gedman there to assist him, that on April 10 every man at Kelvinator but Kavalier and Shannenhouse, and all the dogs but one, had been poisoned by carbon monoxide resulting from poor ventilation in quarters. The replies from Command were terse but reflected a certain amount of shock and confusion. A number of contradictory and impractical orders were issued and remanded. It took Command longer than it had Joe and Shannenhouse to realise that nothing could be done until September at the earliest. The dead men and dogs would keep perfectly well until then; putrefaction was an unknown phenomenon here. The Bay of Whales was frozen solid and impassable and would be for another three months, at least. In any case, Drake Passage, as Joe's own monitoring of short-burst transmissions to BdU had confirmed, was teeming with U-boats. There was no hope of being rescued by some passing whaler without the help of a military escort—the whalers and chasers had, by and large, abandoned the field by now—and even then, not until the barrier ice began to warm and fracture. At last, five days after Joe's first message, Command somewhat superfluously ordered them to sit tight and wait for spring. Joe was, in the meantime, to stay in regular radio contact and continue, so far as he was able, the primary mission (apart from the more elemental one of maintaining an American presence at the pole) of Kelvinator Station: to monitor the airwaves for U-boat transmissions, to transmit all intercepts back to Command, which would relay them to the crypt-analysts back in Washington, with their clacking electronic bombes, and finally to alert Command of any German movements toward the continent itself.

It was in the furtherance of this mission that Joe's sanity entered its period of hibernation. He became as inseparable from the radio as Shannenhouse from his Condor. And, again like Shannenhouse, he could not bring himself to inhabit the rooms that they had formerly shared with twenty other living, breathing men. Instead, Joe made the radio shack his principal lodgings, and although he continued to cook his meals in the Mess Hall, he carried them through the tunnels to the radio shack to eat them. His direction-finding observations, and intercepts of short-burst transmissions of the two German submarines then active in the region, were extensive and accurate, and in time, with some coaching from Command, he learned to handle the quirky and delicate navy code machine nearly as well as Gedman had.

But it was not just military and commercial shipping channels to which Joe tuned in. He listened through his powerful multiband Marconi CSR 9A set to anything and everything the three seventy-five-foot antenna towers could pull down out of the sky, at all hours of the day: AM, FM, shortwave, the amateur bands. It was a kind of ethereal fishing, sending out his line and seeing what he could catch, and how long he could hold on to it: a tango orchestra live from the banks of the Plate, stern biblical exegesis in Afrikaans, an inning and a half of a game between the Red Sox and the White Sox, a Brazilian soap opera, two lonely amateurs in

Nebraska and Suriname droning on about their dogs. He listened for hours to the Morse code alarums of fishermen in squalls and merchant seamen beset by frigates, and once even caught the end of a broadcast of *The Amazing Adventures of the Escapist*, learning thus that Tracy Bacon was no longer playing the title role. Most of all, however, he followed the war. Depending on the hour, the tilt of the planet, the angle of the sun, the cosmic rays, the aurora australis, and the Heaviside layer, he was able to get anywhere from eighteen to thirty-six different news broadcasts every day, from all over the world, though naturally, like most of the world, he favoured those of the BBC. The invasion of Europe was in full swing, and like so many others, he followed its fitful but steady progress with the help of a map that he tacked to the padded wall of the shack and studded with the coloured pins of victory and setback. He listened to H.V. Kaltenborn, Walter Winchell, Edward R. Murrow, and, just as devotedly, to their mocking shadows, to the snide innuendos of Lord Haw-Haw, Patrick Kelly out of Japanese Shanghai, Mr O.K., Mr Guess Who, and to the throaty insinuations of Midge-at-the-Mike, whom he quite often thought of fucking. He would sit, awash in the aqueous burbling of his headphones, for twelve or fifteen hours at a time, getting up from the console only to use the latrine and to feed himself and Oyster.

It may be imagined that this ability to reach out so far and wide from the confines of his deep-buried polar tomb, his only company a half-blind dog, thirty-seven corpses human and animal, and a man in the grip of an idée fixe, might have served as a means of salvation for Joe, connected in his isolation and loneliness to the whole world. But in fact the cumulative effect, as day after day he at last doffed the headphones and lowered himself, stiff, head buzzing, onto the floor of the shack beside Oyster, was only, in the end, to emphasise and to mock him with the one connection he could not make. Just as, in his first months in New York, there had never been any mention in any of the eleven newspapers he bought every day, in any of three languages, about the well-being and disposition of the Kavalier family of Prague, there was now never anything on the radio that gave him any indication of how they might be faring. It was not merely that they were never personally mentioned—even at his most desperate, he didn't seriously imagine this possibility—but that he could never seem to get any information at all about the fate of the Jews of Czechoslovakia.

From time to time there were warnings and reports from escapees of camps in Germany, massacres in Poland, roundups and deportations and trials. But it was, from his admittedly remote and limited point of view, as if the Jews of his country, his Jews, his family, had been slipped unseen into some fold in the pin-bristling map of Europe. And increasingly, as the winter inched on and the darkness deepened around him, Joe began to brood, and the corrosion that had been worked on his inner wiring for so long by his inability to do anything to help or reach his mother and grandfather, the disappointment and anger he had been nursing for so long at the navy's having sent him to the fucking South Pole when all he had wanted to do was drop bombs on Germans and supplies on Czech partisans, began to coalesce into a genuine desperation.

Then one 'evening' toward the end of July, Joe tuned in to a shortwave broadcast from the Reichsrundsfunk directed at Rhodesia, Uganda, and the rest of British Africa. It was an English-language documentary programme cheerfully detailing the creation and flourishing of a marvellous place in the Czech Protectorate, a specially designed 'preserve', as the narrator called it, for the Jews of that part of the Reich. It was called the Theresienstadt Model Ghetto. Joe had been through the town of Terezin once, on an outing with his Makabbi sporting group. Apparently, this town had been transformed from a dull Bohemian backwater into a happy, industrious, even cultivated place, of rose gardens, vocational

223

schools, and a full symphony orchestra made up of what the narrator, who sounded like Emil Jannings trying to sound like Will Rogers, called 'internees'. There was a description of a typical musical evening at the preserve, into the midst of which, to Joe's horror and delight, floated the rich, disembodied tenor of his maternal grandfather, Franz Schonfeld. He was not identified by name, but there was no mistaking the faint whiskey undertones, nor for that matter the selection, 'Der Erlkönig'.

Joe struggled to make sense of what he had heard. The false tone of the programme, the bad accent of the narrator, the obvious euphemisms, the unacknowledged truth underlying the blather about roses and violins—that all of these people had been torn from their homes and put in this place, against their will, because they were Jews—all these inclined him to a feeling of dread. The joy, spontaneous and unreasoning, that had come over him as he heard his little grandfather's sweet voice for the first time in five years subsided quickly under the swelling unease that was inspired in him by the idea of the old man singing Schubert in a prison town for an audience of captives. There had been no date given for the programme, and as the evening went on and he mulled it over, Joe became more and more convinced that the pasteboard cheeriness and vocational training masked some dreadful reality, a witch's house made of candy and gingerbread to lure children and fatten them for the table.

The next night trolling the frequencies around fifteen megacycles on the extremely off chance that there might be a sequel to the previous night's programme, he stumbled onto a transmission in German, one so strong and clear that he suspected it at once of having a local origin. It was sandwiched carefully into an extremely thin interstice of bandwidth between the powerful BBC Asian Service and the equally powerful A.F.R.N. South, and if you were not desperately searching for word of your family, you would have dialled

224

past it without even knowing it was there. The voice was a man's, soft, high-pitched, educated, with a trace of Swabian accent and a distinct note of outrage barely suppressed. Conditions were terrible; the instruments were all either inoperable or unreliable; quarters were intolerably confined, morale low. Joe reached for a pencil and started to transcribe the man's philippic; he could not imagine what would have prompted the fellow to make his presence known in such an open fashion. Then, abruptly, with a sigh and a weary, 'Heil Hitler', the man signed off, leaving a burble of empty airwaves and a single, unavoidable conclusion: there were Germans on the Ice.

This had been a fear of the Allies ever since the Ritscher expedition of 1938–39, when that extremely thorough German scientist, lavishly equipped by the personal order of Hermann Göring, had arrived at the coast of Queen Maud Land in a catapult ship and hurled two excellent Dornier Wal seaplanes again and again into the unexplored hinterland of the Norwegian claim where, using aerial cameras, they had mapped over three hundred and fifty thousand square miles of territory (introducing the art of photogrammetry to the Antarctic) and then pelted the whole thing with five thousand giant steel darts, specially crafted for the expedition, each one topped with an elegant swastika. The land was thus staked and claimed for Germany, and renamed New Schwabia. Initial difficulties with the Norwegians over this presumption had been neatly solved by the conquest of that country in 1940.

Joe put on his boots and parka and went out to tell Shannenhouse of his discovery. The night was windless and mild; the thermometer read 4°F. The stars swarmed in their strange arrangements, and there was a gaudy viridian ring around the low-hanging moon. Thin watery moonlight puddled over the Barrier without seeming to illuminate any part of it. Aside from the radio towers, and the chimneys jutting like the fins of killer whales from the snow, there was

225

nothing to be seen in any direction. The lupine mountains, the jutting pressure ridges like piles of giant bones, the vast tent city of peaked haycocks that lay to the east—he could see none of it. The German base could have lain not ten miles away across level ice, blazing like a carnival, and still remained invisible. When he was halfway to the Hangar, he stopped. The cessation of his crunching footsteps seemed to eliminate the very last sound from the world. The silence was so absolute that the inner processes of his cranium became first audible and then deafening. Surely a concealed German sniper could pick him out, even in this impenetrable gloom, just by hearing the storm-drain roaring of the veins in his ears, the hydraulic pistoning of his salivary glands. He hurried toward the hatch of the Hangar, crunching and stumbling. As he approached it, a breeze kicked up, carrying with it an acrid stench of blood and burning hair potent enough to make Joe gag. Shannenhouse had fired up the Blubberteria.

'Stay out,' said Shannenhouse. 'Get lost. Keep out. Go fuck your dog, you Jew, you bastard.'

Joe was trapped halfway down the stairwell, not yet low enough to see into the Hangar. Every time he tried to get to the bottom, Shannenhouse threw something at his legs, a crankshaft, a dry cell.

'What you are doing?' Joe called to him. 'What is this smell?'

Shannenhouse's odour had grown in the weeks since Joe's last encounter with him, slipping free of the confines of his body, absorbing further constituent smells of burned beans, fried wire, airplane dope, and, nearly drowning out all the others, freshly tanned seal.

'All the canvas I had was ruined,' Shannenhouse said defensively and a little sadly. 'It must have got wet on the trip down.'

'You are covering the airplane in the skin of seals?'

'An airplane *is* a seal, dickhead. A seal that swims through the air.'

'Yes, all right,' Joe said. It is a well-known phenomenon that the Napoleons in the asylums of the world have little patience with one another's Austerlitzes and Marengos. 'I just come to tell you one thing. Jerry is here. On the Ice. I heard him on the radio.'

There was a long, expressive pause, though as to what emotion it expressed, Joe felt none too certain.

'Where?' Shannenhouse said at last.

'I'm not sure. He said something about the thirtieth meridian, but . . . I am not sure.'

'Over there, though. Where they were before.'

Joe nodded, although Shannenhouse couldn't see him.

'That is what, a thousand miles.'

'At least.'

'Fuck them, then. Did you raise Command?'

'No, Johnny, I did not. Not yet.'

'Well, raise them, then. Christ, what the fuck is wrong with you.'

He was right. Joe ought to have contacted Command the moment he finished transcribing the intercepted transmission. And once he had some idea of the nature and source of the transmission, his failure to do so was not only a breach of procedure, and a betrayal of an order—to preserve the continent from Nazi overtures—that had come directly from the president himself, but it also put him and Shannenhouse in potential danger. If Joe knew about them, they almost certainly knew about Joe. And yet, just as he had not reported Carl Ebling after the first bomb threat to Empire Comics, some impulse now prevented him from opening the channel to Cuba and making the report that duty obliged him to make.

'I don't know,' Joe said. 'I don't know what is the fuck wrong with me. I'm sorry.'

'Good. Now get out.'

Joe climbed back up the stairs and out into the mercury-blue night. As he started north, back toward the opening of the radio shack, something flickered in the middle of all the nothing, so tentatively that at first he thought it was an optic phenomenon akin to the effect of the silence on his ears, something bioelectric happening inside his eyeballs. No; there it was, the horizon, a dark seam, piped with an all but imaginary ribbon of pale gold. It was as faint as the glimmer of an idea that began to form, at that moment, in Joe's mind.

'Spring,' said Joe. The cold air crumpled up the word like fish wrap. When he got back to the radio shack, he dug out a broken portable shortwave that Radioman First Class Burnside had been planning to repair, plugged in the soldering iron, and, after a few hours' work, managed to fix up a set that he could dedicate exclusively to monitoring the transmissions of the German station, which, it transpired, was under the direct command of Göring's office, and referred to itself as Jotunheim. The man who made the transmissions was very careful about concealing them, and after the initial outburst that Joe had chanced upon, he limited himself to more spare and factual, but no less anxious, accounts of weather and atmospheric conditions; but with patience, Joe was able to locate and transcribe what he estimated to be around sixty-five per cent of the traffic between Jotunheim and Berlin. He accumulated enough information to confirm the location at the thirtieth meridian, on the coast of Queen Maud Land, and to conclude that the bulk of their enterprise, at least so far, was of a purely observational and scientific character. In the course of two weeks of careful monitoring, he was able to reach a number of positive conclusions, and to listen as a drama unfolded.

The author of these hand-wringing transmissions was a geologist. He took an interest in questions of cloud formations and wind patterns, and he may also have been a meteorologist, but he was primarily a geologist. He was continually pestering Berlin with details of his plans for the spring, the schists and coal seams he intended to unearth. He had just two companions in Jotunheim. One was code-named Bouvard and the other Pecuchet. They had started out their season on the Ice at almost exactly the same time as their American counterparts, of whose existence they were fully aware, though they seemed to have no idea of the catastrophe that had struck Kelvinator Station. Their number had been reduced, too, but only by one, a radioman and Enigma operator who had suffered a nervous collapse and been taken away with the military party when the latter left for the winter; in spite of the risk of exposure without coded transmissions, the Ministry had seen no reason to force soldiers to winter over when there would be neither chance nor need of soldiering. The military party was due back on September 18, or as soon as they could get through the ice.

On the eleventh day following Joe's discovery of Jotunheim, for reasons that the Geologist, in the face of intense pressure and threats from the Ministry, refused to characterise as anything more than 'unbecoming', 'unsuitable', and 'of an intimate nature', Pecuchet shot Bouvard and then turned his weapon fatally on himself. The message announcing the death of Bouvard three days later was filled with intimations of imminent doom that Joe recognised with a chill. The Geologist, too, had sensed that loitering presence in a veil of glittering dust at the fringes of his camp, waiting for its moment.

All this, for two weeks, Joe pieced together in secret and kept to himself. He told himself, each time he dialled in to what he came to call Radio Jotunheim, that he would listen just a little longer, accrue another bit of information, and then pass everything he had along to Command. Surely this was what spies generally did? Better to get it all, and then risk discovery in transmitting it, than tip off the Geologist and his friends before he had acquired the full picture. The shocking murder-suicide, which broke new ground for death on the continent, seemed to put a point on things, however, and Joe typed up a careful report that, conscious as ever of his English, he proofread several times. Then he sat in front of the console. While nothing would have pleased him more than to shoot this haughty-sounding, languid Geologist in the head, he had come to identify so strongly with his enemy that, as he prepared to reveal the man's existence to Command, he felt an odd reluctance, as if in doing so he would betray himself.

As he was attempting to make up his mind what to do with his report, the desire for revenge, for a final expiation of guilt and responsibility, that had been the sole animator of Joe's existence since the night of December 6, 1941, received the final impulse it required to doom the German Geologist.

The coming of spring had brought on another whaling season, and with it a fresh campaign of the undersea boats. *U-1421*, in particular, had been harassing traffic in Drake Passage, Allied and neutral, at a moment when shortages of the oil rendered from whales could mean the difference between victory and defeat in Europe for either side. Joe had been supplying Command with intercepts from *U-1421* for months, as well as providing directional information on the submarine's signals. But the South Atlantic D/F array had, until recently, been incomplete and provisional, and nothing had ever come of Joe's efforts. Tonight, however, as he picked up a burst of chatter on the DAQ huff-duff set that, even in its encrypted state, he could recognise as originating from *U-1421*, there were two other listening posts tuned in as it made its report. When Joe supplied his readings on the signal from Kelvinator's HF/DF array in its cage atop the north aerial, a triangulation was performed at the Submarine Warfare Center in Washington. The resultant position, latitude and longitude, was supplied to the British navy, at which point an attack team was dispatched from the Falkland Islands. The corvettes and sub hunters found *U-1421*, chased it, and pelted it with hedgehogs and depth charges until nothing remained of it but an oily black squiggle scrawled on the water's surface.

Joe exulted in the sinking of *U-1421*, and in his role therein. He wallowed in it, even going so far as to permit himself to imagine that it might have been the boat that had sent the *Ark of Miriam* to the bottom of the Atlantic in 1941.

He trotted down along the tunnel to the Mess Hall and, for the first time in over two weeks, filled and turned on the snow melter, and took a shower. He fixed himself a plate of ham and powdered eggs, and broke out a new parka and pair of mukluks. On his way to the Hangar, he was obliged to pass the door to the Waldorf and the entrance of Dog-town. He shut his eyes and ran past. He did not notice that the dog crates were empty.

The sun, all of it, an entire dull red disk, hung a bare inch above the horizon. He watched it until his cheeks began to feel frostbitten. As it sank slowly back below the Barrier, a lovely salmon-and-violet sunset began to assemble itself. Then, as if to make certain Joe didn't miss the point, the sun rose for a second time, and set once more in a faded but still quite pretty flush of pink and lavender. He knew that this was only an optical illusion, brought on by distortions in the shape of the air, but he accepted it as an omen and an exhortation.

'Shannenhouse,' he said. He had gone barrelling down the steps without giving the pilot any warning and, as it turned out, had caught him during one of his rare periods of sleep. 'Wake up, it's daytime! It's spring! Come on!'

Shannenhouse stumbled out of the plane, which glistened eerily in its tight glossy sheath of seal hides. 'The sun?' he said. 'Are you sure?'

'You just missed it, but it will be back in twenty hours.'

A softness appeared in Shannenhouse's eyes that Joe recognised from their first days on the Ice long ago. 'The sun,' he said. Then, 'What do you want?'

'I want to go kill Jerry.'

Shannenhouse pursed his lips. His beard was a foot long now, his smell excoriating, probing, nearly sentient. 'All right,' he said.

'Can that plane fly or not?'

Joe started around the tail, over to the starboard side of the plane, where he noticed that the hides covering the front part of the fuselage were of a much lighter colour and a different texture than those on the port side.

Stacked in a neat pyramid beside the plane, like cargo waiting to be loaded on board, sat the skulls of seventeen dogs.

Wahoo Fleer, their dead CO, had been at Little America with Richard Byrd in '33 and again in '40. When they went through his files, they found detailed plans and orders for transmontane Antarctic flights. In 1940 Captain Fleer himself had flown over part of the territory they would be crossing to kill the Geologist, over the Rockefeller Mountains, over the Edsel Fords, toward the shattered magnificent vacancy of Queen Maud Land. He had made carefully typed lists of the things a man ought to carry with him.

    1 ice-chisel
    1 pair of snow-shoes
    1 roll toilet paper
    2 handkerchiefs

The great anxiety of such a flight was the possibility of a forced landing. If they crashed, they would be alone and without hope of rescue at the magnetic centre of nothingness itself. They would have to fight their way back to Kelvinator Station on foot, or press on ahead to Jotunheim. Captain Fleer had typed up lists of the emergency gear they would need in such an instance: tents, Primus stove, knives, saws, axe, rope, crampons. Sledges that they would have to drag themselves. Everything had to be considered for the weight it would add to the payload.

Engine muff and blow-torch   4 lbs.
2 reindeer-fur sleeping-bags   18 lbs.
Flare gun and eight cartridges   5 lbs.

The precision and order of Captain Fleer's instructions had a settling effect on their minds, as did the return of the sun, and the idea of killing one of the enemy. They resumed each other's company. Shannenhouse came in from the Hangar, and Joe moved his bedroll into the Mess Hall. They said nothing about their descent over the past three months into some ancient mammalian despair. Together they ransacked Wahoo Fleer's desk. They found a decoded tidbit from Command, received the previous autumn, passing along an unconfirmed report that there might or might not be a German installation on the Ice, code-named Jotunheim. They found a copy of the Book of Mormon, and a letter marked 'In the Event of My Death', which they felt entitled, but could not bring themselves, to open.

Shannenhouse took a shower. This necessitated the melting of forty-five two-pound blocks of snow, which Joe, grunting and cursing in three languages, cut and shovelled, one by one, into the melter on the Mess Hall's roof, whose zinc maw, like the bell of a gramophone, broadcast the thin reedy voice of the pilot singing 'Nearer My God to Thee'. They spoke little, but their exchanges were amiable, and over the course of a week they resumed the air of comradely put-uponness that had been universal among the men before the Wayne disaster. It was as if they had forgotten that flying unsupported and alone across one thousand miles of storm-tossed pack and glacier to shoot a lonely German scientist had been their own idea.

'How would you feel about a nice ten- or twelve-hour stretch of, oh, say *shovelling snow*?' they would call to each other from their bunks in the morning, after they had spent the previous five days doing only that, as if some unfeeling superior had put them on shovel duty and they were just the unlucky stiffs who had to obey the order to dig out the Hangar and the tractor garage. In the evening, when they came aching, faces and fingers seared with cold, back into the tunnels, they filled the Mess Hall with cries of 'Whiskey rations!' and 'Steaks for the men!'

Once they had the snow tractor dug out, it required a full day of tinkering and heating various parts of its balky Kaiser engine to get it running again. They lost an entire day driving it thirty yards across level snow from the garage to the Hangar. They lost another day when the winch on the tractor failed, and the Condor, which they had managed to tow halfway up the snow ramp they'd crafted, snapped loose and went sledding back down into the Hangar, shearing off the tip of its left lower wing. This required another three days of repair, and then Shannenhouse came into the Mess Hall, where Joe had a Royal Canadian Mounted Police manual for 1912 open to the chapter entitled 'Some Particulars of Sledge Maintenance', and was struggling to make sure the man-sledges were properly lashed. MAKE SURE SLEDGES PROPERLY LASHED was item 14 on Captain Fleer's Pre-Flight Checklist. Three languages did not suffice for his cursing needs.

'I'm out of dogs,' Shannenhouse said. The new tip he had grafted on the Condor's wing needed to be covered and doped to the rest of the sheathing, otherwise the plane would not take off.

Joe looked at him, blinking, trying to take in his meaning. It was the twelfth of September. In another few days, perhaps, if it could break through the melting pack, a ship bringing soldiers and planes would be returning to Jotunheim, and if they had not managed to get aloft by then, their mission might have to be called off. That was part of Shannenhouse's meaning.

'You can't use the men,' Joe said.

'I wasn't suggesting that,' Shannenhouse said. 'Though I would be lying, Dopey, if I said the thought hadn't occurred to me.'

He stroked at his whiskers, looking at Joe; he still hadn't shaved his bearish red beard. His eyes rolled toward Joe's bunk, where Oyster lay sleeping.

'There's Mussels,' he said.

They shot Oyster. Shannenhouse lured the not wholly unsuspecting dog topside with a slab of frozen porterhouse and then put a bullet point-blank between the good eye and the pearl. Joe couldn't bear to watch; he lay on his bunk fully dressed, zipped into his parka, and cried. All of Shannenhouse's former loutishness was gone; he respected Joe's grief at the sacrifice of the dog, and handled the grisly work of skinning and flensing and tanning himself. The next day Joe tried to forget about Oyster and to lose himself in vengeful thoughts and the stupendous tedium of adventure. He checked and rechecked their gear against Captain Fleer's lists. He found and removed the ice-hammer that had somehow fallen into the gearbox of the tractor's winch. He waxed the skis and checked the bindings. He dragged the sledges back in from the tunnels, undid them, and lashed them again the Mountie way. He cooked steak and eggs for himself and Shannenhouse. He plucked the steaks from the salted pan, set them steaming on two big metal plates, and deglazed the pan with whiskey. He set the whiskey on fire and then blew the fire out. Shannenhouse came in stinking of processed flesh. He took the plate gratefully from Joe, his expression solemn.

'Just big enough,' he said.

Joe took his plate, sat down at the captain's desk, and, hoping to absorb from the instrument some of the captain's thoroughness, typed the following statement:

*To those who will come searching for Lt John Wesley
Shannenhouse (j.g.) and Radioman Second Class Joseph
Kavalier:*

*I apologise for our presence being elsewhere and probably
in all truth dead.*

*We have confirmed an establishment of a German military
and scientific base located in the Queen Maud Land, also
known as Neuschwabenland. This base is presently manned
by one man only. (See, if you please, attached transcripts,
intercepted radio transmissions A-RRR,1.viii.44-2.ix.44.) As
there are two of us the situation seems clear.*

Here Joe stopped typing and sat chewing for a minute on
a piece of steak. The situation was far from clear. The man
they were going to kill had done nothing to harm either of
them. He was not a soldier. It was unlikely that he had been
involved in any but the most tangential, metaphysical of ways
with the building of the witch's house in Terezin. He had had
nothing to do with the storm that blew up out of the Azores
or the torpedo that had blown a hole in the hull of the *Ark of
Miriam*. But these things had, nonetheless, made Joe want to
kill someone, and he did not know who else to kill.

*To those who quite reasonably inquire as to our motives or
authorities in performing this mission,*

He stopped typing again.

'Johnny,' he said. 'Why are you doing this?'

Shannenhouse looked up from a nine-month-old copy of
All Doll. Cleaned up and bearded, he looked like one of the
faces that had lined the main hall of Joe's old gymnasium, the
portraits of past headmasters, stern and moral men untroubled
by doubt.

'I came here to fly airplanes,' he said.

*let it be not doubtful that we thought only to serve our
country (adopted in my case).*

Please see to the care of the men in quarters who are dead and frozen.
Respectfully,
JOSEPH KAVALIER, Radioman Second Class.
September 12, 1944.

He pulled the sheet of paper out of the typewriter, then rolled it in again, and left it like that. Shannenhouse came over to read it, nodded once, and then went back out to the Hangar to see to the plane.

Joe lay down on his bunk and closed his eyes, but the sense of conclusiveness, of putting his affairs in order, which he had sought in typing up a final statement, eluded him. He lit a cigarette and took a deep draft of it, and tried to clear his mind and conscience so that he could face the next day and its duties untroubled by any scruple or distraction. When he had finished his smoke, he rolled over and tried to sleep, but the memory of Oyster's single trusting blue eye would not leave his mind.

'How Doth My Good Cousin Silence?'

Denis Glover

The one time silent regions of the Pole
Are now vociferous, upon the whole.
Where Amundsen stormed in with cold deceit
And Scott's grim team toiled on to outface defeat
Now Neptune navy boys, pre-heated upper lip,
Roar in to land on Coca-Cola Strip
And great Sir Hillary's ice-breaker jaw
Drums in with tractors. What a bore.

O Pole, thou should'st be silent as before.

But, quoth the London Committee, and the Ross
Sea Committee, and the chewing-gum boys, and the
Ob and the Grab and the IGY scientists
and sickeners, and Life and Time, and all the
quarrel-thickeners,
                    Nevermore.

The Frozen Continents

Owen Marshall

I had never met Beavis before he and I were put on the PEP scheme together. I finished filling in the form promising not to divulge vital and confidential council business which might come my way, and then followed the supervisor to the car. Beavis was already seated. 'This is Beavis,' said the supervisor.

'Typhoon Agnes hit central Philippines on November 5 claiming more than 800 lives,' said Beavis. 'Five hundred on Panay Island alone, 325 kilometres south of Manila; another forty-five killed in Leyte and Eastern Sawar provinces.' The supervisor looked away: I said hello to Beavis.

The PEP scheme was an inside one at the museum because it was winter. Where we were taken, however, it seemed colder than outside. Museums create a chill at the best of times, but in our unused part were ice-floes and penguins. A panorama, the supervisor said. All the penguins were to be handled with care and stored out of harm's way along the wall, but the rest was to be dismantled and carried down to the yard. 'I'll look in tomorrow and see how you're going,' said the supervisor. His nose was dripping in the cold.

'Right,' I said.

'A cold wave at the end of last year claimed at least 290 lives in north and east India. Low temperatures and unseasonal fog and rain caused general disruption to air traffic,' said Beavis with no apparent realisation of irony.

'There's a toilet and tea room at the west end of the corridor on this floor. Ten-thirty and 3.30,' said the supervisor. He started coughing as he left.

The ocean was what we began on first. As it was plywood it was difficult to recover any sheets to use again. When the

239

water was gone we would be able to move about freely and take greater care with the ice-floes and penguins. I found it an odd sensation at first; standing waist deep in Antarctica as we dismantled it. I pointed out to Beavis the clear symbolism relating to man's despoliation of the last natural continent and so on. Beavis in reply told me that fourteen people were killed in a stampede when a fire broke out during a wedding ceremony at Unye in the Turkish province of Ordu.

We had the green sea out by 10.30. Beavis stood shivering by a window we had uncovered and wiped free of dust. He had his arms folded and a hand in each armpit, and he looked wistfully down on to a square of frosted grass, and the neat gravel boundaries. 'It's time for our tea break,' I told him.

An outline of a hand in felt pen and a list of instructions concerning the Zip were the only decorations on the cream walls of the tea room: points about not leaving the Zip unattended when filling and so on. I had it read within the first minute, but then words are always the things I notice. There was one failure in agreement of number between subject and verb, but overall the notice served its purpose. I wasn't as confident in assessing the people. They accepted us with exaggerated comradeship as is the response of people in secure, professional employment when confronted with PEP workers, amputees or Vietnamese refugees. I gave my name and introduced Beavis. Beavis had a classy-looking pair of basketball boots, and the most hair on the backs of his hands that I've ever seen. 'Army worms invaded the Zambezi valley in the north of Zimbabwe and destroyed maize and sorghum crops over more than 100 square kilometres of farmland,' he said. The museum staff present became more amiable still.

One girl had seductive earlobes and dark, close curls. I had a vision in which I persuaded her to come with me, in which I bit her ear beneath the curls and we made the earth move; or at least shook Antarctica with some vehemence. Instead, all of us apart from Beavis shuffled and spoke of inconsequential things. Beavis had several cups of coffee, then abruptly told us of the twenty-four bedridden people who died in a fire which broke out in an old people's home near the town of Beauvais. Impressively recounted, it subdued us all. I guiltily enjoyed the warmth from the wall heaters and my tea—before going back to the South Pole.

Antarctica had been built in sections and we tried to get as much clean timber and plywood sheets out as possible. As we worked I explained to Beavis the Celtic influence in modern poetry, and he told me of the bush fires in south-east Australia, and the earthquake, six on the Richter scale, which killed at least twenty people in India's Assam state. Beavis had a clear, well-modulated voice, and he was deft with the hammer and saw as well. I thought that he'd probably been one of those students, brilliant and compulsive, whose brain had spiralled free of any strict prescription. We had a rest after managing to strip off the first hessian and plaster ice-floe. The sun gradually turned the corner of the museum, melting the frost from a section of the lawn. It caused a precise demarcation between green and white, like the pattern of a flag. Beavis looked out too; and pondered.

We got on well, Beavis and I, although he wasn't light-hearted at all. As he was releasing one penguin the torso came away in his hands, and left the bum and webbed feet on the ice. Beavis stumbled back on to the discarded timber, exposing the heavy treads of his basketball boots, but he didn't laugh with me; just rubbed his shins and looked carefully down the corridor as if expecting a visitor. 'There's got to be some natural mortality amongst penguins,' I said. 'Put it behind the others and it'll hardly show.'

'More than 100 people drowned when a boat capsized in mid-stream on the Kirtonkhola river near the town of Barisal in Bangladesh,' said Beavis.

I carried armfuls of wood and plaster down to the yard before lunchtime. I experimented with several different routes;

partly for variety of experience, partly in the hope of seeing the girl with the dark curls, but she wasn't visible. Somehow I imagined her in the medieval glass and tapestry section rather than in natural history panoramas. I discussed the subject of feminine perfection with Beavis, pointing out the paradox that, in nature as in art, beauty comes not from beauty, but from the combination of the ordinary and the earthly. 'That woman,' I said to Beavis, 'is skin, blood and spittle; that's the wonder of it.' Beavis considered the insight and told me that more than 400 passengers were killed when a crowded train plunged into a ravine near Awash, some 250 kilometres east of Addis Ababa.

Beavis suffered a headache a little before twelve o'clock. I think the cold, and the dust from the penguins, caused it. He sat on a four by four exposed from the display and leant on to the window. His cheek spread out and whitened on the glass. Three times he began to tell me of a tsunami in Hokkaido, but his words slurred into an unintelligible vortex. He burped, and rolled his face on the icy glass. 'It's time for our lunch break anyway,' I said. He rolled his head back and forth in supplication and whispered ahh, ahh, ahh to comfort himself. The penguins refused to become involved; each retained its viewpoint with fixed intensity. Illness isolates more effectively than absence: I knew Beavis wouldn't miss me for a while so I went to the small staffroom and made two cups of sweet tea, and brought them and the yellow seat-cover back to Antarctica.

The yellow cover draped well around Beavis's shoulders, and he held it together at his chest. He had dribbled on the back of his hand and the black hair glistened there. He sipped his tea, though, and listened while I explained why I had given up formal academic studies, and my plan to use the Values Party to restructure education in New Zealand. I think he was pretty much convinced and I let him sit quietly as I worked. Afterwards he seemed to feel better because he wiped his face with the yellow cover, and fluffed up his hair. He told me about the Bhopal poisonous gas discharge which caused more than 2,500 deaths. 'I remember that one,' I said. There was quite a lot I could say about Bhopal, and I said it as we started on the penguins and ice-floes again. Beavis's preoccupation with recent accidental disasters was a salutary thing in some ways: it minimised our own grievance, made even Antarctica's grip bearable.

The sun made steady progress around the building, and the frost cut back across the lawn with surgical precision. Beavis's affliction passed. I went, in all, eleven different ways down to the yard with remains of the southern continent, but I never saw Aphrodite. I stopped the permutations when a gaunt man with the look of an Egyptologist shouted at me that if I dropped any more rubbish in his wing he'd contact the PEP supervisor.

There's a knack to everything, and Beavis and I were getting the hang of our job. We didn't tear any more penguins after that first one in the morning, yet some of them were soft and weakened, and smelt like teddy-bears stored away for coming generations. I said to Beavis that there'd been too much moisture over the years and that a controlled climate was necessary for the sort of exhibits which had stuffed birds. 'Torrential rain caused flooding and mudslides which killed eleven people and swept away dwellings on the outskirts of Belo Horizonte in the south-east state of Minas Gerais, Brazil.'

Before three o'clock I remembered to smuggle the seat-cover back to the tea room, and return our cups. I told Beavis that my estimate was that we'd have the whole panorama cleared out inside four days. PEP schemes lasted three months, therefore obviously a good deal of job variety remained— other panoramas to destroy, perhaps. A nocturnal setting for our kiwis, or an outdated display of feral cat species. Beavis made no reply. He was most moved to conversation by literary and philosophical concerns. It was a credit to him really: he had very little small talk did Beavis.

Do not turn off at the wall, it said by the Zip in the tea room. The Egyptologist was there and he bore a grudge. 'We're going to have three months of this then, are we,' he said. 'A gradual demolition of the institution around us.'

'A Venezuelan freighter was washed ashore in Florida during a storm that caused one death and millions of dollars of damage.'

'For Christ's sake,' said the gaunt man.

The girl with the dark curls didn't come in. The tea room hardly seemed the same place as that of the morning, but I knew from the writing on the wall that it was. As we went away the Egyptologist had a laugh at our expense. Beavis didn't mind: he trailed his hand on the banisters, and made sure he didn't step on any of the triangles in the lino pattern. Circles were safe, it appeared.

The ice-age was in retreat before us. I had fourteen penguins arranged in column of route along the wall, and in the grounds two piles grew—one of rubbish and one of reusable timber. We realised that the sun wasn't going to reach our window, and days start to get colder again in winter after four o'clock. I suggested to Beavis that we leave the penguins in the habitat which suited them, and show our initiative by burning the scraps we'd collected in the yard. We could keep warm with good excuse until knock-off time. I didn't want Beavis to suffer one of his headaches again.

We built a small fire on a garden plot, stood close to it for warmth, and watched the smoke ghost away in the quiet, cold afternoon. Beavis enjoyed the job of putting new pieces on the fire, and I listened as he told of the consequences when the Citarum river overflowed into several villages of Java's Bundung region, and considered myself lucky. The park trees had black, scrawny branches like roots in the air: as if the summer trees had been turned upside down for the season.

244

Deep hidden in the soil were green leaves and scarlet berries.

The museum rose up beyond the yard and the park, but despite all the windows I couldn't see anyone looking out at all. No one to hear us, no one to join us, no one to judge us. The strip of lawn closest to the museum still kept its frost like a snowfall. It would build there day after day. No one to see Beavis and me with our fire. Beavis delicately nudged timber into the fire with his basketball boots, and watched smoke weave through the tree roots. I pointed out to him that we were burning Antarctica to keep ourselves warm, which was an option not available to Scott and Shackleton. 'More than 500 died when a liquid gas depot exploded at San Juan Ixhuatepec, a suburb of Mexico City,' said Beavis.

I felt very hungry by the time the hooters went. Beavis and I had missed lunch because of his headache. If he didn't have something soon I thought he might get another attack because of a low blood-sugar level. My own blood-sugar level was pretty low, it seemed to me. We left the fire to burn itself out, and went three blocks down to the shops. I had enough money for two hot pies, and when I came out of the shop I saw Beavis sitting on the traffic island watching the five o'clock rush. Some people walked; some trotted. Some of the cars had *Turbo* written on their sides and some had only obscure patterns of rust, but they all stormed on past Beavis who was as incongruous there as among the penguins. His lips were moving. I suppose he was reminding the world of earthquakes in Chile, or of an outbreak of cholera in Mali.

I was surprised how satisfied most of the people were, but good on them, good on them. How should they know that the frozen continent was to be found right here in the midst of our city after all.

The Piper and the Penguin

Laurence Fearnley

The cassette tape silenced their relationship. And the relationship dissolved quietly, as if it was no more than a teaspoon of sugar stirred into a mug of warm tea. But the relationship was silent. That was the whole point. The tape was silent and with time, not long, the relationship, too, became silent.

The tape wasn't the beginning. First there had been the photographs. The photographs were also silent of course, but that didn't matter.

The photographs were interesting for other reasons. And by the time she opened the third letter, Kathleen had already made the connection. The photographs, or photocopied images of photographs, were linked by a reference to sound. They were images of sound. Only the tape had confused her, and she admitted she had been stupid not to make the association. She thought Max had made a mistake, that perhaps he had inserted the wrong cassette into the package, that somehow he had become confused. He was often confused or, at least, self-absorbed. But not when it came to sound. Then, as a composer, he was without fault. That was why he was down there, in the Antarctic, as New Zealand's first Antarctic Composer in Residence. And that was why Kathleen had been surprised to receive the blank tape.

She remembered the question Max had asked her when they first met:

—If a tree falls over in a Siberian forest and nobody is there to hear it, can it be said that the tree makes a sound?

Her answer was always the same. It came quickly:

246

—Of course. Sound doesn't need a human ear in order to exist.

But Max wasn't so sure. And late at night when Kathleen watched him standing alone on the verandah staring into space, she knew he was still trying to find an answer to the question.

But first came the photographs. Five of them, and then, finally, the tape. What was the difference between a blank tape and a silent tape? The difference, she learned, was that Max could sit and listen to a silent tape for hours, then days on end, until at last that was all he did. He sat and listened to a tape of nothing. By contrast, the sound of the tape coming to an end, being taken from the tape machine, turned, reinserted and started came like an explosion.

Had the circumstances been different, Kathleen might have laughed. Indeed, she might have tried to snap Max out of his growing fixation. She might have swapped the silent tape for a blank tape. Could he tell the difference? But she respected him too much to play such a trick. She might have taped over the cassette, replacing the silence with any number of popular songs recorded from the radio, but, in the end, she couldn't.

Instead she listened to the room where Max sat hour after hour listening to silence. She thought her ears would break with the attempt to hear something. A breath, a footstep in the snow, the wind against the microphone, but there was nothing. She had listened to the tape herself. Her fingers had automatically adjusted and then readjusted the volume as her ears strained to detect a sound where none was present. And then a taxi had pulled up outside her neighbour's house, a horn had sounded, two short quick bursts, and she suddenly became aware of her surroundings. Sitting in a hibiscus-warm street in Ponsonby, Kathleen was listening to nothing while the rest of the city was moving, regenerating, buzzing, alive. Someone must be playing a cruel joke on her.

247

That was what the photographs had started out as. Jokes. But the photographs were heavy with the intimacy of a private joke. Silent images of captured noise. Riddles which became increasingly obscure as Max's twelve-week absence collected red penned crosses on the calender.

The first photograph was easy. Sent before he left the country, the postmark clearly marked with the city, Christchurch, and the date, 24 November. It was already summer and there, in front of Kathleen, was an image of a man in a kilt standing against a white background of snow, bagpipes drawn to his lips, his audience a single penguin. The penguin's head was tilted back, reminding her not of a penguin, not of a bird at all, but of a dog about to howl. Max must have found the photo during one of his trips to the public library. He must also have known that Kathleen would make her way to the library, find the Antarctic section and leaf through the pages of countless books until she uncovered this particular photo. What Kathleen hadn't known was that the book, a book with a return date of 12 November and before that, a date stamp of 6 September 1981, would also contain a small slip of paper on which was written:

—*I knew you'd come looking . . . I love you.*

It was Max's writing and Kathleen's instant response was to leaf through the pages of the other books on the shelf in case they, too, carried messages of love. The other books were empty save for the remains of a tattered supermarket receipt which someone had used as a bookmark.

But there was the photograph and the caption beneath the image which read:

OFF COATS LAND.
The piper and the penguin.

Kathleen had found the photograph before reading the title of the book. It was a dark book, thick, filled with yellowed newsprint pages. The book was called *A Naturalist at the Poles* and was written by R.N. Rudmose Brown. Rudmose. The name Rudmose. Kathleen's curiosity wasn't enough to make her read the book. Instead she scanned the words printed on the title page: Scottish National Antarctic Expedition . . . 1902–04 . . . Dr W.S. Bruce . . . Modern Whaling and Bear Hunting. . . . Whaling and bear hunting, Scottish and Antarctic. Words and images gathered in her head, their grouping as eccentric as the photograph of the Piper and the Penguin itself.

The photograph belonged to the chapter headed 'Plans for the Scotia Expedition'. Kathleen skimmed through the pages, her glance momentarily arrested by the words: 'Among ice he used to tell the engineer: "When I ring dead slow, dinna gang dead slow *but slower*."' Dinna gang dead slow *but slower*. On the next page, page 114, she saw the name Rudmose. Rudmose Brown: botanist and invertebrate zoologist. And then, at the bottom of the page, she found the information she needed:

> The pipes of the Scotia had an honoured career. After their return from the Antarctic they sounded often in the fjords and glens of Spitsbergen. In the early months of the war, Bruce lent them to the 15th Battalion of the Royal Scots . . . The Battalion was in action in the big attack on the Somme on July 1, 1916. Pipe Major-Sergeant Anderson carried the pipes and was playing them when he was severely wounded. At the time he was reported killed, but fortunately this was not so. The pipes were lost on the field of action. . . .

Bruce's expedition left Scotland in 1902. The date for departure had been delayed and at a final dinner given to the officers and staff, someone called Murray had given a farewell speech, saying: 'You are to do battle with the fiercest forces of nature in the most forbidding region that our planet affords. I hope you will emerge victoriously.'

She smiled as she read the words. A vision of Max dressed for an Antarctic battlefield flashed by as she returned the book to the shelf. And then, because she still wasn't sure where the expedition had gone, she lifted the book once more from its place and flicked through the pages until stopped by the words Weddell Sea and below them: 'Too much imagination in such undertakings is a disqualifying trait.'

The words made her uneasy. The comical image of the piper and the penguin was replaced by a vision of Max standing in front of the house. His head was tilted to face the night sky and he was listening, as if to a sound so distant it might well have been from the stars themselves.

The sense of unease was increased later that evening. Picking up a copy of the Lonely Planet guide to the Antarctic, she searched for more information about the Bruce Expedition. On page thirty she read: 'A remarkable series of photographs, documenting the first known use of bagpipes in the Far South, shows an emperor penguin, head thrown back and beak agape, being serenaded by a kilted piper. Although an observer noted "only sleepy indifference", some of the photos show that the bird had to be tied by a line to prevent its escape.'

Kathleen looked at the photograph once more before fixing it to the fridge door by a plastic-coated magnet. She imagined that the notes from the pipes would freeze in the air and then fall shattered to the ground like small shards of broken glass. Sound must be distorted, unreal, in such an empty and cold environment. There was no reason for her belief, it was merely a feeling she had, and yet, somewhere in Max's notebook she remembered a reference to sound. Was it during Scott's trip that someone had written it was possible to hear voices as far away as two miles? Or was it ten miles? Or thirty? She couldn't remember the details.

*

Max had begun his 'Sound Notebook' on the day he heard he was to go to the Ice. At first, mindful of Kathleen's own unsuccessful application, he had kept the notebook to himself. Their letters of notification had arrived in the same post: his bulky with information and details for the next stage in the process, hers limp with the single typed page informing her of her failed application. A postscript, handwritten at the bottom of the page, wished her luck with her forthcoming exhibition. Kathleen was pleased for Max. It seemed he hadn't had much luck recently and her own appointment to the Sculpture department at the University of Auckland had done nothing for his failing confidence.

Filled with cuttings and accounts gathered from sources as varied as *National Geographic* magazines, diaries and letters, the notebook had brought Max a sense of purpose during the months leading up to his departure. She could remember his smiling face as he told her of Joseph Banks' refusal to join Cook's *Resolution* expedition south. Banks felt there was insufficient accommodation for himself and his entourage of thirteen men, two of whom were French horn players employed by Banks to provide entertainment throughout the long months at sea.

Upon opening the pages of the book, Kathleen had half-expected to hear a faint noise, a musical line, or perhaps the penetrating animal-like call of the French horn, as if the book itself should offer up sounds, become a *note*book rather than a recording only of words. However, the pages had remained silent and for the first time since Max's departure, the house too seemed silent and remote as she turned out the light and lay on the bed.

The second, third and fourth letters arrived together, seven weeks after Max's departure. Kathleen took the letters from the postbox and looked carefully at each envelope, running the smooth paper in her fingers as if expecting the letters to be frozen, or cold, as if recently released from a supermarket coolstore. The letters did not melt in her hands but were laid out carefully on her studio workbench, where, sitting like a box of unopened chocolates, they waited while she continued to work on the carved sculpture she was to have completed in time for the opening of her exhibition. She made several trips to the desk, each time picking up one or more of the letters, noting again the circled number on the bottom left hand corner of each envelope, a number which indicated the order in which the letters should be read.

That evening, sitting alone on the verandah of her house, Kathleen opened the first of the three letters. The words were brief, note-like:

> —*Arrived Thursday. Ears still throbbing from the noise of the aeroplane's engines. An unpleasant reminder of the six-hour flight. Had to shout to make myself heard so I kept quiet and watched my fellow travellers. Apart from the noise I felt as if I had been sprung back in time to some nineteenth-century ocean crossing. Our bodies were rammed together—like those diagrams of the convict ships we saw in Sydney last year. You'll find out what it's like next year! I'm sharing a room in Q Hut with a couple of German scientists. They're here with a group from Waikato University. I tried to engage them in conversation but all they seem interested in is some bacteria found on the slopes of Mt Melbourne—wherever that is. I made some comment about Bach-teria but it went completely beyond them. Hopefully, I'll get out and make some recordings tomorrow though I'm not too sure how the equipment will stand the cold. I'll do my best.*
> *Miss you,*
> *Max.*
> *P.S. Thought you might like this.*

Attached to the letter by a paper clip was a photograph of a group of men sitting in a crowded aeroplane. Max sat closest to the camera, the back of his head and his ear the only features detailed in the slightly blurred image. It was typical of Max not to look at the camera. In fact Kathleen had often wondered if he saw anything at all. He seemed blind to his surroundings, as if he could only gather images through his ears.

Before opening the second of the three letters, she stepped inside the house to fetch a beer from the fridge. She held her hand within the fridge's cool mist, a faint chill seeping up her arm before the heavy white door swung shut.

She began to read the letter:

> Dear K,
> I lay in bed this morning and listened to the floorboards. This probably won't come as too great a surprise to you, you know me so well, but the floorboards here are unbelievably noisy. It's impossible to walk the length of the corridor without setting off a squeaking which rivals the bed in my parents' spare room. You must remember it! I think of that bed each time I hear the floorboards. I think I've managed to talk my way onto the Mt Melbourne trip. I can only go if there's room on the chopper so I won't know for sure until the last minute. It will be good to get out of Scott Base as I still haven't seen much of interest. My recording equipment seems to be holding up in these temperatures, though the batteries aren't all that good. Okay, that's all for now. I haven't taken any photos yet but I'll be sure to take my camera with me if I go on this trip.
> Love M.

Kathleen re-read the words 'I still haven't seen much of interest' and winced. It was now past nine and the street lights flickered on. At Scott Base it would still be daylight. And yet it would be cold. The cold and the light seemed strange companions, especially now as she sat in the warm, yellowed twilight, the heat from the wall of the house seeping through her shirt and touching her back.

*

She had intended to save the third letter for the following morning but, feeling irritated by Max's apparent lack of visual sensitivity, she picked up the envelope, ripping it open as if it was nothing more than a bill from Telecom. She skimmed the letter for information. Max had been included on the Waikato University trip to Mt Melbourne. The flight to the mountain had been extraordinary. The sound of the helicopter had done nothing to dampen the impression of the ice below, a cloud-like surface which extended as far as the eye could see. And then the campsite on the slopes of the volcano, the view of the open sea gleaming in the distance, real water visible beyond the expanse of ice.

Kathleen began to feel calmer as she read on. The scientists had worked late, taking samples from the volcanic soil while Max took sound recordings of the activity around him. He recorded the murmur of quiet conversations, the wind as it moved through the tents and flags scattered around the campsite. The volcano, Max had discovered, was a site of Special Scientific Interest and to reduce the introduction of foreign micro-organisms to the area, boots and all equipment had had to be disinfected and special sterile suits worn. Max's letter continued to describe the day's activities which culminated with dinner, eaten at midnight, beneath a clear blue sky.

A photograph, ripped from a magazine, accompanied the letter. It contained an image of a campsite. Two tents were attached by long lengths of rope to a moving surface of spin drifted ice and snow.

On the second page, the letter continued:

—*I was awakened after only a few hours sleep by the feeling of snow, hard, like sand, blowing against my face. Although our tent was closed, snow was getting in through the small gaps in the door's zip. The wind made a sound unlike any I have heard before. It terrified me. I lay in my sleeping bag waiting for the tent to take off and fly through the air like something from the Wizard of Oz. It was as if the whole world was collapsing—anything that was not tied down was moving and yet the sky remained a clear, cloudless, blue. Although the sky seemed motionless, the ground shifted and disappeared beneath our feet in a wash of snow and ice. Our voices were instantly carried away by the wind and it was almost impossible to hear anyone speak. Fortunately there was someone with us who knew what to do as I was completely disorientated by the experience. The storm continued for the rest of the day and into the night, and finally, when it cleared sufficiently for the helicopter to fly, I almost lost my recordings in my haste to return to civilisation. As I write this, four days later, my knees are still tender and bruised from crawling repeatedly across the hard ground to rescue equipment which had blown away. At one point I narrowly missed being hit by a snow shovel as it flew past my head. Even Axel, who never shows any emotion, seemed somewhat shaken. He didn't respond when the chopper pilot made some joke about the gale force wind being worthy of a Wagnerian Opera. Being at Scott Base you tend not to notice how much space there is 'out there' and how small we are by comparison. It's difficult to describe to someone who hasn't been here to experience it, but it's as if there's some great distance separating me from the other people here—as if I'm suddenly alone. I don't know if that makes sense to you but I feel glad to be back in Q Hut listening to the floorboards again.*

Max.

Kathleen spent the next week in the studio, only returning home late at night in order to wash and sleep. In her pocket she carried Max's letter. The storm seemed to have shaken him and because of this she waited for his next letter with a growing sense of impatience.

A week passed, followed by a few more days, and eventually a letter arrived bearing a New Zealand stamp and posted from Wellington only the day before. The writing on the envelope meant nothing and, as a consequence, she did not open the letter immediately, but waited until later that night when sitting at the kitchen table drinking a final cup of tea before going to bed. The writing, Kathleen was to discover, belonged to a Victoria University scientist. She had spent a few days with Max out in the field before returning to Wellington the previous weekend. The field referred to was not so much an undulating pasture of green grass as a vast expanse of broken ice and snow making up the Nimrod Glacier. This information was supplied by Max in a rather brief note which accompanied two photographs. The first photograph showed an iceberg, crudely carved and mono-lithic, floating in a millpond smooth sea. On the back of the photo Max had scrawled the words: *It looks a bit like one of your sculptures.* The second image contained Scott's last diary entry, a page from a yellowed notebook featuring the message 'I do not think I can write more', followed by the words 'For God's sake look after our people'.

Max's letter made no mention of the photographs. Instead he wrote of the trip to the Nimrod glacier where, using radio-echo sounding equipment, the Victoria University team had been able to investigate the earth's crustal structure beneath the ice. How Max came to be with the group was not mentioned. The letter did, however, describe his day with the team:

> —*Imagine what it's like listening to the sound of the earth. That's what the equipment allowed me to do. But even the sound of the earth was nothing compared to what I heard the following day. I was left completely alone for four hours. Four hours which will remain with me for the rest of my life. I heard a sound which has only ever existed in my deepest imagination . . .*

And there, the letter trailed off. Kathleen turned the page, a page ripped from a music score, but there was nothing to indicate what had happened the next day. There were no more words. The two images came into focus. The iceberg and the page from the diary. Scott's last words.

The package containing the tape arrived two days before Max. Kathleen listened to the tape, but hearing nothing, assumed Max had made a mistake, had posted a blank cassette instead of the recording he had intended to send. She played both sides of the tape, adjusted the volume, and then went back to her work. She smiled as she worked, thinking ahead to Max's return and his embarrassed silence when he realised his mistake in sending the blank tape.

But Max listened to the tape. And as the days went by, and the night of Kathleen's exhibition opening drew nearer, it seemed as if the last-minute frenzy of her work had found its mirror opposite in the silent, brooding figure of Max. And days and weeks later, long after the exhibition had closed and curious friends had stopped dropping by for a cup of tea, she struggled to maintain some semblance of partnership with the withdrawn man who no longer spoke to her, or to any other visitor to the house. And finally, when there seemed no other option, Kathleen left the house and drove across the Harbour Bridge to the home of her parents. Then, silent before so many unspoken questions, she thought of Max, just fifty minutes away, preserved in his own frozen continent.

from

Angels in America

Tony Kushner

Same day. Harper in a very white, cold place, with a brilliant blue sky above; a delicate snowfall. She is dressed in a beautiful snowsuit. The sound of the sea, faint.

HARPER. Snow! Ice! Mountains of ice! Where am I? I . . . I feel better, I do, I . . . feel better. There are ice crystals in my lungs, wonderful and sharp. And the snow smells like cold, crushed peaches. And there's something . . . some current of blood in the wind, how strange, it has that iron taste.

MR LIES. Ozone.

HARPER. Ozone! Wow! Where am I?

MR LIES. The Kingdom of Ice, the bottommost part of the world.

HARPER. *(Looking around, then realising)*: Antarctica. This is Antarctica!

MR LIES. Cold shelter for the shattered. No sorrow here, tears freeze.

HARPER. Antarctica, Antarctica, oh boy oh boy, LOOK at this, I . . . Wow, I must've really snapped the tether, huh?

MR LIES. Apparently . . .

HARPER. That's great. I want to stay here forever. Set up camp. Build things. Build a city, an enormous city made up of frontier forts, dark wood and green roofs and high gates made of pointed logs and bonfires burning on every street corner. I should build by a river. Where are the forests?

MR LIES. No timber here. Too cold. Ice, no trees.

HARPER. Oh details! I'm sick of details! I'll plant them and grow them. I'll live off caribou fat, I'll melt it over the bonfires and drink it from long, curved goat-horn cups. It'll be great. I want to make a new world here. So that I never have to go home again.

MR LIES. As long as it lasts. Ice has a way of melting . . .

HARPER. No. Forever. I can have anything I want here—maybe even companionship, someone who has . . . desire for me. You, maybe.

MR LIES. It's against the by-laws of the International Order of Travel Agents to get involved with clients. Rules are rules. Anyway, I'm not the one you really want.

HARPER. There isn't anyone . . . maybe an Eskimo. Who could ice-fish for food. And help me build a nest for when the baby comes.

MR LIES. There are no Eskimo in Antarctica. And you're not really pregnant. You made that up.

HARPER. Well all of this is made up. So if the snow feels cold I'm pregnant. Right? Here, I can be pregnant. And I can have any kind of a baby I want.

MR LIES. This is a retreat, a vacuum, its virtue is that it lacks everything; deep-freeze for feelings. You can be numb and safe here, that's what you came for. Respect the delicate ecology of your delusions.

HARPER. You mean like no Eskimo in Antarctica.

MR LIES. Correcto. Ice and snow, no Eskimo. Even hallucinations have laws.

HARPER. Well then who's that?

(The Eskimo appears.)

MR LIES. An Eskimo.

HARPER. An antarctic Eskimo. A fisher of the polar deep.

MR LIES. There's something wrong with this picture.

Michel in Antarctica

Kim Stanley Robinson

At first it was fine. The people were nice. Wright Valley was awesome. Each day Michel woke in his cubicle and looked out of his little window (everyone had one) at the frozen surface of Lake Vanda, a flat oval of cracked blue ice, flooding the bottom of the valley. The valley itself was brown and big and deep, its great rock side-walls banded horizontally. Seeing it all he felt a little thrill and the day began well.

There was always a lot to do. They had been dropped there in the largest of the Antarctic dry valleys with a load of disassembled huts and, for immediate occupancy, Scott tents. Their task through the perpetual day of the Antarctic summer was to build their winter home, which on assembly had turned out to be a fairly substantial and luxurious modular array of interconnected red boxes. In many ways it seemed analogous to what the voyagers would be doing when they arrived on Mars, and so of course to Michel it was all very interesting.

There were one hundred and fifty-eight people there, and only a hundred were going to be sent on the first trip out, to establish a permanent colony. This was the plan as designed by the Americans and Russians, who had then convened an international team to enact it. So this stay in Antarctica was a kind of test, or winnowing. But it seemed to Michel that everyone there assumed he or she would be among the chosen, so there was little of the tension one saw in people doing job interviews. As they said, when it was discussed at all—in other words when Michel asked about it—some candidates were going to drop out, others would be invalided out, and others placed on later trips to Mars, at worst. So there was no reason

261

to worry. Most of the people there were not worriers anyway—they were capable, brilliant, assured, used to success. Michel worried about this.

They finished building their winter home by the autumn equinox, March 21st. After that the alternation of day and night was dramatic, the brilliant slanted light of the days ending with the sun sliding off to the north and over the Olympus Range, the long twilights leading to a black starry darkness that eventually would be complete, and last for months. At their latitude, perpetual night would begin a little after mid-April.

The constellations as they revealed themselves were the stars of another sky, foreign and strange to a northerner like Michel, reminding him that the universe was a big place. Each day was shorter than the one before by a palpable degree, and the sun burned lower through the sky, its beams pouring down between the peaks of the Asgaard and Olympus Ranges like vibrant stagelights. People got to know each other.

When they were first introduced, Maya had said 'So you are to evaluate us!' with a look that seemed to suggest this could be a process that went both ways. Michel had been impressed. Frank Chalmers, looking over her shoulder at him, had seen this.

They were a mix of personality types, as one might expect. But they all had the basic social skilfulness that had allowed them to make it this far, so that whether outgoing or withdrawn in their basic nature, they could still all talk easily. They were interested in each other, naturally. Michel saw a lot of relationships beginning to bloom around him. Romances too. Of course.

To Michel all the women in camp were beautiful. He fell a little in love with a lot of them, as was his practice always. Men he loved as elder brothers, women as goddesses he could never quite court (fortunately). Yes: every woman was beautiful, and all men were heroes. Unless of course they weren't. But most were; this was humanity's default state. So Michel felt, he always had. It was an emotional setting that called out for psychoanalysis, and in fact he had undergone analysis, without changing this feeling a bit (fortunately). It was his take on people, as he had said to his therapists. Naïve, credulous, obtusely optimistic—and yet it made him a good clinical psychiatrist. It was his gift.

Tatiana Durova, for instance, he thought as gorgeous as any movie star, with also that intelligence and individuality that derived from life lived in the real world of work and community. Michel loved Tatiana.

And he loved Hiroko Ai, a remote and charismatic human being, withdrawn into her own affairs, but kind. He loved Ann Clayborne, a Martian already. He loved Phyllis Boyle, sister to Machiavelli. He loved Ursula Kohl like the sister he could always talk to. He loved Rya Jimenez for her black hair and bright smile, he loved Marina Tokareva for her tough logic, he loved Sasha Yefremova for her irony.

But most of all he loved Maya Toitovna, who was as exotic to him as Hiroko, but more extroverted. She was not as beautiful as Tatiana, but drew the eye. The natural leader of the Russian contingent, and a bit forbidding—dangerous somehow—watching everyone there in much the same way Michel was, though he was pretty sure she was a tougher judge of people. Most of the Russian men seemed to fear her, like mice under a hawk, or maybe it was that they feared falling hopelessly in love with her. If Michel were going to Mars (he was not) she was the one he would be most interested in.

Of course Michel, as one of the four psychologists there to help evaluate the candidates, could not act on any of these affections. That did not bother him; on the contrary he liked the constraint, which was the same he had with any of his clients. It allowed him to indulge his thoughts without having to consider acting on them. 'If you don't act on it, it wasn't a true feeling'—maybe the old saying was right, but if you were forbidden to act for good reasons, then your feelings might not be false after all. So he could be both true and safe. Besides the saying was wrong, love for one's fellow humans could be a matter of contemplation only. There was nothing wrong with it.

Maya was quite certain she was going to Mars. Michel therefore represented no threat to her, and she treated him like a perfect equal. Several others were like her in this respect—Vlad, Ursula, Arkady, Sax, Spencer, a few others. But Maya took matters beyond that; she was intimate from the very start. She would sit and talk to him about anything, including the selection process itself. They spoke English when they talked, their partial competence and strong accents making for a picturesque music.

'You must be using the objective criteria for selecting people, the psychological profiles and the like.'

'Yes, of course. Tests of various kinds, as you know. Various indexes.'

'But your own personal judgments must count too, right?'

'Yes. Of course.'

'But it must be hard to separate out your personal feelings about people from your professional judgments, yes?'

'I suppose so.'

'How do you do it?'

'Well . . . I suppose you would say it is a habit of mind. I like people, or whatever, for different reasons to the reasons that might make someone good on a project like this.'

'For what reasons do you like people?'

'Well, I try not to be too analytical about that! You know— it's a danger in my job, becoming too analytical. I try to let my own feelings alone, as long as they aren't bothering me somehow.'

She nodded. 'Very sensible, I'm sure. I don't know if I could manage that. I should try. It's all the same to me. That's not always good. Not appropriate.' With a quick sidelong smile at him.

She would say anything to him. He thought about this, and decided that it was a matter of their respective situations: since he was staying behind, and she was going (she seemed so sure), it didn't much matter what she said to him. It was as if he were dying to her, and she therefore giving herself to him, openly, as a farewell gift.

But he wanted her to care about what she said to him.

On April 18th the sun went away. In the morning it sparked in the east, shining directly up the valley for a minute or two, and then with a faint green flash it slipped behind Mount Newell. After that the dark days had midday twilights, shorter every day; then just night. Starry starry night. It was beyond Martian, this constant darkness—living by starlight with the aching cold outside, experiencing sensory deprivation in everything but one's sense of cold. Michel, a Provençal, found that he hated both the cold and the dark. So did many of the others. They had been living in an Antarctic summer, thinking life was good and that Mars would not be such a challenge after all, and then with winter they were suddenly getting a better idea of what Mars would be like—not exactly, but in the sense of experiencing a massive array of deprivations. It was sobering how hard it hit.

Of course some did better than others. Some seemed not even to notice. The Russians had experienced cold and dark almost like this before. Tolerance of confinement was also good among the senior scientists—Sax Russell, Vlad Taneev, Marina Tokareva, Ursula Kohl, Ann Clayborne—these and other dedicated scientists seemed to have the capacity to spend great amounts of their time reading, working at their computers, and talking. Presumably lives spent largely in labs had prepared them.

They also understood that this was the life Mars was waiting to give them. Something not that different from the lives they had always led. So that the best analogy to Mars, perhaps, was not Antarctica, but any intense scientific laboratory.

This led him to thoughts of the optimum life history when considering inclusion in the group: middle-aged lab scientist, dedicated, accomplished; childless; unmarried or divorced. Lots of applicants fitted the criteria. In some ways you had to wonder. Though it wouldn't be fair; it was a life pattern with its own integrity, its own rewards. Michel himself fitted the bill in every respect.

Naturally he had to divide his attention equally among all of the candidates, and he did. But one day he got to accompany Tatiana Durova alone, on a hike up the South Fork of Wright Valley. They hiked to the left of the flat-topped island ridge called the Dais that divided the valley lengthways, and continued up the southern arm of Wright Valley to Don Juan Pond.

Don Juan Pond: what a name for this extraterrestrial desolation! The pond was so salty that it would not freeze until the air chilled to −54 C; then the ice coating the shallow saline pond, having been distilled by the freezing, would be fresh-water ice, and so would not thaw again until the temperature rose above zero, usually in the following summer when trapped sunlight would greenhouse in the water under the ice, and melt it from below. As Tatiana explained the process it hovered in Michel's mind as some kind of analogy to their own situation, hanging right on the edge of his understanding but never coming clear.

'Anyway,' she was saying, 'scientists can use the pond as a single-setting minimum-temperature thermometer. Come here in the spring and you know immediately if the previous winter has got below minus 54.'

266

As it had already, some cold night this autumn; a layer of white ice sheeted the pond. Michel stood with Tatiana on the whitish, humped, salt-crusted shore. Over the Dais the noon sky was blue-black. Around them the steep valley walls fell to the floor of the canyon. Large dark boulders stuck out of the pond's ice sheet.

Tatiana walked out onto the white surface, plunging through it with every step, boots crackling, water splashing—liquid salt water, spilling over the fresh ice, dissolving it and sending up a thin frost smoke. A vision: the Lady of the Lake, become corporeal and thus too heavy to walk on water.

But the pond was only a few centimetres deep, it barely covered the tops of her thick boots. Tatiana reached down and touched the tip of one gloved finger into the water, pulled up her mask to taste the water with her impossibly beautiful mouth—which puckered to a tight square. Then she threw back her head and laughed. 'My God! Come taste, Michel, but just a touch, I warn you. It's terrible!'

And so he clomped through the ice and over the wet sand floor of the pond, stepping awkwardly, a bull in a china shop.

'It's fifty times saltier than the sea, taste it.'

Michel reached down, put his forefinger in the water; the cold was intense, it was amazing that it was liquid still, so cold it was. He raised it to his tongue, touched gingerly: cold fire. It burned like acid. 'My God!' he exclaimed, spitting out involuntarily. 'Is it poison?' Some toxic alkali, or a lake of arsenic—

'No no.' She laughed. 'Salts only. A hundred and twenty-six grams of salt per litre of water. As opposed to three point seven grams per litre, in seawater. Incredible.' Tatiana was a geochemist, and so now shaking her head with amazement. This kind of thing was her work. Michel saw her beauty in a new way, masked but perfectly clear.

'Salt raised to a higher power,' he said absently. A concentrated quality. So it might be in the Mars colony; and suddenly the idea he had felt hovering over him descended: The ordinary sea-salt of humanity would be concentrated by their isolation into a poisonous pond.

He shuddered and spat again, as if he could reject such a bad thought. But the taste remained.

As the perpetual darkness stretches on it becomes hard not to think it permanent, as if we are lingering on after the local star has burnt out. People (some of them) are finally beginning to act as if they are being tested. As if the world has indeed ended, and we existing in some antechamber of the final judgment. Imagine a time of real religion, when everyone felt like this all the time.

Some of them avoided Michel, and Charles and Georgia and Pauline, the other psychologists. Others were too friendly. Mary Dunkel, Janet Blyleven, Frank Chalmers; Michel had to watch himself to avoid ending up alone with these people, or he would fall into a depression witnessing the spectacle of their great charm.

The best solution was to stay active. Remembering the pleasure of his hike with Tatiana, he went out as often as he could, accompanying the others as they performed various maintenance and scientific tasks. The days passed in their artificial rounds, everything measured out and lived just as if the sun were rising in the morning and setting in the evening. Wake, eat, work, eat, work, eat, relax, sleep. Just like home.

One day he went out with Frank on a hike up to an anemometer near the Labyrinth, an interlacing complex of canyons cutting the floor of upper Wright Valley. He wanted to try to see if he could penetrate the man's pleasant surface. In the end it did not work; Frank was too cool, too professional, too friendly. Years of work in Washington DC had made him very smooth indeed. He had been involved in getting the first human expedition to Mars, a few years before; an old friend of John Boone, the first man to set foot on Mars. He was also said to be heavily involved in the planning for this expedition as well. He was certainly one of those who felt they were going to be among the hundred; extremely confident, in fact. He had a very American voice somehow, booming out to Michel's left as they hiked. 'Check those glaciers, falling out of the passes and being blown away before they reach the valley floor. What an awesome place, really.'

'Yes.'

'These katabatic winds—falling off the polar cap—nothing can stop them. Cold as hell. I wonder if that little windvane we set up here will even be there any more.'

It was. They pulled out its data cartridge, put in another one. Around them the huge expanse of brown rock formed a bowl under the starry sky. They started back down.

'Why do you want to go to Mars, Frank?'

'What's this, we're still at work out here are we?'

'No, no. I'm just curious.'

'Sure. Well, I want to try it. I want to try living somewhere where you can actually try to do something new. Set up new systems, you know. I grew up in the South, like you did. Only the American South is a lot different from the French South. We were stuck in our history for a long, long time. Then things opened up, partly because it got so bad. Partly just a lot of hurricanes hitting the coast! And we had a chance to rebuild. And we did, but not much changed. Not enough, Michel. So I have this desire to try it again. That's the truth.' And he glanced over at Michel, as if to emphasise not only that it was the truth, but that it was a truth he seldom talked about. Michel liked him a bit better after that.

Another day (or, in another hour of their endless night) Michel went out with a group, to check on the climatology stations located around the lake shore. They hauled banana sleds loaded with replacement batteries and tanks of compressed nitrogen and the like. Michel, Maya, Charles, Arkady, Iwao, Ben, and Elena.

They walked across Lake Vanda, Ben and Maya pulling the sleds. The valley seemed huge. The frozen surface of the lake gleamed and sparked blackly underfoot. To a northerner the sky already seemed overstuffed with stars, and in the ice underfoot each star was shattered into many pricks of light. Next to him Maya shone her flashlight down, lighting a field of cracks and bubbles under her; it was like shining light into a glass floor that had no bottom. She turned the flashlight off and it suddenly looked to Michel like the stars of the other hemisphere were shining up through a clear world, an alien planet much closer to the centre of its galaxy. Looking down into the black hole at the centre of things, through burred starlight. Like the shattered bottomless pool of the self. Every step broke the sight into a different refraction, a kaleidoscope of white points in black. He could gaze down into Vanda for a long time.

They came to the far shore of the lake. Michel looked back: their complex sparked like a bright winter constellation coming up over the horizon. Inside those boxes their companions were working, talking, cooking, reading, resting. Tensions in there were subtle but high.

A door opened in the complex, a wedge of light was thrown onto rust-coloured rock. It could have been Mars, sure; in a year or two it would be. Many of the current tensions would be resolved. But there would be no air. Outside they would go, yes, sometimes; but in spacesuits. Would that matter? The winter suit he was wearing at that moment was as much like a spacesuit as the designers could make it, and the frigid numbing downvalley breeze was like breathing purified oxygen just gasified from liquid stock, and insufficiently warmed. The sub-biological chill of Antarctica, of Mars; nothing much to choose between them. In that sense this year of training and testing had been a good idea. They were getting at least a taste of what it might be like.

Ben stepped down onto the uneven lower ice of the lake's summertime moat, slipped and went down in a flash. He cried out and the others rushed to him, Michel first because he had seen it happen. Ben groaned and writhed, the others crouched around him—

'Excuse me,' Maya said, and ducked between Michel and Arkady to kneel at Ben's side.

'Is it your hip?'

'Ah—yeah—'

'Hold on. Hold steady.' Ben clutched at her arm and she held him on his other side. 'Here, let's get your harness unclipped from the sled. Okay, slip the sled under him. Move him gently! Okay. Hold still there, we'll get you back to the station. Can you stay steady or should we strap you down? Okay, let's go. Help stabilise the sled. Someone radio the station and tell them to get ready for us.' She clipped her own harness onto the banana sled and started back across the lake, quickly but steadily, almost ice-skating on her boots, flashlight lit to show her the ice underfoot. The others followed beside Ben.

Across the Ross Sea, McMurdo Station had an extra complement of winter staff precisely to help support them out at Vanda, and so the winter helicopter came yammering down in a huge noise only an hour or so after their return to the station. By that time Ben was furious at himself for falling, more angry than hurt, though they found out later that his hip had been fractured.

'He went down in a flash,' Michel said to Maya afterwards. 'So fast he had no time to get a hand out. I'm not surprised it broke something.'

'Too bad,' Maya said.

'You were good out there,' Michel said, surprising himself. 'Very quick.'

She blew this away with a sound and a wave of her hand.

'How many times I've seen it. I spent my whole childhood on ice.'

'Ah, of course.' Expertise. A fund of experience was the basis of all natural decision making. This was true of Maya in many different realms, he felt. Ergonomics, her speciality, was a matter of people getting along well with things. She was going to Mars. He was not. He loved her. Well, but he loved many women. That was just the way it was. But with her . . .

From Michel's personal notes, heavily encrypted:

Maya: very beautiful. A tiger slouches into the room, reeking of sex and murder. The alpha female before whom all submit. Quick in everything, including moods. I can talk to her. We have real conversations because she doesn't care what I'm here for. Can that be true?

Spencer Jackson: a power. A secret soul. Depths beyond all calculation, even for him. The Vanda inside us. His the mind into which the whole community falls, transmuted to art. Can sketch any face in a dozen strokes, and there they are bare as a pebble. But I don't think he's happy.

Tatiana Durova: very beautiful. A goddess trapped in a motel. She's looking for a way out. She knows everyone thinks she is beautiful, and therefore trusts none of us. She needs to get back to Olympus, where her appearance would be taken for granted, and she able to get through to someone. To her peers. Perhaps she takes Mars to be Olympus.

Arkady Bogdanov is a power. A very steady reliable fellow, earnest almost to the point of dullness. One sees everything he's thinking, he doesn't bother to conceal it. What I am is enough to get me to Mars, he says in his manner. Don't you agree? And I do. An engineer, quick and ingenious, not interested in larger issues.

272

Marina Tokareva: a beauty. Very serious and intense, no small talk to her. One is forced to think about things. And she assumes you are as quick as she is. So it can be work to follow her. Narrow chiselled features, thick jet-black hair. Sometimes following her glances I think she is one of the homosexuals who must be among us; other times she seems fixated on Vlad Taneev, the oldest man here.

George Berkovic and Edvard Perrin are paired in their regard for Phyllis Boyle. Yet it is not a competition but a partnership. They both think they like Phyllis, but really what they like is the way the other one mirrors their affection. Phyllis likes this too.

Ivana is quite beautiful, despite a thin face and an overbite; a goofy smile lights up the face of the classic chemist nerd, and suddenly the goddess is revealed. Shared a Nobel Prize in chemistry, but one has to quash the thought that the smile is what won the prize. It makes one happy to see it. One would give her the Nobel Prize just to see that smile.

Simon Frazier: a very quiet power. English; public school education from age nine. He listens very closely, speaks well, but he says about one tenth as much as everyone else, which naturally gains him the reputation of a complete mute. He plays with this image, quietly. I think he likes Ann, who is like him in some ways, though not so extreme; in other ways very unlike. Ann does not joke with her image among the others, she is completely unaware of it—American lack of self-consciousness, versus Simon's Brit irony.

Janet Blyleven: beautiful. Speaks rapidly, confidently. Friendly. Looks healthy. Nice breasts. Doggy friendship is no friendship at all.

Ann is a real beauty, though austere. Tall, angular, bony, strong; both body and face. She draws the eye. She certainly does take Mars seriously. People see that in her and like her for it. Or not, as the case may be. Her shadow is very distinct.

Alexander Zhalin is a power. He likes women with his eyes. Some of them know it, some don't. Mary Dunkel and Janet Blyleven are both with him a lot. He is an enthusiast. Whatever has taken his fancy becomes the horizon of all interest.

Nadia Cherneshevsky: at first you think she is plain, then you see she is one of the most beautiful of all. It has to do with solidity—physical, intellectual, and moral. The rock everyone rests on. Her physical beauty is in her athleticism— short, round, tough, skilful, graceful, strong—and in her eyes, as her irises are parti-coloured, a dense stippled carpet of colour dots, bits of brown and green mostly, with some blue and yellow, all flecked together in concentric rings of pattern, shot by rays of a different pattern, merging in a casual glance to a colour like hazel. You could dive into those eyes and never come out. And she looks back at you without fear.

Frank Chalmers: a power. I think. It's hard not to see him as an adjunct to John Boone. The sidekick, or enabler. On his own out here, not so impressive. Diminished; less an historical character. He's elusive. Big, bulky, dark-complexioned. He keeps a low profile. He is quite friendly, but it doesn't seem to one that it is real friendliness. A political animal, like Phyllis; only they don't like each other. It's Maya he likes. And Maya makes sure he feels part of her world. But what he really wants is not clear. There's a person in there one does not know at all.

More formally, he administered the Revised Minnesota Multiphasic Personality Inventory, giving the questionnaires in groups of ten. Hundreds of questions, calibrated to give statistically significant personality profiles. Only one of several

274

different tests he was giving over the winter; testing was one of the main ways they passed the time.

They were taking this test in the Bright Room, which was lit by scores of high-wattage bulbs, until everything in it seemed incandescent, especially people's faces. Looking at them as they worked, Michel suddenly felt how absurd it was to be schoolmaster to this brilliant crowd. And he saw very clearly in their glowing faces that they were not answering the questions to tell him what they were like, but rather to say what they thought they should in order to get to go to Mars. Of course reading the answers with that in mind would reveal almost as much as if they were being sincere. Still it was a shock to see it so clearly right there on their faces.

He shouldn't have been surprised. Faces revealed mood and much else with extreme precision, in most people anyway. Perhaps all people; a poker face reveals someone who is feeling guarded. No, he thought while watching them, a whole language might be developed from this, if one paid proper attention. Blind people hear actors' voices as completely artificial and false, and in this world they were all blind to faces, but if he looked at them more closely, it might yield a kind of phrenology of sight. He might become the one-eyed man in the kingdom of the blind.

So he watched their faces, fascinated. The Bright Room was very bright indeed; time spent in such spaces had been shown to ward off the worst of seasonal affective disorder. In this luminous glare each translucent face seemed not just to be speaking to him, but also to be a complete rebus of that person's character: variously strong, intelligent, humorous, guarded, whatever, but in any case the entire personality, all right there on the surface. There was Ursula, faintly amused, thinking this was just one of the many silly things psychologists did; she as a medical person recognised that it was both ludicrous and necessary, she knew all the medical sciences were as much art

275

as science. Sax, on the other hand, was taking it all very seriously, as he seemed to take everything: this was a scientific experiment to him, and he trusted that scientists in other disciplines were honestly dealing with the methodological difficulties of that discipline. All right there on his face.

They were all experts. Michel had studied NDM, or Naturalistic Decision Making; he was an expert on the subject; and he knew that experts took the limited data available to them in any situation and compared it to their vast fund of experiences, and then made quick decisions based on analogies to past experience. Thus now, in this situation, this group of experts were doing what they would do to win a grant, or to win over a committee judging a tenure application package. Something like that. The fact that they had never faced a task quite like this one was problematic but not debilitating.

Unless they considered the situation to be unstable beyond the point of prediction. Some situations were like that; even the best meteorologists could not well predict hailstorms, even the best battlefield commanders could not predict the course of surprise attacks. For that matter some recent studies had shown that it was much the same with psychologists when they attempted to predict people's future mental diagnoses from their scores on standard psychological tests. In each case there wasn't enough data. And so Michel stared intently at their faces, pink or brown summaries of their personalities, trying to read the whole in the part.

Except it was not really true. Faces could be deceptive, or uninformative; and personality theory was notoriously vexed by deep uncertainties of all kinds. The same events and environments produced radically different results in people, that was the plain fact. There were too many confounding factors to say much about any aspect of personality. All the models of personality itself—the many, many theories—came down to a matter of individual psychologists codifying their

276

guesses. Perhaps all science had this aspect, but it was so obvious in personality theory, where new propositions were supported by reference to earlier theorists, who often supported their assertions by reference to even earlier theorists, in strings all the way back to Freud and Jung, if not Galen. The fascinating *Psychoanalytic Roots of Patriarchy* was a perfect example of this, as was Jones's classic *The New Psychology of Dreaming*. It was a standard technique: citing a guess by a dead authority added weight to one's assertions. So that often the large statistical tests administered by contemporary psychologists were designed mostly to confirm or disconfirm preliminary intuitive stabs by near-Victorians like Freud, Jung, Adler, Sullivan, Fromm, Maslow, etc. You picked the earlier expert whose guesses seemed right to you, then tested these intuitions using current scientific techniques. If going back to the original either/or, Michel chose Jung over Freud; after that he was partial to the whole utopian self-definition crowd—Fromm, Erikson, Maslow—and the matching philosophers of freedom from the same era, people like Nietzsche and Sartre. And the latest in modern psychology, of course—tested, peer-reviewed, and published in the journals.

But all his ideas were elaborations of an original set of feelings about people. A matter of hunches. On that basis he was supposed to evaluate who would or would not do well if removed to Mars. Predicting hailstorms and surprise attacks. Interpreting personality tests designed according to the paradigms of alchemists. Even asking people about their dreams, as if these were anything more than the detritus of the sleeping brain! Dream interpretation: once Jung dreamed about killing a man named Siegfried, and he struggled mightily to figure out what the dream might have meant, never once wondering if it had anything to do with his immense anger at his old friend Freud. As Fromm noted later, 'the slight change from *Sigmund* to *Siegfried* was enough to enable a man whose greatest skill was the interpretation of dreams, to hide the real meaning of this dream from himself'.

It was a perfect image for the power of their methodology.

Mary Dunkel sat beside him at lunch one day. Her leg pressed against his. This was not an accident. Michel was surprised; it was a tremendous risk on her part, after all. His leg responded with a matching pressure, before he had a chance to think things over. Mary was beautiful. He loved Mary for her dark hair and brown eyes and the turn of her hips as she went through doorways ahead of him, and now for her boldness. Elena he loved for the kindness in her beautiful pale eyes, and for her rangy shoulders, wide as any man's. Tatiana he loved for being so gorgeous and self-contained.

But it was Mary pressed against him. What did she mean by it? Did she mean to influence his recommendation for or against her? But surely she would know this kind of behaviour might very possibly be counted against her. She had to know that. So knowing that and doing this anyway meant that she must be doing it for other reasons, more important to her than going to Mars. Meant it personally, in other words.

How easy he was. A woman only had to look at him right and he was hers forever. She could knock him down with the brush of a fingertip.

Now his body began to fall over yet again, reflexively, like the jerk of the lower leg when the knee is properly tapped. But part of his mind's slow train of thought, trailing behind reality by a matter of some minutes (sometimes it was hours, or days), began to worry. He could not be sure what she meant. She could be a woman willing to risk all on a single throw of the dice. Try sidling up to a man to get on his good side. It often worked like a charm.

He realised that to have power over another's destiny was intolerable. It corrupted everything. He wanted to slip away to the nearest bed with Mary, hers or his, to fall onto it and make love. But making love could by definition only occur between two free human beings. And as he was warden, judge and jury to this group . . .

He moaned at the thought, a little 'uhnn' in his throat as the problem struck him in the solar plexus and forced air upward through his vocal cords. Mary gave him a glance, smiled. Across the table Maya picked this up and looked at them. Maya had perhaps heard him groan. Maya saw everything; and if she saw him wanting silly reckless Mary, when really he wanted Maya with all his heart, then it would be a double disaster. Michel loved Maya for her hawklike vision, her fierce sharp intelligence, now watching him casually but completely.

He got up and went to the counter for a piece of cheesecake, feeling his knees weakly buckling. He dared not look back at either of them.

Though it was possible the leg contact and all their looks had been in his mind only.

It was getting strange.

Two Russians, Sergei and Natasha, had started a relationship soon after their arrival at Lake Vanda. They did not try to hide it, like some other couples Michel knew about or suspected. If anything they were a bit too demonstrative, given the situation; it made some people uncomfortable how affectionate they were with each other. Ordinarily one could ignore strangers kissing in public, watch them or not as one chose. Here there were decisions to be made. Was it worse to be a voyeur or a prude? Did one apply to the programme as an individual or as a part of a couple? Which gave one a better chance? What did Michel think?

Then during the winter solstice party, June 21st, after everyone had drunk a glass of champagne and was feeling good about getting past that ebb tide in the psychological year, Arkady called them out to see the aurora australis, a filmy electric dance of coloured veils and draperies, soft greens and blues and a pale pink flowing across the grain of their reality, shimmering through the black plenum in quick sine waves. And suddenly, in the midst of this magic, shouting erupted from inside the compound—muffled shrieks, bellows. Michel looked around and all the hooded ski-masked figures were looking at him, as if he should have known this was coming and forestalled it somehow, as if it were his fault—and he ran inside and there were Sergei and Natasha, literally at each other's throats.

He tried to detach them and got hit in the side of the face for his trouble.

After that operatic debacle Sergei and Natasha were expelled to McMurdo—which itself took some doing, both getting the helicopter over during a week of stormy weather, and getting Sergei and Natasha to agree to leave. And after that people's trust in Michel was heavily damaged, if not shattered completely. Even the administrators of the programme, back in the north, were faintly over-inquisitive when they asked him about it; they noted that records showed he had had an interview with Natasha the day before the fight, and asked what they had talked about, and if he could please share his notes on the meeting, which he declined to do for reasons of professional confidentiality.

Natasha Romanova: very beautiful. Magnificent posture. The calmest Russian woman I have ever met. Biologist, working in hydroponic farming. Met Sergei Davydov and fell in love with him here in the camp. Very happy now.

But everyone knew he had been involved with the investigation of the incident, and naturally they must have discussed the fact that he was testing and judging them. And keeping records

280

of course. Mary no longer pressed his leg with hers, if she ever had, nor even sat next to him. Maya watched him more closely than ever, without appearing to. Tatiana continued to seek her peers, speaking always to the person inside one, or behind one. Or inside her. And Michel wondered more and more, as the arbitrary divisions of time they called days passed in their cycles—sleep, hunger, work, Bright Room, tests, relaxation, sleep—whether they could hold it together, mentally or socially, when they got to Mars.

This of course had been his worry from the start, expressed to the others on the planning committee only partially, as a nervous joke: Since they're all going to go crazy anyway, why not send insane people in the first place, and save them the trouble?

Now, trying to shake the feeling of anxiety growing in him, in the bright rooms and out in the dark world, the joke got less and less funny. People were furtive. Relationships were forming, and Michel saw these relationships now by the absences created by their concealment. Like tracing footprints in air. People no longer caressed who had before; glances were exchanged, then avoided; some people never looked at each other any more, and yet drew toward each other as they passed in the halls out of an internal magnetism too strong to tell the others about, but also too strong to conceal. There were trips out into the frigid starry night, often timed so that both parties were out there together, although they did not leave or return together, but with other parties. Lookout Point, a knob low on the Dais, could be observed through night IR goggles, and sometimes one saw two flowing green bodies delineated out there against the black phosphor background, the two figures overlapping in a slow dance, a beautiful mime. Michel hummed an old song in English as he watched, absorbed beyond shame: 'I'm a spy, in the house of love—I know the things, that you're thinking of . . .'

Some of these relationships might knit the community together, others might tear it apart. Maya was playing a very dangerous game with Frank Chalmers now, for instance; she went out on walks with him, they talked late into the evenings; unselfconsciously she would put a hand to his arm and laugh, head thrown back, in a way that she never had with Michel. A prelude to a later intensification, Michel judged, as the two were beginning to look like the natural leaders of the expedition. But at the same time she was always playing him off against the Russian men, with whom she would joke in Russian about the non-Russians, unaware perhaps that Frank spoke some Russian, as he did French (atrociously) and several other languages. Frank just watched her, a small inner smile playing over his lips, even when she joked about him and he could understand it. He would even glance at Michel, to see if he too caught what she was doing. As if they were complicit in their interest in Maya!

And of course she played Michel as well. He could see that. Perhaps just instinctively, as a matter of habit. Perhaps something more personal. He couldn't tell. He wanted her to care about him . . .

Meanwhile, other small groups were withdrawing from the main one. Arkady had his admirers, Vlad his close group of intimates; they were harem keepers, perhaps. On the other hand, Hiroko Ai had her group, and Phyllis hers, each distinct; polyandry as well as polygamy, then, or at least it seemed possible to Michel. They all existed already—in potentiality or in his imagination, it was hard to tell. But it was impossible not to perceive at least part of what was going on among them as the group dynamics of a troop of primates, thrown together all unknown to each other, and therefore sorting things out, establishing consorts, dominance hierarchies, and so on. For they were primates; apes shut in cages; and even though they had chosen the cages themselves, still—there they were. In a situation. Like Sartre's *Huis Clos*. No exit. Social life. Lost in a prison of their own devise.

Even the stablest people were affected. Michel watched fascinated as the two most introverted personalities among them, Ann Clayborne and Sax Russell, became interested in each other. It was pure science for both of them, at first; they were very much alike in that, and also in that both were so straightforward and guileless that Michel was able to overhear many of their first conversations. They were all shop talk; Martian geology, with Sax grilling her for the most part, learning from her as from a professor, but always able to contribute from the standpoint of a theoretical physicist, one of the leading lights a decade or two before, in his postgraduate years. Not that Ann seemed to care about that. She was a geologist, a planetologist who had studied Mars ever since grad school, until now in her forties she was one of the acknowledged authorities. A Martian ahead of the fact. So if Sax was interested, she could talk Mars for hours; and Sax was interested. So they talked on and on.

'It's a pure situation, you have to remember that. There might even be indigenous life, left there underground from the early warm wet period. So that we have to make a sterile landing and a sterile colony. Put a cordon sanitaire between us and Mars proper. Then a comprehensive search. If Terran life were allowed to invade the ground before we determined the presence or absence of life, it would be a disaster for science. And the contamination might work the other way too. You can't be too careful. No—if anyone tries to infect Mars, there will be opposition. Maybe even active resistance. Poison the poisoners. You can never tell what people will do.'
Sax said little or nothing in reply to this.

*

Then one day it was those two, appearing as deadpan and phlegmatic as ever, who went out for night walks at the (carefully offset) same time, and, Michel saw through his goggles, made their way to Lookout Point. They might have been among those Michel had already seen out there. They sat there beside each other for some time.

But when they came back Sax's colour was high, and he saw nothing of the world inside the compound. Autistic to all. And Ann's brow was furrowed, her eye distracted. And they did not talk to each other, or even look at each other, for many days after that. Something had happened out there!

But as Michel watched them, fascinated by this turn of events, he came to understand that he would never know what it had been. A wave of—what was it—grief? Or sorrow, at their distance from each other, their isolation—each in his or her own private world, sealed vessels jostling—cut off—the futility of his work—the deathly cold of the black night—the ache of living life so inescapably alone. He fled.

Because he was one of the evaluators, he could flee. He could leave Lake Vanda from time to time on the rare helicopter visits, and though he tried not to, in order to establish better solidarity with the group, still he had done it once before, in the darkest depth of winter before the solstice, after seeing Maya and Frank together. Now, though the midday twilights were returning, he took up an invitation from an acquaintance at McMurdo to visit the Scott and Shackleton huts, just north of McMurdo on Ross Island.

Maya met him in the lock as he left. 'What—running away?'

'No, no—no—I'm going to have a look at the Scott and Shackleton huts. A matter of research. I'll be right back.'

Her look showed that she did not believe it. Also that she cared where he went.

But it was in the nature of research, after all. The little

cabins left behind by the first explorers of Antarctica were the remains of some of the very few expeditions in human history that resembled in any way what they were proposing to do on Mars. Though of course all analogy was false and misleading, and dangerous—this was a new thing they were thinking, a new event in history, nothing like it before.

Still, the first decades of Antarctic exploration had been somewhat like their planned expedition, he had to admit as the helicopter landed on the black rock of Cape Evans, and he followed the other distinguished visitors to the small snow-slabbed wooden hut above the beach. This was the nineteenth-century equivalent of their settlement at Lake Vanda, though their compound was ever so much more luxurious. Here at Cape Evans they had had only the necessities, all the necessities except for some vitamins, and the company of the opposite sex. How pale and odd they had become from those lacks, along with the lack of sunlight itself. Monastic malnourished troglodytes, suffering from seasonal affective disorder without knowing what a ferocious psychological problem this was (so that perhaps it hadn't been). Writing newspapers, acting out sketches, pumping music rolls through player pianos, reading books, doing research, and producing some food, by fishing and killing seals. Yes—they had had their pleasures—deprived as they were, these men had still lived on Mother Earth, in contact with the cold fringe of her bounty. On Mars there would be none of those Inuit raptures to pass the time and ameliorate their confinement.

But the postmodern structure of feeling might already have made them used to disconnection from Earth. Everyone inhabiting their own personal spaceship, carrying it mobile with them like a hermit crab's shell, moving from one component of it to the next: home, office, car, plane, apartment, hotel room, mall. An indoor life, even a virtual life. How many hours a day did they spend in the wind? So that perhaps Mars would not feel very different.

As he considered these matters Michel wandered the big main room of Scott's hut, looking at all the artefacts in the grey light. Scott had erected a wall of boxes to separate the officers and scientists from the common seamen. So many different facets; Michel felt his thoughts ricocheting this way and that.

They flew up the coast to Cape Royds, where Shackleton's hut stood like a rebuke to Scott's—smaller, neater, more wind-sheltered. Everyone together. Shackleton and Scott had fallen out during the first expedition to Antarctica, in 1902. Similar disagreements were likely to occur in the Martian colony; but there would be no chance to build a new home elsewhere. At least not at first. And no going home. At least that was the plan. But was that wise? Here again the analogy to the first Antarcticans fell apart, for no matter how uncomfortable they had been in these huts (and Shackleton's looked quite homely, actually) they knew they were only going to be here for a year or three, and then out and back home to England. Almost anything could be endured if there was some release foreseeable at the end of it, coming closer every day. Without that it would be a life sentence—no exit indeed. Exile, to a sur-antarctic wasteland of frigid airless rock.

Surely it made better sense to cycle the scientists and technicians to Mars in a way similar to that of the early Antarcticans. Tours of duty at small scientific stations, the stations built and then manned continuously, but by rotating teams, with individuals out there for three years each. This would be more in keeping with recommended lifetime maximum radiation doses. Boone and the others on the first trip there and back, two years before, had taken about thirty-five rad. Subsequent visiting scientists could stick to something like that.

But the American and Russian space programmers had decided otherwise. They wanted a permanent base, and they had invited scientists to move there for good. They wanted a commitment from people, no doubt hoping for a similar commitment of public interest back home—interest in a permanent cast of characters that could be learned, their lives become a matter of drama for public consumption back on Earth, with its bottomless addiction to narrative—biography as spectacle. Part of the funding effort. It made sense in its way.

But who would want to do such a thing? This was a matter that troubled Michel greatly; it headed the long list of double-binds he felt applicants were put in by the process of selection. In short, they had to be sane to be selected, but crazy to want to go.

Many other double-binds accompanied that basic one. Applicants had to be extroverted enough to socialise, but introverted enough to have studied a discipline to the point of mastering it. They had to be old enough to have learned these primary, secondary and sometimes tertiary professions, and yet be young enough to withstand the rigours of the trip out and the work there. They had to do well in groups, but want to leave everyone they knew behind forever. They were being asked to tell the truth, but clearly had to lie to increase their chances of getting what they wanted. They had to be both ordinary and extraordinary.

Yes, the double-binds were endless. Nevertheless this nearly final group had come from an initial pool of many thousands of applicants. Double-binds? So what! Nothing new to fear there. Everyone on Earth was strung up in vast networks of double-binds. Going to Mars might actually reduce their number, decrease their strain! Perhaps that was part of the appeal of going!

Perhaps that was why these men of the first Antarctic explorations had volunteered to come south. Still, looking around at the bare wooden room, it was amazing to Michel that those who had wintered down here had managed to stay sane. On the wall of Shackleton's hut there was a photo of them: three men, huddled before a black stove. Michel stared long at this evocative photo. The men were worn-looking, battered, dirty, frostbitten, tired. Also calm, even serene. They could sit and do nothing but watch fire burn in a stove, entirely satisfied. They looked cold but warm. The very structure of the brain had been different then, more inured to hardship and the long slow hours of sheer animal existence. Certainly the structure of feeling had changed; that was culturally determined; and thus the brain must necessarily have changed too. A century later their brains depended on great dollops of mediated stimulation, quick-cut inputs which had not even existed for earlier generations. So that reliance on inner resources was harder. Patience was harder. They were different animals from the people in this photo. The epigenetic interplay of DNA and culture was now changing people so fast that even a century was enough to make a measurable difference. Accelerated evolution. Or one of the punctuations in the long tale of punctuated evolution. And Mars would be more of the same. There was no telling what they would become.

Back to Lake Vanda, and the old huts quickly became like a dream interrupting the only reality, a reality so cold that spacetime itself seemed to have frozen, leaving all of them living the same hour over and over again. Dante's cold circle of hell, the worst of all, as he recalled.

The sensory deprivation was getting to them all. Every 'morning' he found himself waking up in low spirits. It took hours after waking to work the weight out of his stomach and focus on the day. After he reached level neutrality, as it was beginning to turn blue twilight at the windows, he was able to ask to join whoever was going outside that day. Out there in the numbing grey or blue or purple twilight he hiked along, trailing the other thickly clad figures, who looked like pilgrims in a medieval winter, or Prehistoric people struggling through the Ice Age. One slender bundle might be Tatiana, her beauty muffled but not entirely blanketed, for she moved like a dancer over the cracked mirror of the lake, under the high walls of the valley. Another might be Maya, focused on the others, though quite friendly and diplomatic to him too. It worried him. Beside her strode Frank, bulky and muffled.

Tatiana was easier to understand, and so attractive. Across the ice one day he followed her. On the far shore they stopped to inspect the dead body of a mummified seal. These disoriented Weddell seals were found far up all the Dry Valleys, dead for hundreds or thousands of years, frozen all that time, slowly frittered away by the winds, until the skeleton slowly emerged from the body like a soul taking off a fur coat, a soul white and wind-polished and articulated.

Tatiana grabbed his arm, exclaiming at the sight. She spoke French well, and had spent summers as a girl on the beaches of the Côte d'Azur; just the thought of that made him melt. Now they spoke, gloved hand in gloved hand, looking down through ski-masks at the *memento mori* in the grey light. His heart beat hard at the thought of the beauty encased in the chrysalis parka beside him, saying 'It's such a shock to come on one of these poor creatures' vertebra, out on its own in all the rock, like someone's lost bracelet.'

From across the lake Frank watched them.

And after that day Maya dropped Michel completely, with never a word nor any outward sign that things had changed, but only a single swift glance at Tatiana, in his presence, after which a purely formal politeness, no content whatsoever. And now Michel knew, very acutely, whose company in this group he craved the most; but would never have again.

Frank had done that.

And all around him it was happening: the pointless wars of the heart. It was all so small, petty, tawdry. Yet it mattered; it was their life. Sax and Ann had gone dead to each other, likewise Marina and Vlad, and Hiroko and Iwao. New cliques were forming around Hiroko and Vlad and Arkady and Phyllis, as they all spun out into their own separate orbits. No—this group would go dysfunctional. Was going dysfunctional, he could see it right before his eyes. It was too hard to live isolated in this sub-biological sensory deprivation; and this was paradise compared to Mars. There was no such thing as a good test. There was no such thing as a good analogy. There was only reality, unique and different in every moment, to be lived without rehearsal and without revision. Mars would not be like this cold continuous night on the bottom of their world; it would be worse. Worse than this! They would go mad. A hundred people confined in tanks and sent to a poisonous cold dead planet, a place to which winter in Antarctica was like paradise; a prison universe, like the inside of a head when your eyes are closed. They would all go mad.

In the first week of September the noonday twilight grew almost as bright as day, and they could see sunlight on the peaks of the Asgaard and Olympus Ranges, flanking the deep valley. Because the valley was such a narrow slot between such high ranges, it would be perhaps another ten days before the sun fell directly on the base, and Arkady organised a hike up the side of Mount Odin to catch an earlier glimpse of it. This turned into a general expedition, as almost everyone proved interested in seeing the sun again as soon as possible. So early on the morning of September 10th, they stood nearly a thousand metres above Lake Vanda, on a shelf occupied by a small ice pond and tarn. It was windy, so the climb had not warmed them. The sky was a pale starless blue; the east sides of the peaks of both ranges were glazed gold with sunlight. Finally to the east, at the end of the valley, over the burnished plate of the frozen Ross Sea, the sun emerged over the horizon and burned like a flare. They cheered; their eyes ran with emotion, also an excess of new light and cold wind. People hugged each other, bundle after bundle. But Maya kept on the other side of the group from Michel, with Frank always between them. And it seemed to Michel that everyone's joy had a desperate edge to it, as of people who had barely survived an extinction event.

Thus when the time came to make his report to the selection committees, Michel advised against the project as designed. 'No group can stay functional under such conditions indefinitely,' he wrote. In the meetings he made his case point by point. The long list of double-binds was especially impressive.

This was in Houston. The heat and humidity were sauna-like; Antarctica was already a nightmare memory, slipping quickly away.

'But this is just social life,' Charles York pointed out, bemused. 'All social existence is a set of double-binds.'

'No no,' Michel said. 'Social life is a set of contradictory demands. That's normal agreed. But what we're talking about here are *requirements* to be two opposite things at once. Classic double-binds. And they are already causing a lot of the classic responses. Hidden lives. Multiple personalities. Bad faith. Repression, then the return of the repressed. A close look at the results of the tests given down there will show it is not a viable project. I would advise starting with small scientific stations, with rotating crews. As Antarctica itself is operated now.'

This caused a lot of discussion, even controversy. Charles remained committed to sending up a permanent colony, as proposed; but he had grown close to Mary. Georgia and Pauline tended to agree with Michel; though they too had had personal difficulties at Vanda.

Charles dropped by to see Michel in his borrowed office, shaking his head. He looked at Michel, serious but somehow still uninvolved, distanced. Professional. 'Look, Michel,' he said. 'They want to go. They're capable of adapting. A lot of them did very well with that, so well that you couldn't pick them out of a crowd in any kind of blind test. And they want to go, it's clear. That's how we should choose who to send. We should give them their chance to do what they want. It's not really our business to decide for them.'

'But it won't work. We saw that.'

'I didn't see that. They didn't see that. What you saw is your concern, but they have the right to make their try at it. Anything could happen there, Michel. Anything. And this world is not so well arranged that we should deny people who want to take their chance to try something different. It could be good for us all.' He stood abruptly to leave the office. 'Think about it.'

Michel thought about it. Charles was a sensible man, a wise man. What he had said had the ring of truth to it. And a sudden gust of fear blew through Michel, as cold as any katabatic downdraught in Wright Valley: he might, out of his own fear, be stopping something with greatness in it.

He changed his recommendation, describing all the reasons why. He explained his vote for the project to continue; he gave the committees his list of the best hundred candidates. But Georgia and Pauline continued to advise against the project as designed. And so an outside panel was convened to make an evaluation, a recommendation, a judgment. Near the end of the process Michel even found himself in his office with the American president, who sat down with him and told him he had probably been right the first time around, first impressions were usually that way, second-guessing was of little use. Michel could only nod. Later he sat in a meeting attended by both the American and Russian presidents; the stakes were that high. They both wanted a Martian base, for their own political purposes, Michel saw that clearly. But they also wanted a success, a project that worked. In that sense, the hundred permanent colonists as originally conceived was

292

clearly the riskier of the options they had before them now. And neither president was a risk taker. Rotating crews were intrinsically less interesting, but if the crews were large enough, and the base large enough, then the political impact (the publicity) would be almost the same; the science would be the same; and everything would be that much safer, radio-logically as well as psychologically.

So they cancelled the project.

A Site of Special Scientific Interest

Kim Stanley Robinson

Hello again, my friends. As you can see, I am now out on the surface of the Ross Ice Shelf, a few kilometres south of Ross Island. I have come out here to spend a day at the Americans' Happy Camper Camp, where visitors are trained in ice skills to better prepare themselves for their time in Antarctica. The camp is well named; I am happy indeed. The mountaineers have shown us how to light the stoves, to put up the tents and to use the radios. I have learned how to tie several knots. I know now that if you need to get a badly injured person inside a tent but are afraid to move them for fear of injuring them more, you are to slit the bottom of the tent open and erect the tent directly over the unfortunate person. Antarctica is a dangerous place. It is easy, looking around as we are now, to think that I stand on a broad snowy plain; in fact I am standing on cracked ice, with deep fissures all around, and the Antarctic Ocean below me.

Captain Cook, one of the greatest *feng shui* masters of all time, sailed the circumference of this Antarctic Ocean in the 1770s, trying to get as far south as he could. His wooden sailing ships ran into the pack ice at seventy degrees south, and as far as they could see to the south was only more ice. With the technology of his time they could go no farther. Later Cook wrote, 'I can be bold to say, that no man will ever venture farther than I have done and that the lands which may lie to the South will never be explored.'

This sounds odd to us, short-sighted and even a bit foolish. But we must remember that the man who said it was extremely intelligent and capable, accomplishing much more in his life than any of us have. His short-sightedness as exhibited in

294

this remark has to be understood then not as a personal attribute, but as an attribute of his age generally. For Cook lived just before the great accelerations of the industrial age; his time was as it were the foothills of a mountain range so precipitous that the heights could not be guessed. Thus the radical foreshortening of the *kao-yuan* perspective. Cook sailed in wooden ships, which in their materials much resembled those used in ships for the previous two thousand years; only improvements in design had made them more seaworthy, and Cook rightly judged that these improvements, wrested slowly over the centuries out of human experience, had gone about as far with the materials as they could go. Thus he could not foresee the immense changes that would come so rapidly in the industrial decades to follow.

We, however, have no such excuse as Cook. We live on the heights of that mountain range, in a culture changing so rapidly that it is hard to gauge it. We look back on two centuries of continuous acceleration into this unstable moment, so we should be able to foresee that much the same will occur in the time after us. Who can deny that the future will quickly become something very different than our time, quickly become one of any number of possible worlds?

And yet by and large I think we still do no better than Captain Cook. We assume that the conditions that exist now will be permanent, even though every year the laws are amended, and even the ice shelf I am standing on now, that has been here for three million years, is melting away. Even the rocks melt away in time. This moment is like a dragonfly, hovering over a peach blossom; then off and gone.

Look then at this ocean I am camped on in this moment. A white immensity; nothing to say about it. Erebus stands in the air like a powerful deity. Before you can read a landscape, it has to become a part of your inmost heart. When I came before to Antarctica, as a proud young man, I saw the land and it baffled me, and I could not paint it in my poems.

Nothing came to me. As the British explorer Cherry-Garrard said, 'This journey had beggared our language.'

Only later, as I dreamed of it, did I grow to love it. What words I could find were the oldest words, in their simplest combinations. Blue sky; white snow. That is all language can say of this place; all else is footnotes, and the human stories.

Now I am back, and those of you who care to share my voyage, watching and listening in China, or wherever else you may be; I welcome you, because I feel now, all these years later, with the love of these stories in me, that I am ready to film the land I see, and talk to you, my friends, about it; not to reproduce the effects of light, but to tap this light at its source.

Antarctic Stones

Pablo Neruda

There everything ends
and nothing:
there everything begins:
the rivers say farewell in the ice,
the sky has married the snow,
there are neither highways nor horses
and the only building
was raised by the stone.
No one inhabits the castle,
not even lost souls,
those whom the cold and the cold wind
have terrified: there
the solitude of the world is lonely,
and for this the stone
became music, it lifted
its delicate towers, it lifted itself
to cry or to sing
yet it was silent.
Only the wind,
that whip whistling from the pole,
only the empty white
and a murmur of rainbirds
over the castle of solitude.

Visiting Mr Shackleton
(for Chris Cochran)

Bill Manhire

Cool! Wow! Beautiful! Awesome!
Like going back in time.
Amazing! Historic! Finally
I am truly blessed.

Wow! History! Fantastic!
Wonderfully kept.
Shackleton's the man!
Like going back in time.

Wow! Cool! Historic! Yo!
Awesome! Privileged. Unreal!
And Thank you, God. And Happy
Birthday, Dad. And Thailand.

Notes

'Study the treasures under the Antarctic and make use of them even after my death.' (*page 5*)

A *waka*, said to have been composed by Lieutenant Nobu Shirase as a farewell to Antarctica. Nobu Shirase (1861–1946) led a Japanese expedition to Antarctica in 1910–1912. Before leaving Antarctica, he claimed the Ross Ice Shelf, naming it the Yamoto Snow Plain. See Mariska Wouters, 'One Man's Dream: The Antarctic Expedition of Nobu Shirase', *Antarctic: The Journal of the New Zealand Antarctic Society*, vol.20, no.1 & 2, 2002: 21–3.

The Death of Ulysses (*page 31*)

From Book XXVI of Dante's *Inferno*. The shade of Ulysses recounts his final journey, through the Straits of Gibraltar where the Pillars of Hercules mark the limits of the habitable world, and thence south below the equator. This story is thought to be essentially Dante's own invention. The poet can hardly have had Antarctica in mind. But 'the other pole' is no doubt the South Pole, while the details that are clustered here in a context of determined leadership and extraordinary adventure—ship, storm, dangerous current, mysterious peak and shipwreck—will be familiar to many readers of later Antarctic literature. Dante has also been a presence in Antarctic literature in other ways. A copy of the *Inferno* was taken south on the final trek, at least as far as the Beardmore Glacier, by members of Scott's doomed polar party, while Dante's story prompted Tennsyon's famous poem 'Ulysses', whose final line would supply the epitaph for Scott and his companions: 'To strive, to seek, to find, and not to yield.' Bernadette Hince's *The Antarctic Dictionary: A Complete Guide to Antarctic English* (2000) for a number of years had for its working title the acronym *DANTE* (*Dictionary of Antarctic English*). Cherry-Garrard is only one of many to have observed (Cherry-Garrard, 254) that 'Dante was right when he placed the circles of ice below the circles of fire'. See, for example, Kim Stanley Robinson's 'Michel in Antarctica', p.288. Of course, Dante's *Inferno* is another hollow earth (see Introduction, pp.13–14).

The translation is by Laurence Binyon (1869–1943); this episode of the *Inferno* was his favourite, and the first which he translated in 1921.

A more recent version of the travels of Ulysses/Odysseus is Nikos Kazantzakis's *The Odyssey: A Modern Sequel* (1938). In the twenty-second of its twenty-four Books or 'Rhapsodies', Odysseus sails to the South Pole, where there are polar bears and eskimos, as well as ice.

from **Another World and Yet the Same** (*page 33*)

This short selection is from Bishop Joseph Hall's Mundus Alter et Idem (Another World and Yet the Same or The Southern Continent, before this always unknown, through the extended travels of a wandering academic most recently surveyed) which was first published in 1605 in Latin. Hall's satirical narrative purports to be the true story of Mercurius Britannicus and his travels in the as-yet-undiscovered austral continent. Hall's book is sometimes called the first dystopia, as it not only burlesques exploration narratives of the age but also takes a whole range of European tendencies to immoderate and ridiculous extremes. There are four distinct lands: one, *Tenter-belly*, which is populated by gluttons and drunkards; a second named *Viraginia* or *Shee-lande*, where women rule; a third named *Moronia* or *Fooliana*; and a fourth, which is a land of thieves.

As well as general follies and excesses, the geographical location prompts a range of antipodean reverses, as in the notion of a society governed by women, or the assertion that bodily weakness at the North Pole is matched by intellectual weakness at its southern counterpart. This sense of the southern antipodes as a place of contradiction and irrational extremes runs through a number of Antarctic texts. See, for instance, Valery Bryusov's 'The Republic of the Southern Cross'.

The text here is from John Healey's 1609 English translation, *The Discovery of a New World*. The extracts have been lightly edited, and come from the descriptions of *Fooliana*, the southern-most of the lands visited by Mercurius Britannicus. There is a translated edition of the original Latin text, *Another World and Yet the Same: Bishop Joseph Hall's Mundus alter et idem* by John Millar Wands (New Haven: Yale University Press, 1981).

Admiral Richard Byrd, in a foreword to a 1937 reprint of the John Healey translation, expresses mock astonishment at what Joseph Hall reports from,

> *latitudes where I encountered only snow and ice. The only inhabitants of any human interest whom I met there were the penguins, a decent lot on the whole, and perhaps as worthy to dwell in 'Terra Sancta' (as the old geographers called it) as any of God's creatures could be. They are, in any case, quite unlike the guzzlers, the morons, and the rascals of Tenter-Belly, Shee-landt, Fooliana, and Theevingen. . . . Those of us who are especially interested in the Antarctic will find an enduring satisfaction in the knowledge that the land down there, no less than lands more anciently known, can now boast its saga.*

A Gawrey Extended for Flight (*page 40*)

The picture is of a Gawrey, or flying woman, found in Robert Paltock's 1751 imaginary voyage novel *Peter Wilkins*. The novel, much admired by later writers such as Coleridge, who called it 'a work of uncommon beauty', tells of the adventures of the sailor Peter Wilkins:

> *His Shipwreck near the South Pole; his wonderful Passage thro' a subterraneous Cavern into a kind of new World; his there meeting with a Gawrey or flying Woman, whose Life he preserv'd, and afterwards married her; his extraordinary Conveyance to the Country of Glumms and Gawreys, or Men and Women that fly.*

Jorge Luis Borges includes the Gawrey *Youwarkee* in his alphabetical

Book of Imaginary Beings. The wings in the picture can also be reconfigured as a kind of boat.

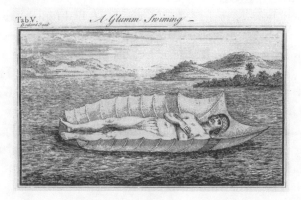

Song (*page 41*)

From *The Journals of Captain James Cook on His Voyages of Discovery* vol.II, ed. J.C. Beaglehole (Cambridge, 1961). Beaglehole quotes a note appended to the original manuscript: 'This song composed by Thomas Perry one of the Sea Men that went round the world with Captain Cook and was very much valued by the Captain. Mrs Cook kept it with the Gold Medal till her death.'

from **The Rime of the Ancient Mariner** (*page 43*)

Coleridge knew Cook's accounts of his voyages to the south, especially the second voyage of 1772–1775, in which Cook concluded that Terra Australis, the Great South Land, did not after all exist—or if it did was a place of ice and uninhabitable.

But, as John Livingston Lowes would memorably demonstrate, *The Ancient Mariner* owes more to Coleridge's extensive readings in voyage narratives involving Arctic journeys. 'There was no lack of ice afloat on the seas of that capacious memory.' (Lowes, 133)

The Ancient Mariner was influential for many subsequent imaginings or transcriptions of Antarctic experience. As Stephen Pyne (Pyne, 162–3) notes, 'In demonstrating how Antarctic nature could be reshaped into a fictional, moral universe, Coleridge introduced many of the enduring images associated with Antarctic literature—the polar spirit, the whirlpool, the spectral mists of snow, the haunted traveller who escapes to tell the tale.'

The image on page 45 is by popular French artist and engraver Gustave Doré (1832–1883), who illustrated an edition of *The Ancient Mariner*. Doré had a taste for the Romantic grotesque and for the atmosphere of 'eerie gloom' invoked by John Martin Leahy (p.119). He also illustrated Dante's *Inferno* and Poe's 'The Raven', along with the works of many other authors (Tennyson, Milton, Rabelais) and the Bible. He was much admired as an artist by Lovecraft and his circle.

from The Narrative of Arthur Gordon Pym of Nantucket (*page 48*)

In this, Edgar Allan Poe's first book-length work of prose fiction, the hero, Arthur Gordon Pym, after a nightmarish sequence of seafaring adventures, finds himself on board a ship which penetrates through the southern ice to find temperate waters and islands populated by dark-skinned natives. The story's attempt to mimic real travellers' tales of extravagant adventure is caught in its long-winded subtitle: *The Narrative of Arthur Gordon Pym of Nantucket. Comprising the Details of a Mutiny and Atrocious Butchery on Board the American Brig* Grampus, *on Her Way to the South Seas, in the Month of June, 1827. With an Account of the Recapture of the Vessel by the Survivers* [sic]; *Their Shipwreck and Subsequent Horrible Sufferings from Famine; Their Deliverance by Means of the British Schooner* Jane Guy; *the Brief Cruise of this Latter Vessel in the Antarctic Ocean; Her Capture, and the Massacre of Her Crew Among a Group of Islands in the Eighty-Fourth Parallel of Southern Latitude; Together with the Incredible Adventures and Discoveries Still Farther South to Which That Distressing Calamity Gave Rise.*

The printed extract is the twenty-sixth and final chapter of *Pym*. This was by no means Poe's first imaginative adventure into Antarctica. He had earlier written the story 'MS. Found in a Bottle', which, like the tale of Arthur Pym, ends with a mysterious disaster in the southern seas. Trapped on board an other-worldly ship with a spirit crew (elements which owe something to Coleridge's *Ancient Mariner*), the narrator is drawn by a current towards the region of the southern pole—'It is evident that we are hurrying onwards to some exciting knowledge—some never-to-be-imparted secret whose attainment is destruction'—where great 'ramparts of ice' tower into a desolate sky, and look 'like the walls of the universe'. The story, which won the young Poe a prize, ends:

> *Oh, horror upon horror!—the ice opens suddenly to the right, and to the left, and we are whirling dizzily, in immense concentric circles, round and round the borders of a gigantic amphitheatre, the summit of whose walls is lost in the darkness and the distance. But little time will be left me to ponder upon my destiny! The circles rapidly grow small—we are plunging madly within the grasp of the whirlpool—and amid a roaring, and bellowing, and thundering of ocean and of tempest, the ship is quivering—oh God! and—going down!*

The idea of the whirlpool and the narrator's terrified yet somehow ecstatic entry into the earth is not entirely transcendental or metaphorical. Poe knew of and seems to have had sympathy with the theories of John Cleves Symmes, who in April 1818 had circulated a manifesto, accompanied by a certificate guaranteeing his own sanity, to universities and government agencies, declaring the earth 'hollow, and habitable within; containing a number of solid concentrick spheres, one within the other; and . . . open at the poles 12 or 16 degrees'.

The last chapter of *Pym* is succeeded by a Note which makes it clear that Pym survived the mysterious embrace of the giant figure, although the remaining chapters, which he had kept 'for the purpose of revision, have been irrecoverably lost through the accident by which he perished himself'.

> *The loss of two or three final chapters (for there were but two or three) is the more deeply to be regretted, as, it cannot be doubted, they contained matter relative to the Pole itself, or at least to regions in its very near proximity; and as, too, the statements of the author in relation to those regions may shortly be verified or contradicted by means of the governmental expedition now preparing for the Southern Ocean.*

The mysterious cry *Tekeli-li!* has been picked up by subsequent 'sequel-writers' such as Charles Romyn Dake (*A Strange Discovery*, 1899), Jules Verne and H.P. Lovecraft (who once remarked that Poe was his 'God of Fiction'). It has also supplied a title for a rich bibliography of Antarctic fiction compiled by Fauno Cordes and available at http://www.antarctic-circle.org/fauno.htm.

from An Antarctic Mystery (*page 54*)

From Jules Verne, *Le Sphinx des Glaces* (1897); translated by Mrs Cashel Hoey (1899) as *An Antarctic Mystery*. In an article about Edgar Allan Poe published in 1864, Jules Verne wondered who might take up the tale of Arthur Gordon Pym, which Poe had broken off in mid-air. Someone, he suggested, more bold than he, who would not be afraid to launch himself into the sphere of the impossible. In the event his own rather perfunctory novel picks up some eleven years after the end of Poe's story and supplies a plausible if reductively scientific explanation for events which Poe was happy to leave entirely in the realm of mystery and supernatural abstraction.

In Verne's famous novel, *Twenty Thousand Leagues Under the Sea*, Captain Nemo's submarine, the *Nautilus*, visits Antarctica, sailing beneath the ice and discovering an open polar sea. Perhaps Verne's novel partly accounts for Shackleton's use of the pen name 'Nemo' in his contributions to *Aurora Australis*?

The Republic of the Southern Cross (*page 65*)

Valery Bryusov (1873–1924) wrote poetry and novels as well as short fiction. 'The Republic of the Southern Cross' was first published in Russian in 1905. The present text is from *The Republic of the Southern Cross and Other Stories* (London: Constable, 1918. Introduction by Stephen Graham; translator is anonymous). With its fabular and parable-like qualities, this story and others by Bryusov have reminded some commentators of Borges and Calvino. Bryusov himself wrote that *the stories are written to show, in various ways, that there is no fixed boundary line between the world of reality and that of the imagination, between the dreaming and the waking world, life and fantasy; that what we commonly call 'imaginary' may be the greatest reality of the world, and that which all call reality the most dreadful delirium.*

The Travellers to the South Pole (*page 87*)

German Expressionist poet and short story writer Georg Heym (1887–1912) was much preoccupied with evil. His South Pole travellers make the opposite decision to Shackleton, who had turned back some ninety-seven miles short of the South Pole, later saying to his wife, 'I thought you'd rather have a live donkey than a dead lion.' Heym wrote one other Antarctic story, 'Das Tagebuch Shakletons' (1911), which also adjusts what was for him contemporary history. The story purports to be the final diary entries of the explorer Shackleton (the odd spelling is Heym's). Shackleton and his fellows enter a warmer area beyond the southern ice where they are turned into zombie-like figures and imprisoned. It is suggested that the diary published under Shackleton's name is a forgery, designed to mask the true fate of Shackleton and his polar expedition.

'Die Südpolfahrer' ('The Travellers to the South Pole', 1911) is collected in *Georg Heym, Dichtungen und Schriften, vol.2: Prosa und Dramen*, ed. Karl Ludwig Schneider, Darmstadt: Wissenschaftliche Buchgesellschaft, 1962, pp.120–23. Both it and 'Das Tagebuch Shakletons' were among Heym's unpublished papers. The translation was especially made for this anthology by Gordon Collier.

Sur (*page 90*)

First published in the *New Yorker*, February 1982, and collected in *The Compass Rose*, New York: Harper & Row, 1982.

Ursula K. Le Guin has written in her essay 'Heroes' of her fascination with books about early Antarctic exploration, and particularly with the narratives of the men who were on those expeditions: Scott, Shackleton, Cherry-Garrard, Wilson, Byrd, and others. (In this, Doris Lessing keeps her company; see her 'Afterword' to *The Making of the Representative for Planet 8* (London: Jonathan Cape, 1982).) 'They were certainly heroes to me, all of them,' notes Le Guin.

> And as I followed them step by frostbitten-toed step across the Ross Ice Barrier and up the Beardmore Glacier to that awful place, the white plateau, and back again, many times, they got into my toes and bones and my books, and I wrote The Left Hand of Darkness, *in which a Black man from Earth and an androgynous extraterrestrial pull Scott's sledge through Shackleton's blizzards across a planet called Winter. And fifteen years or so later I wrote a story, 'Sur', in which a small group of Latin Americans actually reach the South Pole a year before Amundsen and Scott, but decide not to say anything about it, because if the men knew they had got there first—they are all women—it wouldn't do. The men would be so let down. 'We left no footprints, even,' says the narrator.* (Le Guin, 171)

Lucy Kavaler's *Heroes & Lovers* (New York: Dutton, 1995) also supplies an all-female polar expedition, a team of American suffragettes led by one Viola Lambert. We learn that they were first to reach the pole, as the fictional Amundsen and Scott equivalents, Carlsen and Sharp, had been unable to cross a giant abyss.

In fact, the first women to reach the South Pole travelled there by plane, a US Navy Hercules, in 1969.

In Amundsen's Tent (*page 110*)

The story by John Martin Leahy (1886–1967) first appeared in *Weird Tales*, January 1928, where the headnote proclaimed: *A horror lurked in Roald Amundsen's tent at the South Pole—an utterly abominable and terrifying monstrosity.*

Captain Stanley Livingstone and Darwin Frontenac are characters in Leahy's short novel, *The Living Death*, which offers a lost-race adventure in an Antarctic setting. Says Bleiler:

> *Captain Livingstone, an explorer, returns from Antarctica with a strange tale. He had penetrated through a cave system into the heart of the continent and came upon wonders: a beautiful woman frozen*

307

in the ice, horrible monsters, a gigantic headless statue, and a warm
lost land. Darwin Frontenac, a great contemporary biologist, and
his associates decide to return to Antarctica with Livingstone and
investigate. Frontenac, whose speciality is cryogenics, freezes a large
number of dogs for later revival as dog teams. The explorers,
discovering that Livingstone's report was accurate, after great
hardships reach the warm land. It is characterised by octopus-like
plants that grab their prey; gigantic vicious humanoid beings,
evolved out of bears, with a paleolithic culture; and, of course,
Zandara, the frozen woman. Most of the expedition perishes amid
the horrors, but Frontenac escapes, bearing Zandara in an ice cube.
He thaws her out at his leisure, and she proves to be charming,
gracious, and intelligent. (Bleiler, 429)

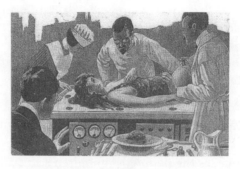

The illustration above is by Frank R. Paul and appeared in the June
1925 edition of *Science and Mechanics*.

The Barrier Silence (*page 132*)

Edward Wilson's poem was first published in the *South Polar Times*,
(vol.3: 151). See also the note (pp.310–11) on 'Edward Wilson' by
Glyn Maxwell.

The poem has given its name to a music album from the group
90 Degrees South. Wilson lived on the hill overlooking the Jaguar
Sound Studio in Cheltenham where the album was recorded. New
Zealand writer Cliff Fell has a poem, 'The Wilsons' (in *The
Adulterer's Bible* (2003)), which recounts his childhood memory
of Edward Wilson's brother 'still waiting, fifty years later, / for his
twin to return / from the assault on the Pole.'

Wilson's Diary (*page 133*)

Australian poet Dorothy Porter (1954–) is best known for her crime novel in verse, *The Monkey's Mask*. 'Wilson's Diary' first appeared in the collection *Driving Too Fast* (Brisbane: University of Queensland Press, 1989), which contains another Antarctic poem, 'Oates' Diary'.

The Photographer in the Antarctic (*page 136*)
The Ice Fleet Sails (*page 139*)

Chris Orsman (1955–) has published two major collections of poetry in New Zealand, *Ornamental Gorse* (1994) and *South* (1996), which retells Scott's last voyage to Antarctica (a revised and expanded edition was published by Faber in 1999). He was a member of New Zealand's inaugural Artists to Antarctica programme in January, 1998. During his time on the ice he designed and printed, in an edition of twenty-three copies, the chapbook *Homelight*, containing work by Nigel Brown, Bill Manhire, and himself (the cover was a linocut, made by Brown with a dessertspoon and handprinted in the TAE Hut at Scott Base). The book is one of the very few literary publications to have been entirely written and produced in Antarctica, and is formally published by Orsman's own, aptly named Pemmican Press.

The photographer in 'The Photographer in the Antarctic' is Herbert Ponting, who recorded in still photography and moving images the early stages of Scott's expedition. The 'Owner' (line 33) is Scott. It is Ponting who speaks in 'The Ice Fleet Sails'. The epigraph is taken from Scott's diary.

Impressions on the March (*page 142*)

From the diary of Robert Falcon Scott (see Introduction, pp.17–19). Scott's journal, open to its 'last entry', is on permanent display in the British Library, Euston Road, London.

Antarctica (*page 144*)

Irish poet Derek Mahon's villanelle takes as one of its refrain lines Oates's famous last words, while its companion rhyme line neatly captures the mixed and shifting responses called forth over the years by the tragedy of Scott's polar expedition. Oates's line has been treated less well in verse, for instance in this passage from Chas. Moss's 1913 poem, 'Commander Scott, R.N., at the South Pole', which also finds its way to the sublime:

> *But further trouble lay in wait*
> *Impossible to over-rate,*
> *And which exceeded human skill,*
> *When Captain Oates was taken ill;*
> *Who grew still worse in fighting on*
> *Through snow and ice till strength was gone:*
> *And soon, alas, the truth was clear—*
> *His work was done, and death was near.*
>
> *His friends he knew*
> *Were staunch and true,*
> *Who could not, would not him forsake,*
> *Their tacit resolution break—*
> *Whate'er befall*
> *Die one die all!*
> *But saw that in his death their safety lay,*
> *And staggered forth to die—the only way.*
>
> *'I'm going out,' said he,*
> *And for some time maybe.'*
> *Some time?*
> *Sublime!*
> *All time for him was at an end,*
> *Except the time to save his friends—*

Edward Wilson (*page 145*)

Wilson, who died with Scott on the return from the Pole, was perhaps the most admired member of Scott's team. His blue eyes were often commented on. Scott wrote in one of his 'final letters', addressed to Wilson's wife, Oriana:

His eyes have a comfortable blue look of hope and his mind is peaceful with the satisfaction of his faith in regarding himself as part of the great scheme of the Almighty. I can do no more to comfort you than to tell you that he died as he lived, a brave, true man—the best of comrades and staunchest of friends.

Glyn Maxwell (1962–) is an English poet and dramatist who now lives in the USA. *Moon Country* (1996) describes a visit to Iceland with the poet Simon Armitage in the steps of W.H. Auden and Louis MacNeice. 'Edward Wilson' first appeared in the *Times Literary Supplement*, 13 March 1998.

from The Fire on the Snow (*page 146*)

These excerpts are from the radio play by Douglas Stewart (1913–1985). Though born and educated in New Zealand, Stewart was a major figure in mid twentieth-century Australian poetry. *The Fire on the Snow* covers the three-month period between 4 January 1912, when the last members of Scott's support party returned to base, and 29 March 1912, when Scott made his final diary entries. It was first broadcast by the Australian Broadcasting Commission in 1941, and subsequently was studied by a whole generation of Australian school children. Stewart noted that his sources were Scott's own diaries and Apsley Cherry-Garrard's *The Worst Journey in the World*. He also wrote another Antarctic sequence, *Worsley Enchanted* (1952), about Shackleton's captain on the *Endurance*.

The Pole (*page 156*)

Vladimir Nabokov (1899–1977) wrote this short verse play in Russian at the age of twenty-four, while working as a summer labourer on a farm in the south of France (1923). Some years earlier he had seen Scott's diaries in their glass case in the British Museum. As his biographer Brian Boyd puts it: 'Themes first sounded in the play—the challenge of courage, the lure of exploration, the timeless romance still left in modern times—would later return in Nabokov's works in more profitable guise.'

This text is from *The Man from the USSR and Other Plays* (1984). Dmitri Nabokov writes there that it is

311

a deliberately free synthesis of the Scott diaries. Nabokov's aim is not a precise journalistic reproduction but a rearrangement of elements into a concentrated interpersonal drama. Even the epigraph and its attribution—

'He was a very gallant gentleman'
(from Scott's notebook)—

are deliberately approximate.

Dmitri Nabokov also notes that, in an early manuscript version, Scott was named 'Bedring'.

The play received perhaps its first production in 1996. According to a note by Dieter E. Zimmer on the Nabokov website, *Zembla*, there were performances of the same production (in a translation by Botho Strauss, and directed by Klaus Michael Grüber) in German in German cities, and in French in French cities:

> *Grüber fans may have expected a hallucinatory fantasy on the subject of coldness, whiteness and death where the spoken word would matter little. Instead, the blizzard has calmed down completely before the transparent curtain opens on the sombre scene, and complete silence reigns so that every word that is uttered assumes additional importance, as if it were a grave revelation about life and death. The only alien elements Grüber adds are plaintive musical fragments by the Hungarian composer György Kurtág (born 1926), performed by six solo instrumentalists and a vocalist. As they walk on and off the stage, for some reason they wear glitzy costumes as if in a vaudeville act, contrasting sharply with the dying men's functional greyish weatherwear.*
>
> *The reviews were rather reserved, though not ferocious.*

Ice House (*page 167*)

The poem is from Canadian poet Anne Michaels's third collection, *Skin Divers* (1999), which includes this note by the author:

> *Kathleen Scott was a sculptor, and the wife of the Antarctic explorer Robert Falcon Scott. They had been married two years, with an eleven-month-old son, when Scott went south to the Pole. Upon parting in New Zealand, they made a pact to keep a daily journal for each other. Scott perished on the return journey from the Pole,*

and when his body and the bodies of his companions were found
in the spring, his diary was brought back to England. On the inside
cover, Scott had written 'Send this diary to my wife.' Then Scott
drew a line through the word 'wife' and wrote instead, 'widow'.

Anne Michaels's novel, *Fugitive Pieces*, also pays considerable attention to the Antarctic, and—in quite another context—along the way offers the tag, 'Many are called but few are frozen.'

Diary Extracts from Scott's Voyage to Discover the West Pole (*page 171*)

James Brown (1966–) has published three books of poetry. This poem is from his first, *Go Round Power Please* (1995). The book's title quotes the last words spoken in the cockpit of the Air New Zealand DC10 which flew into the side of Mount Erebus in November 1979, killing all 237 passengers and twenty crew. Another Antarctic poem in the collection is 'The Poem that Took the Place of a Mountain'. Brown's West Pole extends an idea from A.A. Milne's *Winnie-the-Pooh*. The name 'Bolger', here attributed to a pony, is that of a New Zealand Prime Minister who visited Scott Base and the South Pole in 1997. 'For God's sake, look after our people' are among Scott's very last words.

Scott of the Sahara (*page 173*)

Text from *Monty Python's Flying Circus: Just the Words* (1999). The sketch originally aired 2 December 1970.

Crean. Night Watch (*page 181*)
What the Ice Gets: 23–29 October 1915 (*page 183*)

Both poems are from US poet Melinda Mueller's *What the Ice Gets: Shackleton's Antarctic Expedition, 1914–1916 (A Poem)* (2000). Her book records—in a mixture of narrative poems and dramatic monologues—the story of the 1914–1916 Shackleton expedition in which the *Endurance* was trapped in pack ice, and subsequently sank. The story of how Shackleton and his men sailed to Elephant

Island in three lifeboats, whence he and five others (including Tom Crean) sailed 800 miles in the tiny *James Caird* to South Georgia, has often been told. All were saved. Shackleton himself has related the story in *South* (1919). Probably the most convenient recent retelling is Caroline Alexander's *The Endurance: Shackleton's Legendary Antarctic Expedition* (1998). An earlier book-length poem is Donald Finkel's *Endurance: An Antarctic Idyll* (1978). See also the note (p.311) on Douglas Stewart's *The Fire on the Snow*.

Tom Crean (1877–1938) was second officer on the *Endurance*. He had first sailed to Antarctica with Scott's *Discovery* expedition in 1901, and was subsequently a member of the 1910–1912 expedition. He was a member of the larger polar sledging party led by Scott, but turned back (in tears) with Lashley and Evans on 4 January 1912, while Scott and his four companions continued on. He was also a member of the party which discovered Scott, Wilson, and Bowers dead in their tent. In 'Crean. Night Watch' he recalls the return to New Zealand after the news of Scott's death.

The epigraph of 'Crean. Night Watch' is quoted from Frank Worsley's *Shackleton's Boat Journey* (1931). (Worsley was the New Zealand captain of the *Endurance*.) Crean returned to Ireland and opened a pub, the South Pole Inn, in his birthplace, Annascaul. It is still there and, according to poet Paul Muldoon, filled with southern ghosts: 'At the South Pole Inn / (once owned by Tom Crean) / the ice in your gin / grumbles and groans. // You still hear the yelps / of phantoms—men, dogs— / crying out for help / through tobacco-fog.' The South Pole Inn and the Tom Crean Society share a website: http://www.southpoleinn.ie/index.htm.

The epigraph to 'What the Ice Gets' is from the Book of Job. Shackleton had torn pages containing these words and those of the Twenty-third Psalm from the ship's Bible when the *Endurance* was abandoned. The poem's title is from an earlier remark of Shackleton's to Worsley, after the ship had been drifting some 700 miles while trapped in the ice: 'The ship can't live in this, Skipper. You had better make up your mind that it is only a matter of time . . . what the ice gets, the ice keeps.' The 'Boss' is Shackleton.

from **At the Mountains of Madness** (*page 186*)

These are the final chapters of *At the Mountains of Madness* (1936), by cult horror writer H.P. Lovecraft (1890–1937). Lovecraft was a keen reader of Antarctic texts (his early sonnet 'Antarktos' already speaks of 'vaster parts, that under / The mile-deep ice-shroud crouch and brood and hide'), and while his story explicitly amplifies Poe's *Pym* and revels in phrases such as 'the great unknown continent and its cryptic world of frozen death', it begins as a carefully researched and plausible account of a scientific expedition from Miskatonic University modelled on that of Byrd in 1928–1930. There are also references to Ross, Wilkes, Borchgrevink, Scott, Shackleton, and Mawson. The expeditionary party travels by air far into the unexplored Antarctic interior, discovering in a high, hitherto unknown mountain chain a ruined archaic city which has been abandoned by its makers, the first inhabitants of Earth known as the Old Ones. Some are still alive (or become so after the explorers recklessly thaw them out); so too are the Shoggoths, a race of slave creatures originally created by the star-headed Old Ones and now their nemesis. The only reason this story is being told, we discover, is to warn and dissuade the organisers of a similar proposed scientific expedition. Says the narrator, 'I must break through all reticences at last—even about that ultimate nameless thing beyond the mountains of madness.' Arthur C. Clarke wrote a brief Lovecraft parody, 'At the Mountains of Murkiness'. See *At the Mountains of Murkiness and Other Parodies* (London: Ferret Fantasy, 1973). There is a Lovecraft Antarctic computer game, *Prisoner of Ice*. 'Something monstrous is discovered frozen in the Antarctic ice and you must prevent the Nazis from releasing it.' The game invites you to 'defeat Cthulhu and save the world'.

Byrd in the Antarctic (*page 210*)

Henry Hart's poem was first published in *The Southern Review*, vol.28, no.1, January 1992, and responds to Richard Byrd's near death from carbon monoxide poisoning when in 1934 he wintered over, alone, at the Bolling Advanced Weather Station, some 120 miles inland from the edge of the Ross Ice Shelf, where the main

American base, Little America, was located. He recorded the experience in his book *Alone* (1938). A rescue party reached him on 10 August, but it was still two months before he was sufficiently recovered to be flown back to Little America.

> *Part of me remained forever at latitude 80° 80' South: what survived of my youth, my vanity, perhaps, and certainly my skepticism. On the other hand, I did take away something that I had not fully possessed before: an appreciation of the sheer beauty and miracle of being alive.*

Richard Byrd (1888–1957) made several expeditions to Antarctica, the earliest in 1929 when on 29 November he and three companions became the first to fly over the South Pole. His exploits provided a model for the early sections of H.P. Lovecraft's *At the Mountains of Madness* (see note p.315).

Henry Hart's books of poetry are *The Ghost Ship* (1990) and *The Rooster Mask* (1998). He is an editor of the journal *Verse*.

The Creation of Antarctic Light (*page 212*)

'Ern Malley' is one of the great literary hoaxes of the twentieth century. He and his poems were invented in 1943 by Australian poets James McCauley and Harold Stewart to make a point against modernist verse. Now Ern Malley is better known, and even more admired, than his creators. See Michael Heyward's *The Ern Malley Affair* (1993). Harold Stewart separately made a number of art collages, of which this is one.

from The Amazing Adventures of Kavalier and Clay (*page 213*)

Michael Chabon's *The Amazing Adventures of Kavalier and Clay* is about two comic book artists, one of whom is Joe Kavalier. In this section of the novel, 'Radioman', he has been sent to Antarctica during World War Two.

In an author's note, Chabon gives a list of books consulted on Antarctic matters: '*Little America* and *Discovery*, both by Richard E. Byrd, *A History of Antarctic Science*, by G.E. Fogg, *The White Continent*, by Thomas R. Henry, *Quest for a Continent*, by Walter

Sullivan, and *Antarctic Night*, by Jack Bursey.' Commenting on his research in an interview with comic book artist Jim Steranko, he has said: 'With Antarctica, I took out books prior to 1941 only, read a ton on it, then poured all that knowledge into that section, and then forgot it all.' Elsewhere, Chabon writes:

> At some point, I stumbled across a reference to a mission the United States sent to Antartica in 1941, just before the war began. In case any of the Axis powers made a grab for the Antarctic, the United States wanted to have a foothold. As soon as I read that, it clicked: that's my theater of war. It was exciting to think that I could write about World War Two from a totally new place (http://www. powells.com/authors/chabon.html)

Chabon's account of the Ritscher expedition (see p.225) is historically accurate, but the German camp is his own invention. Indeed, the Nazis never established a land presence on Antarctica, despite subsequent speculation in both fiction and non-fiction. In the bizarre world of occult scholarship, the Nazis hold hands at both the Arctic and Antarctic poles with Lovecraft, Poe, and various proponents of hollow-earth theory. See Joscelyn Godwin's *Arktos: The Polar Myth in Science, Symbolism, and Nazi Survival* (Grand Rapids: Phanes Press, 1993). The carbon monoxide poisoning may have been suggested by Richard Byrd's experience (see the note to 'Byrd in the Antarctic', pp.315–16). Byrd was leader of the United States Services Expedition to the Antarctic between November 1939 and January 1941—there were two bases, one on the Ross Ice Shelf, the other on the Palmer Peninsula.

'How Doth My Good Cousin Silence?' (*page 238*)

Denis Glover (1912–1980) was a New Zealand poet and printer, admired both for his lyric and his satiric poetry. The poem's title is from Shakespeare's *Henry IV Part II* (III, ii). The Ob was a Soviet icebreaker, the Grab presumably some sort of shipboard apparatus used to sample sea bed sediments. The IGY refers to the International Geophysical Year (July 1957–December 1958), in which sixty-seven countries engaged in scientific research throughout the world, but with special emphasis on Antarctica. During this time Sir Edmund

Hillary rode to the South Pole on a converted Ferguson tractor, leading the first overland party to make the journey since Amundsen and Scott. Glover enables Edgar Allan Poe to make yet another Antarctic appearance. 'Nevermore' refers of course to Poe's raven.

The Frozen Continents (*page 239*)

Owen Marshall (1941–) is New Zealand's most admired contemporary short story writer. The story originally appeared in *The Lynx Hunter* (1987); the book's epigraph comes from Oscar Wilde— 'One's real life is often the life one does not lead.'

Aside from the historic huts (see the note on 'Visiting Mr Shackleton', pp.320–21), Antarctic museums are outside the continent they represent. The Scott Polar Research Institute (SPRI), Cambridge, England, and the National Maritime Museum at Greenwich have substantial collections of Antarctic memorabilia (including, at the SPRI, Oates's sleeping bag). The other major Antarctic collection is in the Canterbury Museum, Christchurch, New Zealand. The Shirase Antarctic Expedition Museum is in Konoura, Japan, while a number of famous ships are on display: Scott's *Discovery* in Dundee, Scotland, Shackleton's *James Caird* at Dulwich College, London. Byrd's aircraft, *Floyd Bennet*, the first to fly over the South Pole, is housed in the Henry Ford Museum in Dearborn, Michigan. More popular Antarctic sites include the International Antarctic Centre at Christchurch Airport, which has a gift shop and a café. Then there is Hobart's 'Antarctic Adventure'—'a family-oriented attraction focused on exploration of the cold, white continent'—and 'Kelly Tarlton's Antarctic Encounter' in Auckland, New Zealand. At the latter, tourists can stroll through a replica of Scott's hut at Cape Evans—'lost in time since 1911'—then ride in a snow-cat, plunging below the polar ice to view real penguins and survive the attack of a not-quite-so-real orca. For a vast and growing list of Antarctic sites outside Antarctica, see Robert B. Stephenson's 'A Low-Level Antarctic Gazeteer' at http://www.antarctic-circle.org/llag.htm.

The Piper and the Penguin (*page 246*)

Laurence Fearnley travelled to Antarctica in January 2004 as a New Zealand Antarctic Arts Fellow, and is currently writing a novel with an Antarctic setting. Her earlier novels include *Room* and *Delphine's Run*; this story originally appeared in the literary magazine *Sport*. Perhaps the name Kathleen is significant (for in a sense this is both another artist and Antarctic widow—see the note on Anne Michaels's 'Ice House', pp.312–13). Max is said to be New Zealand's first 'Antarctic Composer in Residence'. In fact, several New Zealand composers and musicians have travelled to Antarctica, including Chris Cree Brown and Phil Dadson. Among British composers who have travelled south are Sir Peter Maxwell Davies, whose *Antarctic Symphony*, a sequel to Vaughan Williams's *Sinfonia Antarctica* (which began life as the sound track for the 1948 feature film *Scott of the Antarctic*), was first performed on 6 May 2001.

from Angels in America (*page 259*)

A brief scene from early in the first part of Tony Kushner's seven-hour theatrical diptych, *Angels in America*. Harper is a valium-dependent Mormon housewife; Mr Lies is both trickster and travel agent, as much a figment of her imagination as the Antarctica which she is hallucinating. Antarctica is part of the astonishing scope of Kushner's play—other settings include Salt Lake City, Washington, Moscow, Earth and Heaven—but incidental to its main concern, an exploration of the deep moral abyss of modern America. Nevertheless, the southern continent represents an old American and European idea of the last frontier as a clean and uncorrupted place of escape, a fantasy locale where you might still remake the world according to your needs.

Michel in Antarctica (*page 261*)
A Site of Special Scientific Interest (*page 294*)

The second extract is from Kim Stanley Robinson's novel *Antarctica* (1997), which is part science fiction eco-thriller, and part environmental meditation. It was written as a direct result of the author's

1995 visit to Antarctica as a member of the US National Science Foundation's artist and writers programme. Ta Shu, a *feng shui* expert, geomancer, and—in a sense—tourist guide, has also travelled to Antarctica as part of the NSF programme. Here, he is broadcasting his impressions of Antarctica to a huge international 'fibrevideo audience'. Ta Shu is a former poet:

> *People said that the book's author had come down as a very long-winded poet, a kind of Chinese Walt Whitman, but after his visit to the ice he had gone silent, and this little chapbook published many years later had been the only poetry ever published by him again. About forty pages of poems, if you could call them that, all of them four words long; things like*
>
> *blue sky*
> *white snow*
>
> *or*
>
> *white cloud*
> *black rock.*

Kim Stanley Robinson is perhaps best known for his Mars trilogy, *Red Mars*, *Blue Mars*, *Green Mars*. 'Michel in Antarctica' is set in a kind of alternative universe to that one, where the original Martian settlers' mission does not take place. It appears in *The Martians*, a short story companion to the Martian novels.

Antarctic Stones (*page 297*)

By Chilean poet and diplomat Pablo Neruda (1904–1973). 'Antarctic Stones' is from his 1961 collection *Las Piedras de Chile*. One other Antarctic poem, 'Antarctic', appeared in *Canto General* (1950). This translation is by Patricia Sarr, Keith Johnston, and Bill Manhire.

Visiting Mr Shackleton (*page 298*)

This poem is composed of comments from the Visitors' Book in Shackleton's hut at Cape Royds. It and Scott's hut at Cape Evans are often visited by scientists and other workers in the McMurdo

320

area, and by passengers on cruise ships. Chris Cochran, to whom the poem is dedicated, is a conservation architect who has advised on the preservation of historic structures in both the Antarctic peninsula and Ross Sea areas. Bill Manhire travelled to Antarctica as an inaugural New Zealand Antarctic Arts Fellow in 1998. A sequence of Antarctic poems, including the long poem 'Hoosh', appears in his *Collected Poems* (2001).

Some Works Cited or Consulted

Ackerman, Diane, *The Moon by Whalelight* (New York: Vintage Books, 1992).

Amundsen, Roald, *The South Pole: An Account of the Norwegian Antarctic Expedition in the 'Fram', 1910–1912* (London: J. Murray, 1912).

Atwood, Margaret, *Strange Things: The Malevolent North in Canadian Literature* (Oxford: Clarendon Press, 1995).

Barnes, Julian, *Flaubert's Parrot* (London: Jonathan Cape, 1984).

Bleiler, Everett F., *Science Fiction: The Early Years* (Kent, Ohio: Kent State University Press, 1990).

Boyd, Brian, *Vladimir Nabokov: The Russian Years* (London: Chatto & Windus, 1990).

Campbell, David, *The Crystal Desert: Summers in Antarctica* (Boston: Houghton Mifflin, 1992).

Cherry-Garrard, Apsley, *The Worst Journey in the World* 1922 (London: Picador, 1994).

Clair, Daphne, *Frozen Heart* (London: Mills & Boon, 1980).

Codling, R., 'Polar Theatre: Two Victorian Plays', *Polar Record* vol.23, no.142, 1986: 67–8.

Diski, Jenny, *Skating to Antarctica* (London: Granta, 1997).

Fox, William L., *Antarctic Image Chronology*, http://www.antarctic-circle.org/fox.htm.

Garner, Helen, *The Feel of Steel* (Sydney: Picador, 2001).

Green, Bill, *Water, Ice and Stone: Science and Memory on the Antarctic Lakes* (New York: Harmony, 1995).

Le Guin, Ursula K., 'Heroes', in *Dancing at the Edge of the World: Thoughts on Women, Words, Places* (New York: Harper & Row, 1989).

Lenz, William E., *The Poetics of the Antarctic: A Study in Nineteenth-Century American Cultural Perceptions* (New York: Garland, 1995).

Lopez, Barry, 'Informed by Indifference: A Walk in Antarctica', *Harpers Magazine,* May 1988.

Lowes, John Livingston, *The Road to Xanadu* (Boston: Houghton Mifflin Company, 1927).

Marx, Friedhelm (ed), *Wege ins Eis. Nord- und Südpolfahrten in der Literatur* (Frankfurt/Main: Insel, 1995).

Matthiessen, Peter, *End of the Earth* (Washington, DC: National Geographic Society, 2003).

Nelson, Victoria, 'Symmes Hole, or the South Polar Romance', *Raritan: A Quarterly Review,* 17.2, 1997: 136–66.

Pyne, Stephen J., *The Ice: A Journey to Antarctica* (Iowa City: University of Iowa Press, 1986).

[Reader's Digest (ed),] *Antarctica: The Extraordinary History of Man's Conquest of the Frozen Continent* (Sydney: Readers Digest, 1990).

Scott, Robert Falcon, *Scott's Last Expedition,* arranged by Leonard Huxley from Scott's journals, 5th edition (London: Smith, Elder & Co, 1914).

[Shackleton, E.H. (ed),] *Aurora Australis* (Sydney: Bay Books, 1988).

Simpson-Housley, Paul, *Antarctica: Exploration, Perception, and Metaphor* (London: Routledge, 1992).

Spufford, Francis, *I May Be Some Time: Ice and the English Imagination* (London: Faber and Faber, 1996).

Tetley, Graeme (ed), *Antarctica 2010: A Notebook* (Christchurch: Antarctica New Zealand, 1998).

Utley, Steven and Harold Waldrop, 'Black as the Pit, From Pole to Pole', in *The Year's Finest Fantasy,* ed. Terry Carr (New York: Berkeley, 1978).

Wheeler, Sara, *Terra Incognita* (London: Random House, 1996).

Woolf, Virginia, *Congenial Spirits: The Selected Letters of Virginia Woolf,* ed. Joanne Trautmann Banks (London: Hogarth, 1989).

Acknowledgements

Many people have helped me in various ways over several years while *The Wide White Page* came into being. Inevitably I have forgotten some of those who have made suggestions, given advice, or answered questions, but my thanks go to: Jeanie Ackley, Beryl Bainbridge, Billy-Ace Baker, James Bellamy, Penelope Bieder, Peter Barrett, James Brown, Nigel Brown, Russell Campbell, David Carnegie, Bernard Carpinter, David Clark, Chris and Margaret Cochran, Gordon Collier, Caroline Dawnay, Chris Elder, Stephen Enniss, Tamsin Falconer, Laurence Fearnley, Thomas Forster, Bill Fox, Katie Hardwick-Smith, Linda Hardy, David L. Harrowfield, Robert Headland, Bernadette Hince, Stuart Hoare, Keith Johnston, Stuart Johnston, Max Jones, Chris Joyner, Elizabeth Leane, William E. Lenz, Chris Mace, Toby Manhire, Vanessa Manhire, Friedhelm Marx, Rick McGregor, Marion McLeod, William Mills, Heather Murray, Anne Noble, Greg O'Brien, Chris Orsman, Harry Orsman, Vincent O'Sullivan, Stephanie Pfennigwerth, Oscar Pinochet de la Barra, Stuart Prior, Peter Robinson, Philip Salom, Patricia Sarr, Shirley Sawtell, Michael Schmidt, Mike Single, Michael Steemson, Stephen Tapscott, John Tranter, Rae Varcoe, Jeffrey Wainwright, Eliot Weinberger, Sara Wheeler, Damien Wilkins, Gillian Wratt, Fiona Wright, and David Young.

Especial thanks to Rowan Gibbs for his early help when this project was a bibliographical pipe-dream; to Fauno Cordes for her generosity; and to Guy Guthridge and Tim Higham who got me to the Pole for forty-five semi-heroic minutes. Thanks, of course, to everyone at Antarctica New Zealand; to the reference staff at the Victoria University Library for their patience and professionalism; and to staff at the British Library, the National Library of New Zealand, and the Scott Polar Research Institute. A small grant from Victoria University's FHSS Research Committee, to meet the cost of international library interloans, made it possible for me to read many texts I could not otherwise have seen. I want to thank Sarah Maxey for the cover. At Victoria University Press, my thanks go to Sue Brown, Anna Smaill, Fergus Barrowman, Heather McKenzie, and Odessa Owens: they can be in my sledging party any day.

Permissions

Monty Python's 'Scott of the Sahara' is from Chapman, Graham et al., *Monty Python's Flying Circus: Just the Words*, vol.1 (London: Methuen, 1989), and reprinted by kind permission.

Melinda Mueller's poems 'Crean. Night Watch' and 'What the Ice Gets: 23–29 October 1915' are from *What the Ice Gets: Shackleton's Antarctic Expedition 1914–1916 [A Poem]* (Seattle: Van West and Co, 2000), and reprinted by kind permission.

The extract from H.P. Lovecraft's 'At the Mountains of Madness' is from *The Thing on the Doorstep and Other Weird Stories* edited by S. T. Joshi (London: Penguin Classics, 2001) and is reprinted by permission of Arkham House Publishers, Inc. and Arkham's agents, JABberwocky Literary Agency, PO Box 4558, Sunnyside, NY 11104-0558.

Henry Hart's poem 'Byrd in Antarctica' was first published in *The Southern Review* (vol.28, no.1, January 1992) and is reproduced with the kind permission of the author.

The 'Ern Malley' collage 'The Creation of Antarctic Light' is by the late Harold Stewart and is reproduced with the kind permission of Lee Riley.

The extract from Michael Chabon's *The Amazing Adventures of Kavalier and Clay* (London: Fourth Estate, 2000) and is reprinted by permission HarperCollins Publishers Ltd. © Michael Chabon 2000.

Denis Glover's poem 'How Doth My Good Cousin Silence' is from *The Bedside Book* (Wellington: Reed, 1963) and is reproduced with the kind permission of the copyright holder, Pia Glover.

Owen Marshall's story 'The Frozen Continents' is from *The Lynx Hunter and Other Stories* (Dunedin: John McIndoe, 1987) and is reproduced with the kind permission of the author.

Laurence Fearnley's story 'The Piper and the Penguin' appeared in *Sport 20* (Autumn 1998: 71–80) and is reproduced with the kind permission of the author.

The extract from Tony Kushner's *Angels in America Part One: The Millenium Approaches* (New York: Theatre Communications Group, March 2001) is reproduced with the kind permission of the author and Theatre Communications Group.

Kim Stanley Robinson's story 'Michel in Antactica' is from *The Martians* (London: HarperCollins Voyager, 1999), and 'A Site of Special Scientific Interest' is from *Antarctica* (London: HarperCollins, 1997). They are reprinted by permission HarperCollins Publishers Ltd. © Kim Stanley Robinson 1999 and 1997.

Every effort has been made to contact the copyright holders for material reproduced in this anthology. The publishers would be grateful to hear from any other copyright holders.